THE
INTERNATIONAL SERIES
OF
MONOGRAPHS ON PHYSICS

THE INTERNATIONAL SERIES OF MONOGRAPHS ON PHYSICS

GENERAL EDITORS

The late Sir RALPH FOWLER   P. KAPITZA

N. F. MOTT   E. C. BULLARD
Henry Overton Wills Professor   Director of the National
of Theoretical Physics in the   Physical Laboratory,
University of Bristol.   Teddington.

THE
OUTER LAYERS
OF A STAR

BY

R. v. d. R. WOOLLEY

COMMONWEALTH ASTRONOMER
PROFESSOR IN THE AUSTRALIAN NATIONAL UNIVERSITY

AND

D. W. N. STIBBS

RADCLIFFE TRAVELLING FELLOW IN ASTRONOMY

OXFORD
AT THE CLARENDON PRESS
1953

Oxford University Press, Amen House, London E.C.4

GLASGOW NEW YORK TORONTO MELBOURNE WELLINGTON
BOMBAY CALCUTTA MADRAS KARACHI CAPE TOWN IBADAN

Geoffrey Cumberlege, Publisher to the University

PRINTED IN GREAT BRITAIN

PREFACE

THIS book is about the relations between the total radiation from a star, its colour, and the lines in the star's spectrum. Considerable reference is made to the Sun, but this is only because the Sun is, for many purposes, the most convenient object to test the general theory: the book is not concerned with solar phenomena—sunspots, flares, prominences, and so on. There are, however, two chapters about specifically solar matters, the solar corona and chromosphere, both of which are considered in their quiet state. These chapters were inserted partly as a matter of general interest in stellar theory, since a corona and a chromosphere may well be features of many stars, and partly from a desire to bring up to date those parts of another book in this series, *Eclipses of the Sun and Moon*, by the late Sir Frank Dyson and one of the present authors, which had become out of date as a result of recent advances. The epoch of this book is 1950.

The main interest of the book is physical, but some mathematical chapters have been inserted for completeness. Physical as distinct from astrophysical theory has been dealt with at length in some instances where experience has suggested that it is not easy to find an account of the precise details that the astrophysicist really wants.

We are grateful to Mrs. Beryl Hall for making some calculations for us, and to Miss Barbara Davson for typing the manuscript.

In conclusion we acknowledge with gratitude our indebtedness to teachers and colleagues, both past and present, whose influence may be seen in this work.

R. v. d. R. W.

D. W. N. S.

Mount Stromlo
Canberra, Australia
   May 1951

CONTENTS

ERRATA

p. 30, Equation (3.1), for $E_2(t)$ read $E_2(\tau - t)$

p. 40, line 4, for $(K0)$ read $K(0)$

p. 45, Equation (61.2), for $(1+\mu^2)^{\frac{1}{2}}$ read $(1+\mu)^{\frac{1}{2}}$

p. 49, footnote, *for* (1948) *read* (1947)

p. 60, after equation (32), insert the condition $\lambda < \lambda_0$

p. 67, Table IX, title, for *Variation of* $k_\lambda/\bar{k}(\text{H-})$ *with Optical Depth* read *Variation of* $k_\lambda/\bar{k}(\text{H-})$ *with Optical Depth in the Solar Atmosphere*

p. 73, line 6, for $p' = \dfrac{3}{2}\dfrac{1-n}{1+n}\dfrac{\bar{k}}{k_\nu}$. read $p' = \dfrac{3}{2}\dfrac{1-n}{1+n}\dfrac{\bar{k}}{k_\nu}\cos\theta$.

p. 80, note to Table XIII, *for* (S. Raudenbusch, *A.N.* **263**, 300 (1938)) ; *read* (H. Raudenbusch, *A.N.* **266**, 301 (1938)) ;

p. 103, expression before equation (47), *insert*) *after* σ

p. 138, line 5 from foot, *for* (51). *read* (50).

p. 174, ll. 4 and 7, for q_ν^2 read p_μ^2

p. 197, Expression for $\frac{1}{2}w^*$ between equations (55) and (56), for $(q-3)^{\frac{1}{2}}$ read $(q^2-3)^{\frac{1}{2}}$

p. 234, line 12, for $C = \dfrac{75}{16}\left(\dfrac{R}{\pi m}\right)^{\frac{1}{2}}\dfrac{R^3}{e^4} T^{\frac{5}{2}}/A_2(2)$

read $C = \dfrac{75}{16}\left(\dfrac{R}{\pi m}\right)^{\frac{1}{2}}\dfrac{R^3}{e^4}\dfrac{1}{A_2(2)}$

p. 257, line 16, *for* Section 9. *read* Section 6.

p. 272, Equation (16), for λ_0 read λ_E

p. 289, line 15, for $p_e \sim p$ read $p_e \sim \frac{1}{2}p$
for $p\,dp = (g/k_0)\,d\tau$ read $p\,dp = 2(g/k_0)\,d\tau$

Equation (42) for $p^2 = (2g/k_0)\tau$ read $p^2 = (4g/k_0)\tau$

p. 298, Table of Physical Constants, Unit for Planck's constant, *for* erg sec.$^{-1}$ *read* erg sec.

Table of Physical Constants, Unit for Stefan's constant, *for* erg cm.$^{-1}$ sec.$^{-1}$ deg.$^{-4}$ *read* erg cm.$^{-2}$ sec.$^{-1}$ deg.$^{-4}$

Table of Astronomical Constants, *for* Angular diameter of the Sun *read* Angular semi-diameter of the Sun

p. 300 footnote, *for* **20** *read* **30**

I

RADIATIVE EQUILIBRIUM OF THE OUTER LAYERS

1. Introduction

THE study of the stars, not as moving points, but as physical entities, is based almost entirely on spectroscopic analysis of the radiation which comes from them; indeed the only physical attribute of a star which may be inferred without the help of spectrum analysis is the mass of the star, which is known from the gravitational field. In the case of the Sun, this gravitational field is measured by observing the motion of the planets, and in the case of certain stars which are double and show orbital motion, the mass may be determined from the parallax and the orbit.

The information given by spectrum analysis falls into two broad divisions. Except in rare cases, the stellar spectrum is a continuous spectrum interrupted by certain lines which may be either emission lines or absorption lines, and the two directions in which the study of stellar spectra may be pursued are the study of the continuous spectrum, and the study of the line spectrum. While this division is, from a formal point of view, artificial, it has been very distinct in the history of the development of astrophysics. From the continuous spectra have been deduced stellar temperatures and, indirectly, stellar radii. The presence or absence of lines was at first held to be an indication of the presence or absence of the elements concerned in their formation in various stars, but further analysis led to the view that the chemical composition of most stellar atmospheres is practically the same, and the evidence given by the lines has turned out to be evidence of the temperatures, and also of the surface gravities of the stars. Thus the two types of analysis have converged to a common goal—the determination of stellar surface temperatures, surface gravities, and radii.

2. The transfer of radiation

To provide the mathematical means with which to treat the matter, we have to develop a theory of the transfer of radiation in the outer layers of a star, in the presence of appropriate absorption coefficients for the continuous spectrum and the line spectrum. The absorption coefficient is a function of the wave-length or frequency of the radiation, and for convenience may be considered to be composed of two parts:

a slowly varying part, the continuous absorption coefficient, and a rapidly varying part which is effectively zero where there is no line, and which rises sharply to large values in the centre of the various absorption lines.

The *specific intensity* of radiation is defined as follows. Consider a point P inside an area $d\sigma$ whose normal is inclined at an angle θ to some

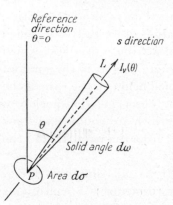

axis of reference, and draw PL normal to $d\sigma$. With vertex P and axis PL describe a cone subtending an elementary solid angle $d\omega$ at P, and describe similar cones through every point on $d\sigma$. The cones generate a semi-infinite truncated cone which passes through the perimeter of $d\sigma$. Let $E_\nu\,d\nu$ be the energy in frequencies between ν and $\nu+d\nu$ of the radiation which passes through $d\sigma$ in time dt and remains within the cone. Then the specific intensity $I_\nu(\theta)$ of the ν-radiation at the point P is given by

FIG. 1. Specific intensity of radiation.

$$I_\nu(\theta)\,d\nu\,d\omega\,d\sigma\,dt = E_\nu\,d\nu.$$

Radiation traversing a medium will be weakened by absorption, and may gain in intensity by emission. For the moment we draw no distinction between different kinds of absorption, such as conversion into heat on the one hand and scattering of light on the other, but define a mass absorption coefficient by supposing that radiation of intensity I_ν traversing an element of length in the s-direction in a medium of density ρ loses by absorption the amount $k_\nu\rho I_\nu\,ds$. Let $4\pi j_\nu\,d\nu$ be the rate of emission of energy in the frequency interval ν to $\nu+d\nu$ per unit mass of the material. If this emission is isotropic the fraction $d\omega/4\pi$ will go into directions within $d\omega$. Since the increase in the flow of radiation in the s-direction is equal to the emission within the solid angle minus the absorption by the mass element, it follows that the differential equation for the transfer of radiation is

$$\frac{dI_\nu}{ds} = -k_\nu\rho I_\nu + j_\nu\rho. \tag{1}$$

We now suppose that k_ν is independent of frequency ν and is equal to k, and we write $\int I_\nu\,d\nu = I$, $\int j_\nu\,d\nu = j$. Then equation (1), integrated with respect to ν, gives

$$\frac{dI}{\rho\,ds} = -kI + j. \tag{2}$$

Since the total thickness of the outer layers is small compared with the stellar radius, we neglect curvature and treat the atmosphere as stratified in plane parallel layers as shown in Fig. 2. We take the axis of x normal to these layers and positive outwards, the origin of x being the surface of the star. This axis is also taken as the direction of reference $\theta = 0$, so that an element of path in the s-direction at an angle θ

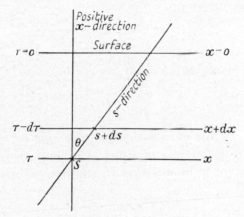

FIG. 2. Relation between geometrical and optical depth in the outer layers.

to the x-axis is $ds = dx \sec \theta$. Since there is symmetry about the outward normal the quantities ρ, $I(\theta)$, and j are only functions of the depth x beneath the surface of the star. Equation (2) now becomes

$$\cos \theta \frac{dI(\theta)}{k\rho \, dx} = -I(\theta) + j/k. \qquad (3)$$

We now define the optical depth τ of a point x beneath the surface by the relation

$$\tau = \int_x^0 k\rho \, dx,$$

giving $d\tau = -k\rho \, dx$. The optical depth is zero when $x = 0$, i.e. outside the star. The equation of transfer now becomes

$$\cos \theta \frac{dI(\theta)}{d\tau} = I(\theta) - j/k. \qquad (4)$$

Define the following quantities

$$J = \frac{1}{4\pi} \int I(\theta) \, d\omega, \qquad H = \frac{1}{4\pi} \int I(\theta) \cos \theta \, d\omega,$$

$$K = \frac{1}{4\pi} \int I(\theta) \cos^2\theta \, d\omega$$

in which the integrals are taken over a sphere, J being the average flowof radiation, $4\pi H$ the net flux F, and the quantity K being related to the radiation pressure. Since the radiation field is axially symmetric about the direction $\theta = 0$, we take $d\omega = 2\pi \sin\theta\, d\theta$, integrating from $\theta = 0$ to π to cover the complete solid angle. Multiplying (4) by $d\omega$ and integrating in this way, after changing the order of differentiation and integration in the first term, we get

$$\frac{dH}{d\tau} = J - j/k, \tag{5}$$

and multiplying (4) by $d\omega \cos\theta$ and integrating,

$$\frac{dK}{d\tau} = H. \tag{6}$$

Now $4\pi H$ is the net flux of radiation per unit area per second from the star. If there are no sources or sinks of radiant energy in the outer layers, H is constant from one layer to another, and equations (5) and (6) give

$$j = kJ, \tag{7}$$

$$K = H\tau + \text{constant.} \tag{8}$$

3. Eddington's treatment. The first approximation

The solution of equation (4) cannot be carried out in a simple manner without approximation because j/k does not depend on any particular value of $I(\theta)$ but, by (7), on $J(\tau)$, the average value of $I(\theta)$ integrated over all directions.

The following approximate treatment is due to Eddington. Suppose that $I(\theta) = I_1$ when $0 < \theta < \tfrac{1}{2}\pi$, and $I(\theta) = I_2$ when $\tfrac{1}{2}\pi < \theta < \pi$, both I_1 and I_2 being constants with respect to θ but, of course, being functions of τ. This approximation to the θ distribution of I is discontinuous at the boundary $\theta = \tfrac{1}{2}\pi$, between the upper and lower hemispheres of directions, but it avoids the occurrence of integral equations and leads to a satisfactory first approximation. The second approximation is dealt with in Section 5.

Evaluating the integrals for J, H, and K we find

$$J = \tfrac{1}{2}(I_1 + I_2), \qquad H = \tfrac{1}{4}(I_1 - I_2), \qquad K = \tfrac{1}{3}J. \tag{9}$$

If we take as our boundary condition that there is no inflowing radiation at the surface of the star, then $I_2 = 0$ and $J = 2H$ at $\tau = 0$. Hence, from equation (8),

$$J = H(2 + 3\tau). \tag{10}$$

Solving for the outward and inward intensities we find

$$I_1(\tau) = H(4+3\tau), \qquad I_2(\tau) = 3H\tau.$$

Since $K/J = \int I\cos^2\theta\, d\omega / \int I\, d\omega$, we may regard this ratio as the mean value of $\cos^2\theta$ weighted by the intensity I. We refer to the result $K = \tfrac{1}{3}J$ in (9) as the geometrical approximation. It is an exact relation if $I(\theta)$ can be expressed in the form

$$I(\theta) = a + b\cos\theta + c\cos^3\theta + ...,$$

a convergent series in odd powers of $\cos\theta$. If we take only the first two terms, we find

$$J = a, \qquad H = \tfrac{1}{3}b, \qquad K = \tfrac{1}{3}a.$$

Since H is constant, b is independent of τ. Equation (8) then gives $a = b\tau + \text{const}$. To determine the constant, we note that the approximation $I(\theta) = a + b\cos\theta$ breaks down at the boundary, where $I(\theta)$ should vanish for $\theta > \tfrac{1}{2}\pi$. If we take as an alternative boundary condition that there is no inward *flux* at $\tau = 0$, we find $J(0) = a(0) = \tfrac{2}{3}b$. Thus the boundary condition is $J = 2H$ as before.

3.1. *The darkening of the limb*

We now determine the amount of radiation leaving the surface of the star at different inclinations to the normal. The emission per unit mass of the stellar atmosphere is $4\pi j$, and the total emission from an elementary cylindrical volume with its axis inclined at an angle θ to the x-axis, and of unit cross-section and length $ds = dx\sec\theta$, is $4\pi kJ\rho\, dx\sec\theta$. If the emission is isotropic, the emission in the s-direction into the solid angle $d\omega$ will be $kJ\rho\, d\omega dx\sec\theta$. At the surface of the star this emission is reduced to

$$k\rho\, dx\sec\theta J\, d\omega \times e^{-\tau\sec\theta},$$

since it has to traverse an optical path length $\tau\sec\theta$ through the superincumbent layers before emergence. With $d\tau = -k\rho\, dx$, the contribution to the emergent intensity by emission from the element of volume at optical depth τ is given by

$$-J(\tau)\, d\omega\, e^{-\tau\sec\theta}\, d\tau\sec\theta.$$

Evidently the total radiation which emerges from the surface of the star is the sum of the emissions from each level reduced by the extinction along the path between each source of emission and the surface. We refer to $J(\tau)$ as the *source function*. The intensity $I(0, \theta)$ at the surface in the direction θ is

$$\int_0^\infty e^{-\tau\sec\theta}J(\tau)\, d\tau\sec\theta.$$

Using $J(\tau)$ from equation (10) we find

$$I(0, \theta) = H(2+3\cos\theta). \tag{11}$$

This is the law of darkening from the centre of the disk to the limb, illustrated in Fig. 3. Equation (11) shows that the integrated brightness of the apparent disk varies in the ratio 5 to 2 from the centre $\theta = 0$ to the limb $\theta = \tfrac{1}{2}\pi$. This approximate theoretical formula is in good agreement with observations of the darkening of the limb of the Sun.

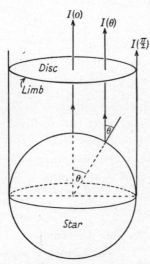

We now apply a check to the limb-darkening formula (11) by calculating the flux F at the surface of the star, which should be equal to $4\pi H$. The amount of radiation emerging at an angle θ to the surface of the star per unit area of the star itself is

$$I(0, \theta)\cos\theta \, d\omega.$$

With $d\omega = 2\pi\sin\theta \, d\theta$, the flux at the surface is given by

$$F = \int_0^{\frac{1}{2}\pi} 2\pi I(0, \theta)\sin\theta\cos\theta \, d\theta. \tag{12}$$

FIG. 3. Distribution of light across the apparent disk—the darkening of the limb.

Using the limb-darkening formula (11), the flux integral has the value $4\pi H$. The limb-darkening formula therefore leads to the correct flux at the boundary, a check which the early approximations of Schwarzschild and Jeans do not satisfy.

3.2. *The equivalent mean intensity*

Let $d\sigma$ be an element of area on the apparent disk of the star at an angular distance θ from the centre. The mean intensity over the observed disk is given by the ratio

$$\mathfrak{F} = \int I(0, \theta) \, d\sigma \Big/ \int d\sigma. \tag{13}$$

Now with $d\sigma = 2\pi a^2\sin\theta\cos\theta \, d\theta$, a being the radius of the star, integrating from $\theta = 0$ to $\tfrac{1}{2}\pi$ we find that $\mathfrak{F}$ is given by

$$2\int_0^{\frac{1}{2}\pi} I(0, \theta)\cos\theta\sin\theta \, d\theta,$$

a result which is simply related to the flux integral (12). Thus

$$F = \pi\mathfrak{F}. \tag{14}$$

This expresses that a surface radiating with an intensity $\mathfrak{F}$ independent of direction gives the same flux as the star itself.

The equivalent mean intensity of a star radiating according to equation (11) is the same as the intensity at a point on the disk where $\cos\theta = \frac{2}{3}$.

4. Some radiation laws

Let $B(\nu, T)$ denote the intensity of equilibrium radiation with frequency ν and temperature T. This refers to the intensity of the isotropic radiation field within an enclosure at temperature T, and is given by Planck's law, namely

$$B(\nu, T) = \frac{2h\nu^3/c^2}{e^{h\nu/RT}-1},$$

h being Planck's constant and R Boltzmann's constant. According to Kirchhoff's law if j_ν and k_ν are the emission and absorption coefficients of matter in thermodynamic equilibrium at temperature T within the enclosure, then

$$j_\nu = k_\nu\, B(\nu, T). \tag{15}$$

If matter at temperature T emits radiation as it would in an equilibrium enclosure at that temperature, it is said to be in a state of *local thermodynamic equilibrium* at temperature T. If k_ν is independent of ν, the emission integrated over all frequencies will be

$$j = k \int B(\nu, T)\, d\nu = k\frac{\sigma}{\pi}T^4, \tag{16}$$

where σ is Stefan's constant $\dfrac{2\pi^5}{15}\dfrac{R^4}{c^2h^3}$.

4.1. *The effective temperature of radiation*

A radiation field of arbitrary constitution is not, in general, in equilibrium with matter at any particular temperature: the integrated radiation has, however, the same density as equilibrium radiation at some temperature T; we call T the effective temperature of the radiation. Then $J = (\sigma/\pi)T^4$, and since $j = kJ$ from equation (7), we see that the temperature of the matter operative in local thermodynamic equilibrium is equal to the effective temperature of the radiation when k is independent of ν. In these circumstances equation (10) becomes

$$\frac{\sigma}{\pi}T^4 = H(2+3\tau).$$

The temperature T_0 at the surface, $\tau = 0$, is given by

$$T_0^4 = 2\pi H/\sigma = F/2\sigma. \tag{17}$$

The distribution of temperature in the outer layers in the first approximation will then be

$$T^4 = T_0^4(1 + \tfrac{3}{2}\tau),\tag{18}$$

a result due to Milne.

The effective temperature of the star as a whole is the temperature T_e of a surface emitting a flux of radiation of equilibrium constitution equal to the actual flux F from the star. Hence $F = \sigma T_e^4$ and equation (17) gives

$$T_e = 2^{\frac{1}{4}}T_0 = 1\cdot 189 T_0.\tag{19}$$

At a point on the disk corresponding to the angular distance θ from the centre, we see only the flow of radiation emerging from the surface at an angle θ to the normal. The effective temperature of this emergent radiation is simply the temperature of equilibrium radiation having the same flow in all directions. Putting $(\sigma/\pi)T^4$ for $I(0, \theta)$ in equation (11) we obtain $T^4 = \tfrac{1}{2}T_e^4(1 + \tfrac{3}{2}\cos\theta)$. The effective temperature at the centre of the disk is $(5/4)^{\frac{1}{4}}$ times the temperature of the star as a whole. Radiation from the limb has the effective temperature of the boundary, whilst the temperature of radiation emerging at an angle θ is the same as the temperature at a depth where $\tau = \cos\theta$.

4.2. *The effective temperature of the Sun*

Let r be the mean radius of the Earth's orbit, and a the radius of the Sun. From every square cm. of the surface of the Sun an amount F of radiation is emitted per second, so that $F \times 4\pi a^2$ is the total output of energy by the Sun per second. All of this energy passes through a sphere of radius r, and the fraction $1/4\pi r^2$ passes through each square cm. of the surface of that sphere. The flux Q at the Earth is therefore $F(a/r)^2$. But $F = \sigma T_e^4$, where T_e is the effective temperature of the Sun. Hence

$$T_e^4 = \frac{Q}{\sigma}\left(\frac{r}{a}\right)^2.\tag{20}$$

The quantity Q is the solar constant; it is usually expressed as the number of calories per minute per square cm. outside the Earth's atmosphere. The ratio a/r is the apparent semi-diameter of the Sun at the Earth's mean distance. Adopting $1\cdot 932$ cals. min.$^{-1}$ cm.$^{-2}$ for the solar constant from Abbot's observations, and $959\cdot 6''$ for the apparent semi-diameter of the Sun according to Auwers, and using $\sigma = 5\cdot 70 \times 10^{-5}$ ergs sec.$^{-1}$ cm.$^{-2}$ or $8\cdot 19 \times 10^{-11}$ cals. min.$^{-1}$ cm.$^{-2}$, Milne (1922) found

$$T_e = 5,740^\circ \text{ K.}$$

The mean value of the solar constants published by Abbot† since 1927 is 1·946 cals. min.$^{-1}$ cm.$^{-2}$ But the Smithsonian Revised Scale (1913), on which all the figures are based, is acknowledged‡ to be 2·4 per cent. too high. This reduces the solar constant to 1·90 cals. min.$^{-1}$ cm.$^{-2}$ However, the observations exclude radiation in the ultra-violet region below λ2,900 A, and according to rocket research the ultra-violet extension of the spectrum contributes 0·014 calories to the solar constant. Allen§ suggests that the solar constant should be further increased by 3 per cent. due to uncounted contributions in the infra-red region beyond 2·5 μ. Thus to allow for the ultra-violet and infra-red extensions, the solar constant should be increased by approximately 3·7 per cent., giving a revised estimate of 1·970 cals. min.$^{-1}$ cm.$^{-2}$ With the latest values of Stefan's constant $\sigma = 5·670 \times 10^{-5}$ ergs sec.$^{-1}$ cm.$^{-2}$ deg.$^{-4}$ and Joule's equivalent $4·1855 \times 10^{7}$ ergs cal.$^{-1}$, equation (20) gives $T_e = 5,784°$ K. Throughout this book we have, however, used the value 5,740° K. for the solar effective temperature to avoid differing needlessly from previous work.

5. Eddington's second approximation

5.1. *The boundary condition*

Since the integrated net flux is constant with depth, we have $j = kJ$, and equation (3) becomes

$$\cos \theta \frac{dI(\theta)}{d\tau} = I(\theta) - J(\tau). \tag{21}$$

In the first approximation to the solution a zero approximation to the θ distribution of I was made by supposing that $I(\theta) = I_1$ when $0 < \theta < \frac{1}{2}\pi$, and $I(\theta) = I_2$ when $\frac{1}{2}\pi < \theta < \pi$. This gave a first approximation to the source function $J(\tau) = H(2 + 3\tau)$, and led to an expression for $I(\theta)$ at the surface, namely

$$I(\theta) = H(2 + 3\cos \theta) \quad (0 < \theta < \frac{1}{2}\pi).$$

For $\theta > \frac{1}{2}\pi$, $I(\theta) = 0$ at the surface. These results enable us to calculate a second approximation to the boundary condition. We had before $I_2 = 0$, $J = \frac{1}{2}I_1$ and $H = \frac{1}{4}I_1$ at $\tau = 0$, giving the condition

---

† C. G. Abbot, L. B. Aldrich, and W. H. Hoover, *Ann. Ap. Obs. Smithsonian Inst.* **6** (1942).

‡ L. B. Aldrich and C. G. Abbot, *Smithsonian Misc. Coll.* **110**, No. 5 (1948).

§ C. W. Allen, *Observatory*, **70**, 154 (1950).

$J = 2H$ at $\tau = 0$. We now have from $J = \dfrac{1}{4\pi}\displaystyle\int I(\theta)\,d\omega$,

$$J(0) = \frac{H}{4\pi}\int\limits_{0}^{\frac{1}{2}\pi} (2+3\cos\theta)2\pi\sin\theta\,d\theta = \tfrac{7}{4}H.$$

This is our new boundary condition. From it we derive the temperature at the boundary in the second approximation. Using $J(0) = \dfrac{\sigma}{\pi} T_0^4$, $H = \sigma T_e^4/4\pi$ we find $T_0^4 = \tfrac{7}{16}T_e^4$, giving

$$T_e = (\tfrac{16}{7})^{\frac14}T_0 = 1{\cdot}230T_0. \tag{22}$$

To find a second approximation to the source function at any optical depth we calculate integral forms for $I(\theta)$ which involve $J(\tau)$ explicitly. When the first approximation $J = H(2+3\tau)$ is substituted in the integrals we find the second approximation to $J(\tau)$ by evaluating

$$\frac{1}{4\pi}\int I(\tau,\theta)\,d\omega.$$

5.2. *Integral forms for $I(\tau,\theta)$ involving the source function*

Equation (21) is a linear differential equation of the form

$$\frac{dy}{dx} + Py = Q, \tag{23}$$

where y is the intensity in any given direction θ, and $P = -\sec\theta$, $Q = -J(\tau)\sec\theta$. The solution of (23) may be written as

$$y\exp\!\left[\int P\,dx\right] = \text{constant} + \int Q\exp\!\left[\int P\,dx\right]dx.$$

Let the constant of integration be determined by the intensity $I(\tau^{*},\theta)$ at optical depth τ^{*} in the prescribed direction θ. The solution of (23) then takes the form

$$e^{-\tau\sec\theta}I(\tau,\theta) = e^{-\tau^{*}\sec\theta}I(\tau^{*},\theta) + \int\limits_{\tau}^{\tau^{*}} e^{-t\sec\theta}J(t)\sec\theta\,dt. \tag{24}$$

We suppose that $I(\tau^{*},\theta)$ does not increase exponentially as $\tau^{*}\to\infty$, so that

$$0 \leqslant \theta \leqslant \tfrac12\pi, \qquad I(\tau,\theta) = \int\limits_{\tau}^{\infty} e^{-(t-\tau)\sec\theta}J(t)\sec\theta\,dt. \tag{25}$$

If we set $\tau^{*} = 0$ in (24) we get

$$I(\tau,\theta) = e^{\tau\sec\theta}I(0,\theta) - \int\limits_{0}^{\tau} e^{-(t-\tau)\sec\theta}J(t)\sec\theta\,dt.$$

When the prescribed direction lies within the range $\tfrac12\pi \leqslant \theta \leqslant \pi$ we have

$I(0,\theta) = 0$, since there is no inflowing radiation at the surface. It is convenient to write $\theta = \pi - \varphi$ so that $\varphi < \frac{1}{2}\pi$ and $\sec\varphi = |\sec\theta|$. We then obtain

$$\begin{array}{l} \frac{1}{2}\pi \leqslant \theta \leqslant \pi \\ (\varphi = \pi - \theta), \end{array} \qquad I(\tau,\varphi) = \int_0^\tau e^{-(\tau-t)\sec\varphi} J(t)\sec\varphi \, dt. \qquad (26)$$

5.21. *Physical interpretation of the integrals for* $I(\tau,\theta)$

Consider the emission of radiation by matter within an elementary cylindrical volume of unit section and axial length $ds = dx \sec\theta$.

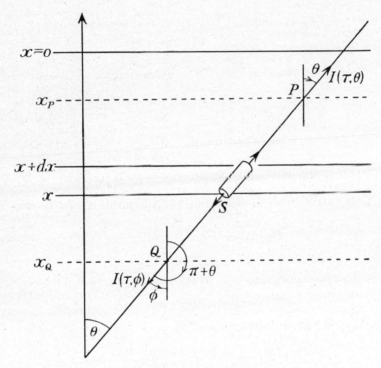

FIG. 4. The emission from matter within an elementary cylindrical volume in relation to the inward and outward intensity at any optical depth.

The total emission of *isotropic* radiation from the volume element is $4\pi j\rho \, dx \sec\theta$, of which the fraction $d\omega/4\pi$ lies within the solid angle $d\omega$. Hence the emission in the directions θ and $\pi+\theta$ will be

$$(j/k)k\rho \, dx \sec\theta. \qquad (27)$$

(i) *The outward intensity at* P. In traversing the optical path $\int_x^{x_P} k\rho \, dx \sec\theta$ between S and P in Fig. 4, the emission (27) is diminished by the absorption factor $\exp\left[-\int_{x}^{x_P} k\rho\, dx \sec\theta\right]$. This reduced emission gives the contribution to the intensity at the point P by the emission from matter between parallel planes at x and $x+dx$. The intensity at P is evidently the summed contributions from elementary layers below P, and is given by

$$\int_{x=-\infty}^{x_P} (j/k)k\rho\, dx \sec\theta \exp\left[-\int_{x}^{x_P} k\rho\, dx \sec\theta\right].$$

If we put $t = \int_{x}^{0} k\rho\, dx$, and $\tau = \int_{x_P}^{0} k\rho\, dx$ we recover equation (25) for the outward intensity.

(ii) *The inward intensity at Q.* The optical path between S and Q being $\int_{x_Q}^{x} k\rho\, dx \sec\theta$, the intensity at Q in the direction $\pi+\theta$ will be

$$\int_{x_Q}^{0} (j/k)k\rho\, dx \sec\theta \exp\left[-\int_{x_Q}^{x} k\rho\, dx \sec\theta\right],$$

since all layers above x contribute to the inward intensity at Q. With $\tau = \int_{x_Q}^{0} k\rho\, dx$ this reduces to equation (26), the intensity in the direction $\pi+\theta$ being the same as for $\pi-\theta$.

5.3. *J, H, and K in the second approximation*

From the first approximation to the source function we have

$$J(t) = H(2+3t).$$

Substituting in (25) and integrating, we find

$$I(\tau,\theta) = H(2+3\cos\theta+3\tau). \tag{28}$$

In like manner (26) gives

$$I(\tau,\varphi) = H\{(2-3\cos\varphi)(1-e^{-\tau\sec\varphi})+3\tau\}. \tag{29}$$

We may now evaluate

$$J = \frac{1}{4\pi}\int I(\theta)\, d\omega, \qquad H = \frac{1}{4\pi}\int I(\theta)\cos\theta\, d\omega,$$

$$K = \frac{1}{4\pi}\int I(\theta)\cos^2\theta\, d\omega \tag{30}$$

by means of (28) and (29) using $d\omega = 2\pi\sin\theta\, d\theta$, integrating over θ

from 0 to π and writing $\theta = \pi - \varphi$ in the range of integration where $\theta > \frac{1}{2}\pi$. We find

$$J(\tau) = H[2 + 3\tau - E_2(\tau) + \tfrac{3}{2}E_3(\tau)], \tag{31}$$

$$H(\tau) = H[1 + \tfrac{1}{2}\tau\{E_2(\tau) - E_3(\tau)\}], \tag{32}$$

$$K(\tau) = \tfrac{1}{3}H[2 + 3\tau - 3E_4(\tau) + \tfrac{9}{2}E_5(\tau)], \tag{33}$$

where
$$E_n(\tau) = \int_1^\infty e^{-\tau x} x^{-n}\, dx$$

is the exponential integral function.

The source function given by (31) agrees with the first approximation $J(\tau) = H(2 + 3\tau)$ at an optical depth where $2E_2(\tau) = 3E_3(\tau)$. This occurs when $\tau \doteq 0\cdot 42$ and also as $\tau \to \infty$, when both E_2 and $E_3 \to 0$. Hence radiation in the surface layers down to $\tau \doteq 0\cdot 42$ is less intense than on the first approximation, and slightly exceeds the first approximation at greater optical depths. Equation (32) gives $H(\tau) = H$ only at $\tau = 0$ and $\tau = \infty$. The constancy of H is, of course, an essential feature of the problem. This departure of the net flux in the outer layers from the prescribed boundary value $4\pi H$ is due to the deficiencies in the first approximation to the source function, from which (32) was calculated. For the same reason equation (33) does not reproduce the *exact* linearity required by (8) namely $K = H\tau + \text{constant}$. It is possible to amend the approximation (31) and construct an 'amended second approximation' which makes a small adjustment to (31) in order to rectify this deficiency.

5.31. *The amended second approximation*

From equations (31) and (33) we find

$$Kf(\tau) = \tfrac{1}{3}J,$$

where
$$f(\tau) = \frac{2 + 3\tau - E_2(\tau) + \tfrac{3}{2}E_3(\tau)}{2 + 3\tau - 3E_4(\tau) + \tfrac{9}{2}E_5(\tau)}.$$

This replaces the result $K = \tfrac{1}{3}J$ used in the first approximation. Now equation (8), $K = H\tau + \text{const}$, is an *exact* condition of the problem, and we therefore have

$$J(\tau) = 3f(\tau)[H\tau + \text{const}].$$

Since $E_n(0) = 1/(n-1)$, we find $f(0) = \tfrac{14}{17}$. Applying the boundary condition $J(0) = \tfrac{7}{4}H$, we find

$$J(\tau) = Hf(\tau)[\tfrac{17}{8} + 3\tau]. \tag{34}$$

With $J = (\sigma/\pi)T^4$, the temperature distribution is given by

$$T^4 = \tfrac{3}{4}T_e^4 f(\tau)[\tau+\tfrac{17}{24}].\tag{35}$$

It is convenient to write (34) and (35) in the alternative forms

$$J(\tau) = \tfrac{3}{4}\mathfrak{F}[\tau+q(\tau)],$$

$$T^4 = \tfrac{3}{4}T_e^4[\tau+q(\tau)],$$

where $\qquad\qquad q(\tau) = f(\tau)(\tau+\tfrac{17}{24})-\tau.\tag{36}$

In this notation the first approximation gave $q(\tau) = \tfrac{2}{3}$. Equation (32) gives $q(\tau) = \tfrac{2}{3}-\tfrac{1}{3}E_2(\tau)+\tfrac{1}{2}E_3(\tau)$. The amended second approximation (34) (which was given by Eddington) goes one step higher than (31) by restoring the constancy of H.

5.32. *Limb darkening*

Equation (25) with $\tau = 0$ gives the limb darkening formula

$$I(0,\mu) = \int_0^\infty e^{-t/\mu}J(t)\,dt/\mu \quad (\mu = \cos\theta).$$

The first approximation gave $J(t) = H(2+3t)$ and

$$I(0,\mu) = H(2+3\mu) = \tfrac{3}{4}\mathfrak{F}(\tfrac{2}{3}+\mu).\tag{37}$$

Equation (31) may be used to give a higher approximation to the darkening of the limb. From it we find

$$I(0,\mu) = \tfrac{3}{4}\mathfrak{F}\left[\tfrac{7}{12}+\tfrac{1}{2}\mu+(\tfrac{1}{2}\mu^2+\tfrac{1}{3}\mu)\ln\frac{1+\mu}{\mu}\right].\tag{38}$$

Since $\lim\limits_{\mu\to 0}\mu\ln\mu = 0$ we have in this approximation $I(0,0) = \tfrac{7}{16}\mathfrak{F}$, a result which also follows from the second approximation to the boundary condition.

The amended second approximation to the limb darkening follows from Eddington's approximation to $J(\tau)$ given by equation (34). The function $f(\tau)$ is an increasing function of the optical depth taking the value $\tfrac{14}{17}$ at $\tau = 0$, and $f(\tau)\to 1$ as $\tau\to\infty$. Accordingly we set $f(\tau) = 1-g(\tau)$, and express $g(\tau)$ as a sum of exponential terms. Thus we write

$$g(\tau) = \sum_j \alpha_j e^{-\beta_j\tau}.$$

Writing equation (34) in the form

$$J(t) = \tfrac{3}{4}\mathfrak{F}[\tfrac{17}{24}+t-(\tfrac{17}{24}+t)g(t)],$$

the limb darkening is now given by

$$I(0,\mu) = \tfrac{3}{4}\mathfrak{F}\left[\tfrac{17}{24}+\mu-\int_0^\infty (\tfrac{17}{24}+t)e^{-t/\mu}\sum_j \alpha_j e^{-\beta_j t}\,dt/\mu\right].$$

The integral within the square brackets may be written as

$$\sum_j \frac{\alpha_j}{1+\mu\beta_j}\int_0^\infty e^{-t/\mu_j}(\tfrac{17}{24}+t)\,dt/\mu_j,$$

where $\mu_j = \mu/(1+\mu\beta_j)$. Hence

$$I(0,\mu) = \tfrac{3}{4}\mathfrak{F}\left[\tfrac{17}{24}+\mu-\sum_j \frac{\alpha_j}{1+\mu\beta_j}\left(\frac{17}{24}+\frac{\mu}{1+\mu\beta_j}\right)\right]. \tag{39}$$

The darkening ratios $I(0,\mu)/\mathfrak{F}$ in the first approximation, the second approximation, and the amended (Eddington) second approximation are given in Table I.

TABLE I

$$I(0,\mu)/\mathfrak{F}$$

μ	First approximation eqn. (37)	Second approximations	
		eqn. (38)	eqn. (39)
0·0	0·5000	0·4375	0·4375
0·1	0·5750	0·5439	0·5430
0·2	0·6500	0·6290	0·6303
0·3	0·7250	0·7095	0·7128
0·4	0·8000	0·7880	0·7930
0·5	0·8750	0·8653	0·8719
0·6	0·9500	0·9420	0·9500
0·7	1·0250	1·0185	1·0276
0·8	1·1000	1·0942	1·1046
0·9	1·1750	1·1702	1·1815
1·0	1·2500	1·2457	1·2581

OTHER APPROXIMATE METHODS OF SOLVING THE EQUATION OF TRANSFER

1. Schwarzschild's approximate solution

THE necessary condition of the radiative equilibrium of the outer layers is that the net flux

$$\pi \mathfrak{F} = \int I(\tau, \theta) \cos \theta \, d\omega \tag{1}$$

is constant from one layer to another, since there are no sources or sinks of energy in the atmosphere. Although the fundamental property (1) is not satisfied by an approximate solution due to Schwarzschild, we give a discussion of this early approximation for the purpose of comparison with other approximate solutions.

1.1. *Equations for the mean intensities*

We define the mean outward and inward intensities by the relations

$$\left.\begin{aligned} I_+ &= \frac{1}{2\pi} \int_+ I \, d\omega \\[2mm] I_- &= \frac{1}{2\pi} \int_- I \, d\omega \end{aligned}\right\}, \tag{2}$$

the integrals being taken over the outward hemisphere of directions for I_+, and over the inward hemisphere for I_-. In the equation of transfer

$$\cos \theta \frac{dI}{d\tau} = I - J \tag{3}$$

we now have

$$J(\tau) = \frac{1}{4\pi} \int I \, d\omega = \tfrac{1}{2}(I_+ + I_-). \tag{4}$$

Multiplying equation (3) by $d\omega = 2\pi \sin \theta \, d\theta$ and integrating over the outward directions from $\theta = 0$ to $\tfrac{1}{2}\pi$, we find

$$\frac{d}{d\tau} \int_0^{\frac{1}{2}\pi} I(\tau, \theta) \sin \theta \cos \theta \, d\theta = I_+ - \tfrac{1}{2}(I_+ + I_-). \tag{5}$$

We write $\theta = \pi - \varphi$ for the inward directions and multiply (3) by $d\omega = 2\pi \sin \varphi \, d\varphi$ and integrate from $\varphi = 0$ to $\tfrac{1}{2}\pi$. This gives

$$-\frac{d}{d\tau} \int_0^{\frac{1}{2}\pi} I(\tau, \varphi) \sin \varphi \cos \varphi \, d\varphi = I_- - \tfrac{1}{2}(I_+ + I_-). \tag{6}$$

As an approximation we replace the intensity in the integrals in equations (5) and (6) by the mean intensities in the outward and inward directions. This amounts to ignoring the dependence of the radiation intensity on direction, and calculating the outward and inward flux when the radiation field is considered as an inward and outward stream with intensities defined by equation (2). Using this approximation, equation (1) gives

$$\mathfrak{F} = I_+ - I_-, \tag{7}$$

and the pair of equations (5) and (6) take the approximate forms

$$\frac{1}{2}\frac{dI_+}{d\tau} = I_+ - \tfrac{1}{2}(I_+ + I_-), \tag{8}$$

$$-\frac{1}{2}\frac{dI_-}{d\tau} = I_- - \tfrac{1}{2}(I_+ + I_-), \tag{9}$$

which are Schwarzschild's equations for the mean intensities. Adding equations (8) and (9) we get

$$\frac{d\mathfrak{F}}{d\tau} = 0, \tag{10}$$

and subtracting (9) from (8)

$$\frac{dJ}{d\tau} = \mathfrak{F}. \tag{11}$$

The boundary condition is that there is no inflow of radiation at $\tau = 0$, or $I_- = 0$ at $\tau = 0$. Then at the surface $\mathfrak{F} = I_+$ and $J = \tfrac{1}{2}I_+$, so that the condition is $J = \tfrac{1}{2}\mathfrak{F}$. Equations (10) and (11) therefore give

$$J = \tfrac{1}{2}\mathfrak{F}(1 + 2\tau). \tag{12}$$

Notice that the use of mean intensities I_+ and I_- is similar to the approximation $I(\theta) = I_1$ for $0 < \theta < \tfrac{1}{2}\pi$, and $I(\theta) = I_2$ for $\tfrac{1}{2}\pi < \theta < \pi$ used in Eddington's first approximation, and Eddington's boundary condition $J = 2H$ is exactly the same as Schwarzschild's $J = \tfrac{1}{2}\mathfrak{F}$. The approximations differ because, apart from the boundary condition, Eddington only uses the mean intensities to establish the result $K = \tfrac{1}{3}J$, which does not, in fact (Section 3 of Chapter I), imply the restriction on $I(\theta)$, and the equation which Eddington uses, $K = H\tau + \text{constant}$, is exact. His approximation is, accordingly, higher than Schwarzschild's.

1.2. *Limb darkening and the net flux*

With the source function given by (12), equations (25) and (26) of Chapter I for the angular distribution of the intensity at any depth give

$$I(\tau, \theta) = \tfrac{1}{2}\mathfrak{F}(1 + 2\cos\theta + 2\tau), \tag{13}$$

$$I(\tau, \varphi) = \tfrac{1}{2}\mathfrak{F}\{(1 - 2\cos\varphi)(1 - e^{-\tau\sec\varphi}) + 2\tau\}. \tag{14}$$

C

From equation (13) we obtain the limb darkening formula

$$I(0, \theta) = \tfrac{1}{2}\mathfrak{F}(1 + 2\cos\theta). \tag{15}$$

We now apply a check to the limb darkening formula by calculating the flux F at the surface, where

$$F = \int_0^{\frac{1}{2}\pi} 2\pi I(0, \theta)\sin\theta\cos\theta \, d\theta,$$

which should be equal to $\pi\mathfrak{F}$. With $I(0, \theta)$ given by (15) we find $F = \tfrac{7}{6}\pi\mathfrak{F}$. Neglecting the exponential term in (14) for large values of τ, the net flux in the innermost layers is readily found to be equal to $\tfrac{4}{3}\pi\mathfrak{F}$. Schwarzschild's approximation therefore leads to different values of the net flux at the boundary of the star and in the deep interior.

Milne, who discovered the relation $T^4 = T_0^4(1 + \tfrac{3}{2}\tau)$ before Eddington's treatment appeared, did so by considering the asymptotic behaviour of $J(\tau)$ at great depths. Since the radiation there tends to become isotropic, $K = \tfrac{1}{3}J$. Milne therefore abandoned (11), wrote

$$J(\tau) = J(0) + \tfrac{3}{4}\mathfrak{F}\tau,$$

and took $J(0)$ from Schwarzschild's boundary condition. As has been said in Chapter I, the Milne–Eddington treatment removes the flux errors in Schwarzschild's approximation.

2. Chandrasekhar's approximations

We write the equation of transfer in the form

$$\mu\frac{dI}{d\tau} = I - \tfrac{1}{2}\int_{-1}^{+1} I \, d\mu. \tag{16}$$

The principle of the method used by Chandrasekhar[†] to solve the integro-differential equation (16) was originally introduced by Wick[‡] in connexion with a diffusion problem. The integral in (16) is expressed as a sum of weighted intensities by means of a formula in numerical integration given by Gauss. This reduces (16) to a system of linear differential equations for the intensities in directions corresponding to the points of subdivision of the range of integration. From these equations the source function

$$J = \tfrac{1}{2}\int_{-1}^{+1} I \, d\mu$$

is found from the Gaussian sum. The intensity in any direction then

† S. Chandrasekhar, *Ap. J.* **100**, 76 (1944); *Radiative Transfer* (Oxford), chap. ii.
‡ G. C. Wick, *Zs. f. Phys.* **121**, 702 (1943).

follows from equations (25) and (26) of Chapter I. The use of Gauss's quadrature formula amounts to assuming an expansion of the intensity $I(\mu)$ in powers of μ ($= \cos\theta$), the highest power depending upon the number of divisions of the range of integration used in constructing the Gaussian sum for $J(\tau)$.

The Gaussian sum for the source function. The integral for J may be represented approximately by a weighted average of the intensities at suitably selected points in the range of integration, as in numerical integration. We write

$$J \simeq \tfrac{1}{2} \sum_{j=1}^{m} a_j I_j,$$

where m is the number of points into which the range of integration is divided, and a_j are the weight factors. Gauss has shown that for a given number of divisions the best representation of an integral is obtained when the spacing of the division points is symmetrical about the mid-point of the range of integration, the interval being divided according to the zeros μ_j of a Legendre polynomial $P_m(\mu)$. The weight factors are given by

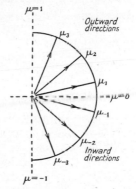

Fig. 5. Gaussian division of the interval from $\mu = -1$ to $+1$ for $n = 3$.

$$a_j = \frac{1}{P'_m(\mu_j)} \int_{-1}^{+1} \frac{P_m(\mu)}{\mu - \mu_j} \, d\mu.$$

The Gaussian sum would give exact values of the integral if $I(\mu)$ could be written down as a polynomial in μ of degree less than or equal to $2m-1$.

It is convenient to use the even order polynomials $P_{2n}(\mu)$ with zeros $\mu_{-n}, \ldots, \mu_{-1}, \mu_1, \ldots, \mu_n$. Gauss's formula for numerical quadrature then gives

$$\int_{-1}^{+1} I(\tau, \mu) \, d\mu \simeq \sum_{j=-n}^{+n} a_j I(\tau, \mu_j), \qquad (17)$$

the summation not including the term $j = 0$. The weight factors a_j (Christoffel numbers), and the subdivision points μ_j, have the properties $a_j = a_{-j}$; $\mu_j = -\mu_{-j}$. Formula (17) is exact for any polynomial of degree $m \leqslant 4n-1$, and in particular

$$\sum_{j=-n}^{+n} a_j \mu_j^m = \int_{-1}^{+1} \mu^m \, d\mu = \begin{cases} \text{zero,} & m \text{ odd,} \\ \dfrac{2}{m+1}, & m \text{ even.} \end{cases} \qquad (18)$$

2.1. *Equations for the intensities, and the general solution*

The integral representation as a finite sum according to equation (17) can be made as accurate as we please by choosing n sufficiently large. Chandrasekhar calls the process in which there are $2n$ divisions of the range of integration, the nth approximation. Equation (16) is now replaced by $2n$ equations, each being a linear equation for the intensity in a direction corresponding to the zero μ_i of the polynomial $P_{2n}(\mu)$. The linear system of simultaneous equations for the intensity in the $2n$ directions μ_i are

$$\mu_i \frac{dI_i}{d\tau} = I_i - \tfrac{1}{2} \sum_{j=-n}^{+n} a_j I_j \qquad (i = \pm 1, \pm 2, ..., \pm n), \qquad (19)$$

the positive signs for i corresponding to the outward intensity in the n directions μ_i, and the negative signs corresponding to the inward directions. When the general solution of (19) is known, we may calculate the source function $J(\tau) = \tfrac{1}{2} \sum_{-n}^{n} a_i I_i$ on the nth approximation, and hence the intensity $I(\tau, \mu)$ in any direction from equations (25) and (26) of Chapter I.

The general solution. We find the linearly independent solutions of equation (19) and then combine them to obtain the general solution.

A solution of the form

$$I_i = g_{i,\alpha} e^{-k_\alpha \tau}, \qquad (20)$$

with $g_{i,\alpha}$ and k_α constant, satisfies equation (19) if

$$g_{i,\alpha}(1 + \mu_i k_\alpha) = \tfrac{1}{2} \sum_{-n}^{+n} a_j g_{j,\alpha}. \qquad (21)$$

Calling the right-hand side of (21) C_α, a constant independent of i, we have

$$g_{i,\alpha} = \frac{C_\alpha}{1 + \mu_i k_\alpha}.$$

Substituting this form for $g_{i,\alpha}$ into equation (21) we obtain the following equation for k_α:

$$1 = \frac{1}{2} \sum_{-n}^{+n} \frac{a_j}{1 + \mu_j k_\alpha}. \qquad (22)$$

Introducing into this summation the properties $a_{-j} = a_j$, $\mu_{-j} = -\mu_j$ and multiplying numerator and denominator of the first n terms by $1 + \mu_j k_\alpha$, and of the last n terms by $1 - \mu_j k_\alpha$, we rewrite equation (22) in the form

$$1 = \sum_{j=1}^{n} \frac{a_j}{1 - \mu_j^2 k_\alpha^2}. \qquad (23)$$

Consequently k_α^2 satisfies an algebraic equation of order n, and since $\sum_{j=1}^{n} a_j = 1$ by equation (18), $k_\alpha^2 = 0$ is a root of equation (23). Hence (22) gives only $2n-2$ distinct roots for k_α in the pairs $\pm k_\alpha$, $\alpha = 1, 2,..., n-1$. We therefore seek another solution of equation (19) in the linear form

$$I_i = b(\tau + q_i), \tag{24}$$

where b is an arbitrary constant. Substituting (24) in (19) we find

$$\mu_i = q_i - \tfrac{1}{2} \sum_{-n}^{+n} a_j q_j$$

or

$$q_i = \mu_i + Q \tag{25}$$

where Q is a constant, independent of i. Equation (24) now becomes

$$I_i = b(\tau + Q + \mu_i). \tag{26}$$

Combining the linearly independent solutions (20) and (26) we have for the general solution of equation (19)

$$I_i = b\left\{ \sum_{\alpha=1}^{n-1} \left[\frac{L_\alpha e^{-k_\alpha \tau}}{1 + \mu_i k_\alpha} + \frac{L_{-\alpha} e^{+k_\alpha \tau}}{1 - \mu_i k_\alpha} \right] + \mu_i + Q + \tau \right\}, \tag{27}$$

where b, $L_{\pm\alpha}$ ($\alpha = 1, 2,..., n-1$), and Q are $2n$ arbitrary constants.

Boundary conditions. Since none of the I_i's increase exponentially as $\tau \to \infty$ we must have all $L_{-\alpha} = 0$. Thus

$$I_i = b\left\{ \sum_{\alpha=1}^{n-1} \frac{L_\alpha e^{-k_\alpha \tau}}{1 + \mu_i k_\alpha} + \mu_i + Q + \tau \right\} \qquad (i = \pm 1,..., \pm n). \tag{28}$$

The $n-1$ constants L_α and also Q may be determined by the condition that at the boundary $\tau = 0$ there is no inflowing radiation, and consequently all the I_i's are zero for $i = -1, -2,..., -n$. Using $\mu_{-i} = -\mu_i$, equation (27) gives the following n equations:

$$\sum_{\alpha=1}^{n-1} \frac{L_\alpha}{1 - \mu_i k_\alpha} + Q = \mu_i \qquad (i = 1, 2,..., n). \tag{29}$$

The roots k_α being given by (23), the simultaneous equations (29) may be solved for the L_α, and Q.

The remaining constant b may be found by evaluating the Gaussian sum for the net flux $F \ (= \pi \mathfrak{F})$. We have

$$\mathfrak{F} = 2 \int_{-1}^{+1} \mu I \, d\mu \simeq 2 \sum a_i \mu_i I_i, \tag{30}$$

where the I_i are given by equation (28). Equation (30) gives

$$\mathfrak{F} = \tfrac{4}{3} b. \tag{31}$$

2.2. *The source function in the n-th approximation*

Having found the general solution of equation (19) we now calculate $J(\tau)$. This is given by $\frac{1}{2} \sum\limits_{-n}^{+n} a_i I_i$. We therefore have

$$J(\tau) = \tfrac{1}{2}b\left\{ \sum_{-n}^{+n} a_i\left(\sum_{\alpha=1}^{n-1} \frac{L_\alpha e^{-k_\alpha \tau}}{1+\mu_i k_\alpha} +\mu_i+Q+\tau \right) \right\}$$

$$= \tfrac{1}{2}b\left\{ \sum_{\alpha=1}^{n-1}\left(L_\alpha e^{-k_\alpha\tau} \sum_{-n}^{+n} \frac{a_i}{1+\mu_i k_\alpha} \right) + \sum_{-n}^{+n} a_i\mu_i + (Q+\tau)\sum_{-n}^{+n} a_i \right\}.$$

Using results from equation (18), together with equations (22) and (31), this reduces to

$$J(\tau) = \tfrac{3}{4}\mathfrak{F}[\tau+q(\tau)],\tag{32}$$

where
$$q(\tau) = Q + \sum_{\alpha=1}^{n-1} L_\alpha e^{-k_\alpha\tau}.$$

Consider the function

$$S(\mu) = Q-\mu+ \sum_{\alpha=1}^{n-1} \frac{L_\alpha}{1-\mu k_\alpha}.\tag{33}$$

From equation (32) and (33) we have

$$q(0) = Q + \sum_{\alpha=1}^{n-1} L_\alpha = S(0).\tag{34}$$

If we multiply (33) by the function

$$R(\mu) = (1-\mu k_1)(1-\mu k_2)...(1-\mu k_{n-1}),$$

we obtain $P(\mu) = R(\mu)S(\mu)$, a polynomial of degree n. According to the boundary relation (29) we have

$$S(\mu_i) = 0 \qquad (i = 1, 2,..., n),$$

so that $P(\mu)$ vanishes for $\mu = \mu_i$, $i = 1, 2,..., n$. Hence

$$P(\mu) = C(\mu-\mu_1)(\mu-\mu_2)...(\mu-\mu_n),\tag{35}$$

where C is a constant. Comparing the coefficients of μ^n in (35) and in the product $R(\mu)S(\mu)$ we find

$$C = (-1)^n k_1 k_2 ... k_{n-1}.$$

Since $P(0) = C\mu_1\mu_2...\mu_n(-1)^n$ and $R(0) = 1$, equation (34) gives

$$q(0) = P(0)/R(0) = k_1 k_2 ... k_{n-1}\mu_1\mu_2...\mu_n.\tag{36}$$

The product $k_1^2 k_2^2 ... k_{n-1}^2$ follows from equation (23), which gives

$$\prod_{i=1}^{n} (1-\mu_i^2 k^2) = \sum_{i=1}^{n} a_i - \sum_{i=1}^{n} a_i\left(\sum_{j=1}^{n} \mu_j^2 - \mu_i^2 \right) k^2 + ...$$

$$... + \mu_1^2\mu_2^2 ... \mu_n^2(-1)^{n-1}k^{2n-2} \sum_{i=1}^{n} a_i/\mu_i^2.\tag{37}$$

Since $\sum a_i = 1$ and $\sum a_i \mu_i^2 = \frac{1}{3}$ the right-hand side of (37) gives

$$1-\left(\sum_{i=1}^{n}\mu_i^2-\tfrac{1}{3}\right)k^2+\ldots+\mu_1^2\mu_2^2\ldots\mu_n^2(-1)^{n-1}k^{2n-2}\sum_{i=1}^{n}a_i/\mu_i^2.$$

The left-hand side of (37) is simply

$$1-k^2\sum_{i=1}^{n}\mu_i^2+\ldots-\mu_1^2\mu_2^2\ldots\mu_n^2(-1)^{n-1}k^{2n}.$$

Hence $$\mu_1^2\mu_2^2\ldots\mu_n^2(-1)^{n-1}k^{2n-2}+\ldots+\tfrac{1}{3}=0$$

is the required polynomial form for the $n-1$ non-zero roots of k^2. Writing the polynomial in its factorized form

$$(k^2-k_1^2)(k^2-k_2^2)\ldots(k^2-k_{n-1}^2)=0$$

we find $$k_1^2 k_2^2\ldots k_{n-1}^2(-1)^{n-1}=\frac{1}{3\mu_1^2\mu_2^2\ldots\mu_n^2(-1)^{n-1}}.\qquad(38)$$

Substituting for the product of the roots in (36) we find

$$q(0)=\frac{1}{\sqrt{3}},$$

which is independent of n and is therefore an exact relation. With this value of $q(0)$ equation (32) gives

$$J(0)=\tfrac{3}{4}\Im q(0)=\tfrac{1}{4}\sqrt{3}\Im,\qquad(39)$$

a result originally derived by Hopf and Bronstein from the integral equations of radiative equilibrium, as shown in Section 2.2 of Chapter III.

2.21. *The intensity in any direction*

The source function being given by equation (32), the intensity $I(\tau,\mu)$ may be found from equations (25) and (26) of Chapter I, namely

$$1\geqslant\mu\geqslant0,\qquad I(\tau,\mu)=\int_{\tau}^{\infty}e^{-(t-\tau)/\mu}J(t)\,dt/\mu,\qquad(40)$$

$$0\geqslant\mu\geqslant-1\qquad I(\tau,\mu')=\int_{0}^{\tau}e^{-(\tau-t)/\mu'}J(t)\,dt/\mu'.\qquad(41)$$

$$(\mu=-\mu'),$$

When the source function is given, these two equations are the solution of the equation of transfer. From (32) we have in the nth approximation

$$J(t)=\tfrac{3}{4}\Im\Big\{t+Q+\sum_{\alpha=1}^{n-1}L_\alpha e^{-k_\alpha t}\Big\}.$$

Equation (40) gives

$$I(\tau,\mu)=\tfrac{3}{4}\Im\Big\{\tau+Q+\mu+\sum_{\alpha=1}^{n-1}\frac{L_\alpha e^{-k_\alpha\tau}}{1+\mu k_\alpha}\Big\},\qquad(42)$$

which is the same as the intensity $I(\tau, \mu_i)$, given by (28) but with the suffix i deleted. The result is, however, different for the inward intensity. From (41) we obtain

$$I(\tau, \mu') = \tfrac{3}{4}\mathfrak{F}\left\{\tau + (Q - \mu')(1 - e^{-\tau/\mu'}) + \sum_{\alpha=1}^{n-1} \frac{L_\alpha}{1 - \mu' k_\alpha}(e^{-k_\alpha \tau} - e^{-\tau/\mu'})\right\}, \quad (43)$$

whereas equation (28) gives

$$I(\tau, \mu_{-i}) = \tfrac{3}{4}\mathfrak{F}\left\{\tau + Q - \mu_i + \sum_{\alpha=1}^{n-1} \frac{L_\alpha e^{-k_\alpha \tau}}{1 - \mu_i k_\alpha}\right\}.$$

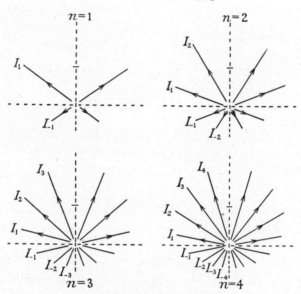

$n=1$ $n=2$

$n=3$ $n=4$

Fig. 6. The intensities I_i in the first four approximations at $\tau = 1$ with the equivalent mean intensity $\mathfrak{F}$ as unit.

There is no difficulty about points of infinite discontinuity for certain inward directions in the summation in equation (43). If we set $1/\mu' = k_\alpha + \epsilon$, we readily find

$$\lim_{\epsilon \to 0} \frac{L_\alpha}{1 - \mu' k_\alpha}(e^{-k_\alpha \tau} - e^{-\tau/\mu'}) = L_\alpha k_\alpha \tau e^{-k_\alpha \tau}.$$

Thus if β be any one of the $n-1$ positive non-zero roots of k, and $\mu'_\beta = \dfrac{1}{k_\beta}$ we have

$$I(\tau, \mu'_\beta) = \tfrac{3}{4}\mathfrak{F}\left\{\tau + (Q - \mu'_\beta)(1 - e^{-k_\beta \tau}) + L_\beta k_\beta \tau e^{-k_\beta \tau} + \right.$$
$$\left. + \sum_{\alpha=1}^{n-1}{}' \frac{L_\alpha}{1 - k_\alpha/k_\beta}(e^{-k_\alpha \tau} - e^{-k_\beta \tau})\right\},$$

in which the prime on the summation indicates the omission of the term with $\alpha = \beta$.

2.3. *Calculation of the integration constants*

In the nth approximation the Gaussian points of division of the range of integration in equation (16) are given by the zeros of the Legendre polynomial $P_{2n}(\mu)$. Since

$$P_m(\mu) = \frac{1}{2^m m!} \frac{d^m}{d\mu^m} (\mu^2 - 1)^m,$$

the zeros are given by the roots of the equation

$$\frac{d^m}{d\mu^m} (\mu^2 - 1)^m = 0.$$

The roots μ_j and the weights a_j are tabulated quantities.†

The values of k_α follow from equation (23), a polynomial of order n in k^2 and having $n-1$ non-zero roots. The $n-1$ constants L_α and Q may be found either by solving the n simultaneous equations (29), or more conveniently as follows: from (33) and (35) we find

$$S(\mu) = Q - \mu + \sum_{\alpha=1}^{n-1} \frac{L_\alpha}{1 - \mu k_\alpha}$$

$$= (-1)^n k_1 k_2 \ldots k_{n-1} \frac{(\mu - \mu_1)(\mu - \mu_2)\ldots(\mu - \mu_n)}{(1 - \mu k_1)(1 - \mu k_2)\ldots(1 - \mu k_{n-1})}. \quad (44)$$

The $n-1$ values of L_α may be readily obtained from (44), as in partial fractions, by multiplying throughout by $1 - \mu k_\alpha$ and then setting $\mu = 1/k_\alpha$ This gives

$$L_\alpha = (-1)^n \frac{k_1 k_2 \ldots k_{n-1}}{k_\alpha^n} \frac{\prod_{i=1}^{n} (1 - \mu_i k_\alpha)}{\prod_{i=1}^{n-1}{}' (1 - k_i/k_\alpha)}, \quad (45)$$

the prime on the product in the denominator indicating the omission of the factor for which $i = \alpha$. Since the left-hand side of (44) vanishes for $\mu = \mu_i$, we have

$$Q = \mu_i - \sum_{\alpha=1}^{n-1} \frac{L_\alpha}{1 - \mu_i k_\alpha}. \quad (46)$$

2.4. *Limb darkening in the n-th approximation*

The darkening of the limb in the nth approximation is given by (42) with $\tau = 0$. We have

$$I(0, \mu) = \tfrac{3}{4} \mathfrak{F} \left[\mu + Q + \sum_{\alpha=1}^{n-1} \frac{L_\alpha}{1 + \mu k_\alpha} \right]. \quad (47)$$

† A. N. Lowan, N. Davids, and A. Levenson, *Bull. American Math. Soc.* **48**, 739 (1942).

Using equation (44) defining $S(\mu)$, the limb darkening formula (47) may be written
$$I(0,\mu) = \tfrac{3}{4}\mathfrak{F}S(-\mu),$$

where
$$S(\mu) = (-1)^n k_1 k_2 \dots k_{n-1} \frac{\prod\limits_{i=1}^{n}(\mu-\mu_i)}{\prod\limits_{\alpha=1}^{n-1}(1-\mu k_\alpha)}.$$

According to (38),
$$k_1 k_2 \dots k_{n-1} \mu_1 \mu_2 \dots \mu_n = 1/\sqrt{3},$$

and we write $S(-\mu) = \dfrac{1}{\sqrt{3}}H(\mu)$, where

$$H(\mu) = \frac{1}{\mu_1 \mu_2 \dots \mu_n} \frac{\prod\limits_{i=1}^{n}(\mu+\mu_i)}{\prod\limits_{\alpha=1}^{n-1}(1+\mu k_\alpha)}. \tag{48}$$

In terms of the function $H(\mu)$, the limb darkening is given by

$$I(0,\mu) = \frac{\sqrt{3}}{4}\mathfrak{F}H(\mu). \tag{49}$$

Equation (47) for the limb darkening involved the integration constants L_α and Q which have been eliminated in (49), a closed form in the general nth approximation. The elimination of the integration constants is possible because the limb darkening is described by a function in the range $0 \leqslant \mu \leqslant 1$, while the boundary conditions specify the zeros of the same function in the complementary interval $-1 \leqslant \mu \leqslant 0$.

It may be shown† that the function $H(\mu)$ defined by equation (48) satisfies the equation

$$H(\mu) = 1 + \tfrac{1}{2}\mu H(\mu) \sum_{j=1}^{n} \frac{a_j H(\mu_j)}{\mu+\mu_j}.$$

Now the summation in this equation is the Gaussian sum for the integral

$$\int_0^1 \frac{H(x)}{\mu+x}\,dx,$$

and the approximation to this integral can be made as accurate as we please by taking n sufficiently large. Therefore the limit function

$$\lim_{n\to\infty} \frac{1}{\mu_1 \mu_2 \dots \mu_n} \frac{\prod\limits_{i=1}^{n}(\mu+\mu_i)}{\prod\limits_{\alpha=1}^{n-1}(1+\mu k_\alpha)}$$

---

† S. Chandrasekhar. *Ap. J.* **105**, 164 (1947); *Radiative Transfer* (Oxford), chap. v.

satisfies
$$H(\mu) = 1 + \tfrac{1}{2}\mu H(\mu) \int_0^1 \frac{H(x)}{\mu + x}\, dx,$$

an equation known as Ambarzumian's functional equation. The solution for $H(\mu)$ may be obtained by iteration, starting with the evaluation of the integral by means of an approximate form for $H(\mu)$ from equation (48). When $H(\mu)$ satisfies the functional equation, Chandrasekhar's solution (49) for the emergent intensity becomes an exact solution. This is sometimes referred to as the solution in the infinite approximation.

2.5. *The first approximation and higher approximations*

In the first approximation we have $n = 1$, and (17) becomes a two point quadrature formula with $a_1 = a_{-1} = 1$ and $\mu_1 = -\mu_{-1} = 1/\sqrt{3}$. To determine the integration constants in this simple case, we notice that equation (23) only gives $k^2 = 0$. Since there are no non-zero roots for k^2, the exponential part (20) of the general solution for the intensities does not appear. Hence equation (29) gives $Q = \mu_1 = 1/\sqrt{3}$, and from (32) we therefore have $q(\tau) = 1/\sqrt{3}$. According to (47), the darkening of the limb is then given by

$$I(0, \mu) = \tfrac{3}{4}\mathfrak{F}\left(\mu + \frac{1}{\sqrt{3}}\right). \tag{50}$$

The Gaussian sums for J, H, and K give

$$J = \tfrac{1}{2}\sum a_j I_j = \tfrac{1}{2}(I_1 + I_{-1}), \tag{51}$$

$$H = \tfrac{1}{2}\sum a_j \mu_j I_j = \tfrac{1}{2}(I_1 - I_{-1})/\sqrt{3}, \tag{52}$$

$$K = \tfrac{1}{2}\sum a_j \mu_j^2 I_j = \tfrac{1}{6}(I_1 + I_{-1}). \tag{53}$$

Using equation (51), the simultaneous differential equations (19) for the intensities take the form

$$\frac{1}{\sqrt{3}}\frac{dI_1}{d\tau} = I_1 - \tfrac{1}{2}(I_1 + I_{-1}), \tag{54}$$

$$-\frac{1}{\sqrt{3}}\frac{dI_{-1}}{d\tau} = I_{-1} - \tfrac{1}{2}(I_1 + I_{-1}). \tag{55}$$

Except for the appearance of the factor $1/\sqrt{3}$ on the left-hand side, equations (54) and (55) are essentially the same as Schwarzschild's equations (8) and (9) for the mean intensities. Schwarzschild's net flux equation (7) is here replaced by (52) which gives

$$\mathfrak{F} = \frac{2}{\sqrt{3}}(I_1 - I_{-1}). \tag{56}$$

The solution of (54) and (55) for the intensities is given directly by equation (28). We have

$$I_1 = \tfrac{3}{4}\mathfrak{F}\left(\frac{2}{\sqrt{3}} + \tau\right), \qquad I_{-1} = \tfrac{3}{4}\mathfrak{F}\tau.$$

With $I_{-1} = 0$ in equations (51) and (52), we get the boundary condition $J = \sqrt{3}\,H = \tfrac{1}{4}\sqrt{3}\,\mathfrak{F}$. According to (39), this boundary value of J is the same in all approximations.

Consider the Gaussian summations (51), (52), and (53) for J, H, and K. Since the quadrature formula

$$\int\limits_{-1}^{+1} f(\mu)\,d\mu \simeq \sum_{-n}^{+n} a_j\,f(\mu_j)$$

is exact when $f(\mu)$ can be expressed as a polynomial of degree $4n-1$ or less, the sum for K in equation (53) will be exact if $f(\mu) = \mu^2 I(\mu)$ is a polynomial of the third degree in μ. Thus if $I(\mu)$ is of the form $a + b\mu$, the Gaussian sums for J, H, and K in the first approximation are *all* exact. From (51) and (53) we have $K = \tfrac{1}{3}J$, a result which is also true if $I(\mu)$ can be expressed as a convergent series in odd powers of μ.

Chandrasekhar's solution in the first approximation is in some respects equivalent to the Milne–Eddington approximation. The following differences at the boundary should be noted:

(i) If we use the linear form $I(\mu) = a + b\mu$ directly, as in Chapter 1, § 2, we have to adopt the vanishing of the inward flux as the boundary condition, and *not* the vanishing of the inward intensity at the surface. This is necessary because the condition of zero intensity inwards at the surface is satisfied by the linear form for $I(\mu)$ only for one direction given by $\mu = -J(0)/3H$. This direction is unknown until we know the boundary value of J. The alternative condition, the vanishing of the inward flux at $\tau = 0$, gives $J(0) = 2H$. This is equivalent to making the intensity vanish for $\mu = -\tfrac{2}{3}$. On the other hand, by using the Gaussian formula we do not have to deal with the coefficients in the polynomial form for $I(\mu)$, but we find exact values of the integrals for J, H, and K in terms of the intensities in certain directions. In the first approximation the directions are $\mu = 1/\sqrt{3}$ and $-1/\sqrt{3}$. Taking the boundary condition as the vanishing of the intensity in the direction $\mu = -1/\sqrt{3}$, we get $J(0) = \sqrt{3}\,H$. This happens to be the exact value of J at the boundary.

(ii) From Chandrasekhar's solution (50) for the emergent intensity in the first approximation we find

$$\frac{1}{2} \int_0^1 \mu I(0,\mu)\, d\mu = H\left(\frac{1}{2}+\frac{\sqrt{3}}{4}\right). \tag{57}$$

Since this should be equal to H, there is an error in the net flux at the boundary as computed from the solution for the emergent intensity.

In the second approximation, the intensity $I(\mu)$ is really approximated by a polynomial of the seventh degree in μ, since the Gaussian sum then evaluates the integral for J exactly. In general, the Gaussian sum in the nth approximation evaluates J exactly if $I(\mu)$ can be expressed as a polynomial of degree $4n-1$. The boundary value of J is exact in all the approximations. The defect in the net flux at the boundary is present in all approximations, but it vanishes in the limit as n tends to infinity.

Table II gives the solution for the limb darkening in the first four approximations, together with the solution in the infinite approximation.

TABLE II

Limb Darkening $I(0,\mu)/\mathfrak{F}$ according to Chandrasekhar

	Approximation				
μ	First	Second	Third	Fourth	Infinite
0·0	0·4330	0·4330	0·4330	0·4330	0·4330
0·1	0·5080	0·5224	0·5285	0·5319	0·5401
0·2	0·5830	0·6078	0·6164	0·6205	0·6280
0·3	0·6580	0·6905	0·7003	0·7046	0·7112
0·4	0·7330	0·7716	0·7819	0·7861	0·7921
0·5	0·8080	0·8515	0·8620	0·8660	0·8716
0·6	0·8830	0·9304	0·9410	0·9449	0·9501
0·7	0·9580	1·0088	1·0193	1·0231	1·0280
0·8	1·0330	1·0866	1·0970	1·1007	1·1053
0·9	1·1080	1·1640	1·1743	1·1779	1·1824
1·0	1·1830	1·2411	1·2513	1·2548	1·2591

THE INTEGRAL EQUATIONS OF RADIATIVE EQUILIBRIUM: EXACT SOLUTIONS

1. The integral equations of Schwarzschild and Milne

AN integral equation for $J(\tau)$ may be obtained by introducing the integral forms for $I(\tau, \theta)$ into the expression

$$J(\tau) = \frac{1}{4\pi} \int I(\tau, \theta) \, d\omega. \tag{1}$$

With $d\omega = 2\pi \sin \theta \, d\theta$, we substitute equations (25) and (26) of Chapter I in (1) and invert the order of integration. This gives

$$J(\tau) = \tfrac{1}{2} \int_{\tau}^{\infty} J(t) \, dt \int_{0}^{\frac{1}{2}\pi} e^{-(t-\tau)\sec\theta} \sec \theta \sin \theta \, d\theta +$$

$$+ \tfrac{1}{2} \int_{0}^{\tau} J(t) \, dt \int_{0}^{\frac{1}{2}\pi} e^{-(\tau-t)\sec\varphi} \sec \varphi \sin \varphi \, d\varphi.$$

Following Schwarzschild we find the kernel of this linear integral equation by means of the substitution $x = \sec \theta$, so that $\sec \theta \sin \theta \, d\theta = dx/x$. Thus

$$\int_{0}^{\frac{1}{2}\pi} e^{-(t-\tau)\sec\theta} \sec \theta \sin \theta \, d\theta = \int_{1}^{\infty} e^{-(t-\tau)x} \frac{dx}{x},$$

which is the exponential integral function $E(t-\tau)$. Hence

$$J(\tau) = \tfrac{1}{2} \int_{\tau}^{\infty} J(t) E(t-\tau) \, dt + \tfrac{1}{2} \int_{0}^{\tau} J(t) E(\tau-t) \, dt.$$

We combine the two integrals to give

$$J(\tau) = \tfrac{1}{2} \int_{0}^{\infty} J(t) E(|t-\tau|) \, dt, \tag{2}$$

an equation due to Schwarzschild and Milne.

Milne has given a second equation which contains the net flux explicitly. Evaluating the integral

$$H = \frac{1}{4\pi} \int I(\tau, \theta) \cos \theta \, d\omega$$

we find
$$\mathfrak{F} = 2 \int_{\tau}^{\infty} J(t) E_2(t-\tau) \, dt - 2 \int_{0}^{\tau} J(t) E_2(t) \, dt, \tag{3.1}$$

a result which is true for all τ. In particular at the boundary where $\tau = 0$ the source function $J(\tau)$ satisfies the equation

$$\mathfrak{F} = 2 \int_0^\infty J(t)E_2(t)\,dt. \tag{3.2}$$

We make use of equation (3.2) later when calculating the boundary value of J.

1.1. *The asymptotic behaviour of $J(\tau)$*

We first investigate the asymptotic behaviour of the solution of equation (2) for τ large. As we go into the interior of the star the radiation field tends to become isotropic. When $I(\tau, \theta)$ is independent of θ the approximate relation $K = \frac{1}{3}J$ in equations (9) of Chapter I is an exact result. Equation (6) of Chapter I therefore gives

$$\lim_{\tau \to \infty} J(\tau) = 3H\tau = \tfrac{3}{4}\mathfrak{F}\tau.$$

The solution of (2) being asymptotically linear for large values of τ, we set
$$J(\tau) = \tfrac{3}{4}\mathfrak{F}f(\tau) = \tfrac{3}{4}\mathfrak{F}[\tau \mid q(\tau)],$$

where $q(\tau)$ is a function to be determined; for τ large $q(\tau)$ approaches a constant, which we denote by $q(\infty)$.

1.2. *Hopf's solution by iteration†*

For the treatment of the problem it is convenient to use the positive linear integral operator

$$\Lambda(\ldots) = \tfrac{1}{2} \int_0^\infty (\ldots)E(|t-\tau|)\,dt.$$

In this notation we write the integral equation (2) in the form
$$J(\tau) = \Lambda(J) \quad \text{or} \quad f(\tau) = \Lambda(f).$$

Hopf has shown that when one starts with an approximate solution $f_0(\tau)$ of the integral equation $f(\tau) = \Lambda(f)$, satisfying the condition $\tau + \tfrac{1}{2} \leqslant f_0(\tau) \leqslant \tau + 1$ for all τ, one can obtain by repeated application of the Λ-operator an increasingly better approximation to the solution $f(\tau)$. The successive applications of the operation $\Lambda(\ldots)$ to the trial function $f_0(\tau)$ give rise to a sequence of functions

$$f_1(\tau) = \Lambda(f_0), \quad f_2(\tau) = \Lambda(f_1), \quad \ldots, \quad f_n(\tau) = \Lambda(f_{n-1}), \quad \ldots,$$

† E. Hopf, *Zs. f. Phys.* **46**, 374 (1928); *Mathematical Problems of Radiative Equilibrium* (Cambridge, 1934), chap. ii, § 9.

the limit function $\lim_{n=\infty} f_n(\tau)$ being the solution of the equation $f(\tau) = \Lambda(f)$.

Hopf's proof proceeds as follows: it may be shown that if c is a constant

$$\Lambda(t+c) = \tau+c-\tfrac{1}{2}\{cE_2(\tau)-E_3(\tau)\}.$$

Since $E_3(\tau) \geqslant \tfrac{1}{2}E_2(\tau)$ for $0 \leqslant \tau < \infty$, it follows that the greatest value of c which makes $\Lambda(t+c) \geqslant \tau+c$ is $c = \tfrac{1}{2}$. Again, since $E_2(\tau) > E_3(\tau)$, and $E_2 \sim E_3$ for large τ, we see that $c = 1$ is the smallest value of c which makes $\Lambda(t+c) < \tau+c$. Accordingly when $\tfrac{1}{2} < c < 1$, $\Lambda(t+c)-(\tau+c)$ changes sign at some value of τ. Thus $c = 1$, and $c = \tfrac{1}{2}$ are the two critical values of c above and below which the function $\Lambda(t+c)-(\tau+c)$ does not change sign. Using these values of c, we now construct two sequences of functions, $g_n(\tau)$ and $h_n(\tau)$, as follows:

$$g(\tau) = \tau+\tfrac{1}{2} \qquad\qquad h(\tau) = \tau+1$$
$$g_1(\tau) = \Lambda(g) \qquad\qquad h_1(\tau) = \Lambda(h)$$
$$g_2(\tau) = \Lambda(g_1) \qquad\qquad h_2(\tau) = \Lambda(h_1)$$
$$\quad = \Lambda^2(g) \qquad\qquad\quad = \Lambda^2(h)$$

$$\cdot\ \cdot\ \cdot\ \cdot\ \cdot \qquad\qquad \cdot\ \cdot\ \cdot\ \cdot\ \cdot$$

$$g_n(\tau) = \Lambda(g_{n-1}) \qquad\qquad h_n(\tau) = \Lambda(h_{n-1})$$
$$\quad = \Lambda^n(g) \qquad\qquad\qquad = \Lambda^n(h)$$

$$\cdot\ \cdot\ \cdot\ \cdot\ \cdot \qquad\qquad \cdot\ \cdot\ \cdot\ \cdot\ \cdot$$

In the g sequence $c = \tfrac{1}{2}$, so that $g_1(\tau)-g(\tau) \geqslant 0$ for $0 \leqslant \tau < \infty$, and in the h sequence, $c = 1$ and $h_1(\tau)-h(\tau) < 0$ for all τ. On account of the positivity of the Λ-operator $\Lambda[g_1(t)-g(t)] > 0$, so that $\Lambda^2(g) > \Lambda(g)$, also $\Lambda[h_1(t)-h(t)] < 0$ giving $\Lambda^2(h) < \Lambda(h)$. Hence

$$g(\tau) < g_1(\tau) < g_2(\tau) < \ldots < g_n(\tau) < \ldots$$

and $\qquad\qquad h(\tau) > h_1(\tau) > h_2(\tau) > \ldots > h_n(\tau) > \ldots$

giving a sequence of ascending functions g_n and a descending sequence h_n.

Now $h(\tau)-g(\tau) = \tfrac{1}{2}$, and in general we have

$$h_n(\tau)-g_n(\tau) = \tfrac{1}{2}\Lambda^n(1) \qquad\qquad (4)$$

where $\Lambda^n(1) > 0$ on account of the positivity of the Λ-operator. Hopf has shown that $\lim_{n\to\infty} \Lambda^n(1) = 0$, and equation (4) therefore implies the existence of a function to which the g and h sequences converge as $n \to \infty$. This limit function is approached from below by the sequence of functions $g_n(\tau)$, and from above by the sequence $h_n(\tau)$. Denoting by $f_n(\tau)$ the general term in either sequence of functions, and proceeding to the limit, we have

$$\lim_{n\to\infty} f_n(\tau) = \lim_{n\to\infty} \Lambda(f_{n-1}) = \Lambda(\lim_{n\to\infty} f_{n-1}).$$

Let the limit function be $f(\tau)$, then

$$f(\tau) = \Lambda(f) \qquad (5)$$

is the equation satisfied by this limit function. The solution $y = f(\tau)$ of equation (5) therefore lies between the two straight lines $y = \tau + \frac{1}{2}$, and $y = \tau + 1$. If we choose $y = f_0(\tau)$ as a trial solution which lies within this strip, we have

$$\tau + \tfrac{1}{2} \leqslant f_0(\tau) \leqslant \tau + 1. \qquad (6)$$

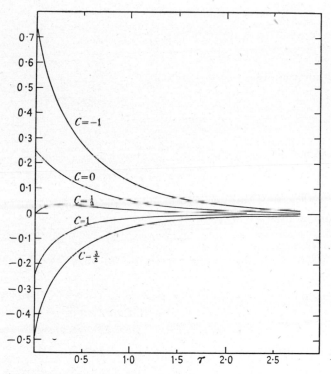

Fig. 7. Behaviour of $\Lambda(f) - f(\tau)$ when $f(\tau) = \tau + c$; $c = 1$ and $c = \frac{1}{2}$ are the two critical values of c above and below which the function $\Lambda(f) - f(\tau)$ does not change sign.

Performing the operation $\Lambda(...)$ n times this inequality becomes

$$g_n(\tau) \leqslant f_n(\tau) \leqslant h_n(\tau),$$

where $f_n(\tau) = \Lambda^n(f_0)$. By virtue of the increasing of the g sequence and the decreasing of the h sequence, we see that the Λ-operations gradually reduce the strip $\tau + \frac{1}{2} \leqslant y \leqslant \tau + 1$ to the curve $y = f(\tau)$ of the solution of equation (5). This process for improving an approximate solution will also work outside the limits given in (6), but the closer the initial function $f_0(\tau)$ is to the solution $f(\tau)$, the more quickly the iteration leads to the limit.

To gain some idea of the effectiveness of each Λ-operation in removing the error in the trial solution $f_0(\tau)$, we set

$$f_0(\tau) = f(\tau) + \epsilon(\tau),$$

where $\epsilon(\tau)$ is the correction function. Let $|\epsilon| \leqslant \delta$, so that δ is the maximum correction. The next approximation to the solution is given by

$$f_1(\tau) = \Lambda[f(t) + \epsilon(t)] = f(\tau) + \Lambda(\epsilon).$$

Since the Λ-operator is positive, we have

$$|\Lambda(\epsilon)| < \Lambda(\delta) = \delta\Lambda(1). \tag{7}$$

Carrying out the operation n times gives

$$f_n(\tau) = f(\tau) + \Lambda^n(\epsilon).$$

Now $|\Lambda^n(\epsilon)| < \delta\Lambda^n(1)$, and since $\lim_{n\to\infty} \Lambda^n(1) = 0$, we must have

$$\lim_{n\to\infty} |\Lambda^n(\epsilon)| = 0,$$

the correction function being reduced to zero in the limit. As before, this gives rise to the limit function $f(\tau) = \lim_{n\to\infty} f_n(\tau)$. Now it may be shown that $\Lambda(1) = 1 - \frac{1}{2}E_2(\tau)$, and hence equation (7) gives

$$|\Lambda(\epsilon)| < \delta[1 - \tfrac{1}{2}E_2(\tau)] < \delta.$$

This gives the magnitude of the correction for any τ after one operation $\Lambda(...)$. Since $E_2(\tau)$ has the value unity at $\tau = 0$, and decreases to zero for large τ, the convergence of the process of successive approximation to $f(\tau)$ is greater for smaller than for larger values of τ, being in fact most rapid at $\tau = 0$. The operation $\Lambda(...)$ leaves the approximate solution unchanged at infinity.

2. An integral equation for $q(\tau)$

If we write $f(\tau) = \tau + q(\tau)$ for the asymptotically linear solution of the integral equation $f(\tau) = \Lambda(f)$, we find

$$\tau + q(\tau) = \Lambda[t + q(t)] = \tau + \tfrac{1}{2}E_3(\tau) + \Lambda(q).$$

Hence q is given by the non-homogeneous integral equation

$$q(\tau) = \Lambda(q) + \tfrac{1}{2}E_3(\tau). \tag{8}$$

Differentiating, we find

$$q'(\tau) = \Lambda(q') + \tfrac{1}{2}q(0)E(\tau) - \tfrac{1}{2}E_2(\tau). \tag{9}$$

From this we deduce that the derivative of $J(\tau) = \tfrac{3}{4}\mathfrak{F}[\tau + q(\tau)]$ becomes logarithmically infinite at $\tau = 0$. This effect was noted by Milne, and is interpreted as a rapid fall in temperature as the surface of the star is approached, the temperature gradient becoming theoretically infinite at the boundary.

2.1. *The Liouville–Neumann solution*

The solution of the equation

$$q(\tau) = \Lambda(q) + p(\tau)$$

is the convergent series $\sum\limits_{n=0}^{\infty} \Lambda^n(p)$, where Λ^n is the nth iterate of the operator $\Lambda(...)$ and $\Lambda^0(p) = p$. The solution of equation (8) will therefore be

$$q(\tau) = \tfrac{1}{2}[E_3(\tau) + \Lambda(E_3) + \Lambda^2(E_3) + ... + \Lambda^n(E_3) + ...].$$

This is the exact solution of the integral equation (8), but the complexity of the terms and the slowness of the convergence of the series makes it of little practical value. Although the Liouville–Neumann solution does not lead to a reasonably convergent series of known functions, it is possible, however, to derive from the solution the exact value of $q(\tau)$ at $\tau = 0$.

2.2. *The Hopf–Bronstein boundary value* $q(0) = 1/\sqrt3$

We find an expression for $q(0)$ starting from equation (3.2) in which we put $J(t) = \tfrac{3}{4}\mathfrak{F}[t + q(t)]$. This gives

$$\tfrac{2}{3} = \int\limits_0^\infty [t + q(t)]E_2(t)\,dt = \tfrac{1}{3} + \int\limits_0^\infty q(t)E_2(t)\,dt.$$

Since $E_2(t) = -dE_3/dt$, integrating by parts we find

$$\int\limits_0^\infty q(t)E_2(t)\,dt = \tfrac{1}{2}q(0) + \int\limits_0^\infty q'(t)E_3(t)\,dt.$$

Hence

$$\tfrac{1}{2}q(0) = \tfrac{1}{3} - \int\limits_0^\infty q'(t)E_3(t)\,dt. \tag{10}$$

The derivative $q'(t)$ is given by the solution of the integral equation (9) for which the Liouville–Neumann solution is

$$q'(\tau) = \tfrac{1}{2}q(0)\sum\limits_{n=0}^{\infty}\Lambda^n(E) - \tfrac{1}{2}\sum\limits_{n=0}^{\infty}\Lambda^n(E_2).$$

The second series may be readily evaluated by means of the results $\tfrac{1}{2}E_2(\tau) = 1 - \Lambda(1)$, and $\lim\limits_{n\to\infty}\Lambda^n(1) = 0$. This gives

$$E_2(\tau) + \Lambda(E_2) + ... + \Lambda^n(E_2) + ... = 2.$$

Hence

$$q'(\tau) = -1 + \tfrac{1}{2}q(0)\sum\limits_{n=0}^{\infty}\Lambda^n(E). \tag{11}$$

Substituting (11) in (10), and using $\int_0^\infty E_3(t)\,dt = \frac{1}{3}$, equation (10) becomes

$$q(0) = \tfrac{4}{3} - q(0) \int_0^\infty E_3(t) \sum_{n=0}^\infty \Lambda^n(E)\,dt. \tag{12}$$

Since it is permissible here to integrate term by term and then carry out the summation, it remains to evaluate

$$\sum_{n=0}^\infty \int_0^\infty E_3(t)\Lambda^n(E)\,dt. \tag{13}$$

To obtain the general term in the summation (13), we multiply equation (8) by $\Lambda^n(E)\,d\tau$ and integrate from 0 to ∞. Using the abbreviation

$$[x,y] = \int_0^\infty x(t)y(t)\,dt$$

the integration gives

$$\tfrac{1}{2}[E_3, \Lambda^n(E)] = [q, \Lambda^n(E)] - [\Lambda(q), \Lambda^n(E)]. \tag{14}$$

We make use of the fact that the kernel $E(|t-\tau|)$ of the Λ-operator is symmetrical. This property may be seen from the relations

$$\int_0^\infty f(\tau)\Lambda(g)\,d\tau = \tfrac{1}{2}\int_0^\infty f(\tau)\,d\tau \int_0^\infty g(t)E(|t-\tau|)\,dt$$

$$= \tfrac{1}{2}\int_0^\infty g(t)\,dt \int_0^\infty f(\tau)E(|\tau-t|)\,d\tau.$$

Hence $\qquad \displaystyle\int_0^\infty f(\tau)\Lambda(g)\,d\tau = \int_0^\infty g(\tau)\Lambda(f)\,d\tau,$

or $\qquad\qquad\qquad [f, \Lambda(g)] = [g, \Lambda(f)]. \tag{15}$

Making use of this symmetry property equation (14) may now be written as

$$\tfrac{1}{2}[E_3, \Lambda^n(E)] = [q, \Lambda^n(E)] - [q, \Lambda^{n+1}(E)]. \tag{16}$$

It is convenient to put $m = 1+n$, so that the summation (13) will be the limit as $m \to \infty$ of the sum to m terms in equation (16). Making the summation to m terms, equation (16) gives

$$\tfrac{1}{2}\sum_1^m [E_3, \Lambda^{m-1}(E)] = \sum_1^m \{[q, \Lambda^{m-1}(E)] - [q, \Lambda^m(E)]\}$$

$$= [q, E] - [q, \Lambda^m(E)].$$

But, according to (15),

$$[q, \Lambda^m(E)] = [\Lambda(q), \Lambda^{m-1}(E)] = \dots = [\Lambda^m(q), E].$$

Therefore
$$\tfrac{1}{2} \sum_{1}^{m} [E_3, \Lambda^{m-1}(E)] = [q, E] - [\Lambda^m(q), E]. \qquad (17)$$

Now $[q, E]$ is simply the value of $2\Lambda(q)$ at $\tau = 0$. Equation (8) gives for $\tau = 0$, $2\Lambda(q) = 2q(0) - \tfrac{1}{2}$. We also deduce from (8) that $\Lambda^m(q) < q$, and since $\tfrac{1}{2} < q < 1$ the result

$$\Lambda^m(q) < \Lambda^m(1) < 1$$

gives $[\Lambda^m(q), E] < [\Lambda^m(1), E]$. But $\lim\limits_{m \to \infty} \Lambda^m(1) = 0$, hence

$$\lim_{m \to \infty} [q, \Lambda^m(E)] = 0.$$

Proceeding to the limit in equation (17) we find

$$\lim_{m \to \infty} \sum_{1}^{m} [E_3, \Lambda^{m-1}(E)] = 4q(0) - 1. \qquad (18)$$

This is the value of the required summation (13). Equation (12) for $q(0)$ now becomes
$$q(0) = \tfrac{4}{3} - q(0)\{4q(0) - 1\}.$$

Hence $q(0) = 1/\sqrt{3}$, a result due to Bronstein and Hopf.†

3. Exact solutions for the emergent intensity and the source function

3.1. *Significance of the Laplace transform*

Instead of starting the treatment of the problem from the integral equation

$$J(\tau) = \tfrac{1}{2} \int_{0}^{\infty} J(t) E(|\tau - t|) \, dt,$$

we go back to the equation of transfer

$$\mu \frac{dI(\tau, \mu)}{d\tau} = I(\tau, \mu) - J(\tau) \qquad (19)$$

in which $I(0, \mu) = 0$ for $0 \geqslant \mu \geqslant -1$. The solution of the linear differential equation (19) for $0 \leqslant \mu \leqslant 1$ will be

$$I(0, \mu) = \int_{0}^{\infty} e^{-t/\mu} J(t) \, dt/\mu. \qquad (20)$$

Now $\mu I(0, \mu)$ may be regarded as the Laplace transform of $J(t)$, so that the problem of determining the emergent intensity is simply that of evaluating the Laplace transform of the source function. The source function itself then follows from the inversion of its Laplace transform.

† M. Bronstein, *Zs. f. Phys.* **59**, 144 (1929); E. Hopf, *M.N.* **90**, 287 (1930).

3.2. *An integral equation for the Laplace transform of the source function*

We introduce the Laplace transforms of $I(\tau,\mu)$ and $J(\tau)$ by the relations

$$\bar{I}(p,\mu) = \int_0^\infty e^{-pt}I(t,\mu)\,dt, \tag{21}$$

$$\bar{J}(p) = \int_0^\infty e^{-pt}J(t)\,dt, \tag{22}$$

where p is complex, and $\mathscr{R}(p) > 0$. Multiplying (19) by $e^{-p\tau}$ and integrating over τ from 0 to ∞, we find

$$\mu \int_0^\infty e^{-p\tau}(dI/d\tau)\,d\tau = \bar{I}(p,\mu) - \bar{J}(p). \tag{23}$$

Integrating by parts, we find

$$\int_0^\infty e^{-p\tau}(dI/d\tau)\,d\tau = [e^{-p\tau}I(\tau,\mu)]_0^\infty + p\int_0^\infty e^{-p\tau}I(\tau,\mu)\,d\tau$$

$$= -I(0,\mu) + p\bar{I}(p,\mu).$$

Equation (23) now gives

$$\bar{I}(p,\mu) = \frac{\bar{J}(p) - \mu I(0,\mu)}{1 - \mu p}. \tag{24}$$

Now $J(\tau) = \frac{1}{2}\int_{-1}^{+1} I(\tau,\mu)\,d\mu$, so that equation (22) may also be written as

$$\bar{J}(p) = \frac{1}{2}\int_{-1}^{+1} \bar{I}(p,\mu)\,d\mu.$$

Hence multiplying (24) by $d\mu$ and integrating from $\mu = -1$ to $+1$,

$$\left\{1 - \frac{1}{2}\int_{-1}^{+1} \frac{d\mu}{1-\mu p}\right\}\bar{J}(p) = -\frac{1}{2}\int_{-1}^{+1} \frac{\mu}{1-\mu p}I(0,\mu)\,d\mu$$

$$= -\frac{1}{2}\int_0^1 \frac{\mu}{1-\mu p}I(0,\mu)\,d\mu, \tag{25}$$

since $I(0,\mu) = 0$ when $0 \geqslant \mu \geqslant -1$. We have

$$\frac{1}{2}\int_{-1}^{+1} \frac{d\mu}{1-\mu p} = \frac{1}{2p}\ln\frac{1+p}{1-p} = \frac{1}{p}\tanh^{-1}p,$$

and equation (25) becomes

$$\left\{1-\frac{1}{p}\tanh^{-1}p\right\}\bar{J}(p)=-\frac{1}{2}\int_{0}^{1}\frac{\mu}{1-\mu p}I(0,\mu)\,d\mu. \qquad (26)$$

Comparing (20) and (22) we get

$$\mu I(0,\mu)=\bar{J}\left(\frac{1}{\mu}\right). \qquad (27)$$

Hence

$$\left\{1-\frac{1}{p}\tanh^{-1}p\right\}\bar{J}(p)=-\frac{1}{2}\int_{0}^{1}\frac{1}{1-\mu p}\bar{J}\left(\frac{1}{\mu}\right)d\mu, \qquad (28)$$

an integral equation for the Laplace transform of the source function. When the solution of (28) is known, the emergent intensity $I(0,\mu)$ follows from equation (27).

3.3. *Limit forms for $q(0)$ and $q(\infty)$*

From the equation

$$J(\tau)=3H[\tau+q(\tau)] \quad (H=\tfrac{1}{4}\mathfrak{F}) \qquad (29)$$

we obtain the Laplace transform .

$$\bar{J}(p)=3H\left[\frac{1}{p^2}+\bar{q}(p)\right], \qquad (30)$$

where

$$\bar{q}(p)=\int_{0}^{\infty}e^{-pt}q(t)\,dt. \qquad (31)$$

By means of the substitution $u=pt$, equation (31) becomes

$$p\bar{q}(p)=\int_{0}^{\infty}e^{-u}q(u/p)\,du. \qquad (32)$$

Proceeding to the limit with respect to p in equation (32), and interchanging the order of the limit and integration processes, we find

$$q(0)=\lim_{p\to\infty}p\bar{q}(p), \qquad (33)$$

$$q(\infty)=\lim_{p\to 0}p\bar{q}(p). \qquad (34)$$

The relation $q(\infty)=K(0)/H$. The asymptotic behaviour of $J(\tau)$ for large τ being determined, according to (34), by $\bar{J}(p)$ at $p=0$, we find a series expansion for $\bar{J}(p)$ for small values of p from equation (26). Now $\tanh^{-1}p=p+\tfrac{1}{3}p^3+...$ and we have

$$\frac{1}{2}\int_{0}^{1}\frac{\mu}{1-\mu p}I(0,\mu)\,d\mu=\frac{1}{2}\int_{0}^{1}\mu(1+\mu p+\mu^2 p^2+...)I(0,\mu)\,d\mu$$

$$=H+pK(0)+...,$$

where $K(\tau) = \frac{1}{2} \int_{-1}^{+1} \mu^2 I(\tau, \mu) \, d\mu$. Hence equation (26) gives

$$\bar{J}(p) = 3H\left[\frac{1}{p^2} + \frac{1}{p}\frac{K(0)}{H} + \ldots\right],\tag{35}$$

which is the Laurent expansion of $\bar{J}(p)$ about the double pole at $p = 0$. From (30) and (35), $\bar{q}(p) = \frac{1}{p}\frac{(K0)}{H} + \ldots$, hence, by equation (34),

$$q(\infty) = K(0)/H.\tag{36}$$

From (29) and (36) we obtain the asymptotic form

$$J(\tau) \sim 3[H\tau + K(0)].\tag{37}$$

We now find the relation (36) without using the limit form (34). Consider the Laplace transform of $\dfrac{dJ}{dt} = 3H\left(1 + \dfrac{dq}{dt}\right)$. This is given by

$$\int_0^\infty e^{-pt}\frac{dJ}{dt}\,dt = \left[e^{-pt}J(t)\right]_0^\infty + p\int_0^\infty e^{-pt}J(t)\,dt = -J(0) + p\bar{J}(p).$$

Hence

$$p\bar{J}(p) = 3H\left[q(0) + \int_0^\infty e^{-pt}\left(1 + \frac{dq}{dt}\right)dt\right].\tag{38}$$

But

$$\int_0^\infty e^{-pt}\left(1 + \frac{dq}{dt}\right)dt = \frac{1}{p} + \int_0^\infty (1 - pt + \tfrac{1}{2}p^2t^2 + \ldots)\frac{dq}{dt}\,dt$$

$$= \frac{1}{p} + q(\infty) - q(0) + O(p).$$

Equation (38) may now be written

$$\bar{J}(p) = 3H\left[\frac{1}{p^2} + \frac{1}{p}q(\infty) + \ldots\right].\tag{39}$$

A comparison of the asymptotic expansions (35) and (39) yields the relation (36).

3.4. *The Wiener–Hopf solution*†

If we set

$$f(p) = 1 - \frac{1}{2}\int_{-1}^{+1}\frac{d\mu}{1 - \mu p} = -p^2\int_0^1\frac{\mu^2}{1 - \mu^2 p^2}\,d\mu,\tag{40}$$

$$g(p) = -\frac{1}{2}\int_0^1\frac{\mu}{1 - \mu p}\,I(0, \mu)\,d\mu,\tag{41}$$

equation (25) becomes $f(p)\bar{J}(p) = g(p).$ (42)

† N. Wiener and E. Hopf, *Berliner Ber.*, Math. Phys. Klasse, 696 (1931); G. Placzek and W. Seidel, *Phys. Rev.* **72**, 550 (1947).

Consider the domains in the complex p-plane in which the functions occurring in equation (42) are analytic. In the neighbourhood of the origin

$$f(p) = -p^2(\tfrac{1}{3} + \tfrac{1}{5}p^2 + \dots)$$

so that $f(p)$ has a double zero at the origin. The function $f(p)$ is analytic in the strip $-1 < \mathscr{R}(p) < +1$ and has no other zeros in the strip except the double zero at the origin. Since the only singularities of $g(p)$ occur for values of p for which the denominator of the integrand vanishes, $g(p)$ is analytic in the domain $\mathscr{R}(p) < 1$.

Construct a function $\phi(p)$ such that $\phi(p) \to 0$ as $|p| \to \infty$. Now $\dfrac{1}{p^2} f(p)$ has no zero in the strip $-1 < \mathscr{R}(p) < +1$, and, further, the function

$$\tau(p) = \frac{1}{p^2}(p^2-1)f(p) \qquad (43)$$

has the value $\tfrac{1}{3}$ at the origin, and tends to unity as $|p| > \infty$ in the strip. Consider therefore the function

$$\phi(p) = \ln \tau(p) \quad (\ln 1 = 0), \qquad (44)$$

which is single valued within the strip; also $\phi(p) > 0$ as $|p| \to \infty$. By Cauchy's integral formula

$$\phi(p) = \frac{1}{2\pi i} \int_C \frac{\phi(w)}{w-p}\,dw = \frac{1}{2\pi i} \left\{ \int_{\beta-i\infty}^{\beta+i\infty} - \int_{-\beta-i\infty}^{-\beta+i\infty} \right\} \frac{\phi(w)}{w-p}\,dw, \qquad (45)$$

where $0 < \beta < 1$, and $-\beta < \mathscr{R}(p) < \beta$. We write equation (45) as

$$\phi(p) = \phi_+(p) - \phi_-(p),$$

so that from (44) $\phi_+(p) = \ln \tau_+(p)$, $\phi_-(p) = \ln \tau_-(p)$ and we have

$$\tau(p) = \frac{\tau_+(p)}{\tau_-(p)}. \qquad (46)$$

From equations (42), (43), and (46) we obtain

$$\frac{p^2 \bar{J}(p)}{(p+1)\tau_-(p)} = \frac{(p-1)g(p)}{\tau_+(p)}. \qquad (47)$$

Now the left hand side of equation (47) is regular in the half plane $\mathscr{R}(p) > 0$, and the right-hand side is regular in the half plane $\mathscr{R}(p) < \beta$. These two domains of regularity overlap in the strip $0 < \mathscr{R}(p) < \beta$, and each side of equation (47) is the analytic continuation of the other. Therefore the left-hand function and the right-hand function are different forms of a function which is regular in the whole p-plane. It may be shown that each side of equation (47) is bounded at infinity, and therefore must be bounded in the whole plane. According to Liouville's theorem, a function which is analytic and bounded in the whole complex plane must be a constant. Accordingly

$$\bar{J}(p) = C(p+1)\tau_-(p)/p^2,$$

where C is the constant. Expanding $\bar{J}(p)$ as a Laurent series about $p = 0$

$$\bar{J}(p) = C\frac{\tau_-(0)}{p^2} + C\frac{\tau_-(0)+\tau'_-(0)}{p} + \dots. \tag{48}$$

Comparing (35) with (48), we find $C = 3H/\tau_-(0)$. It now remains to evaluate $\tau_-(0)$, where

$$\ln\tau_-(0) = \frac{1}{2\pi i}\int_{-\beta-i\infty}^{-\beta+i\infty}\frac{1}{w}\ln\tau(w)\,dw. \tag{49}$$

The integrand has a simple pole at $w = 0$ which we circumvent by the semicircular path γ (Fig. 8), the path of integration in equation (49) being

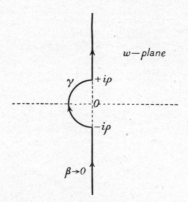

FIG. 8. Path of integration for the evaluation of $\tau_-(0)$.

deformed into two segments along the imaginary axis from $-i\infty$ to $-i\rho$, $+i\rho$ to $i\infty$, and the semicircle of radius ρ. Now, from equation (43), $\tau(w)$ is an even function, so that $(1/w)\ln\tau(w)$ is odd, and the integrals over the two segments cancel. On γ we have $w = \rho e^{i\theta}$, and

$$\ln\tau_-(0) = \frac{1}{2\pi i}\lim_{\rho\to 0}\int_{\frac{3}{2}\pi}^{\frac{1}{2}\pi}\ln\tau(\rho e^{i\theta})i\,d\theta = -\tfrac{1}{2}\ln\tau(0).$$

Since $\tau(0) = \tfrac{1}{3}$, we have $\tau_-(0) = \sqrt{3}$. Hence $C = \sqrt{3}H \ (= \tfrac{1}{4}\sqrt{3}\mathfrak{F})$, and we now have

$$\bar{J}(p) = \sqrt{3}H(p+1)\tau_-(p)/p^2, \tag{50}$$

where

$$\ln\tau_-(p) = \frac{1}{2\pi i}\int_{-\beta-i\infty}^{-\beta+i\infty}\frac{1}{w-p}\ln\tau(w)\,dw. \tag{51}$$

3.41. *Determination of $q(0)$ and $q(\infty)$*

Equations (30) and (33) give

$$q(0) = \frac{1}{3H} \lim_{p \to \infty} p\bar{J}(p). \tag{52}$$

But from (51) $\ln \tau_-(p) \to 0$ as $w \to \infty$, so that $\lim\limits_{p \to \infty} \tau_-(p) = 1$. Hence, proceeding to the limit in equation (52), we find

$$q(0) = \frac{1}{\sqrt{3}}.$$

From equations (39) and (48),

$$q(\infty) = 1 + \frac{\tau'_-(0)}{\tau_-(0)}. \tag{53}$$

Differentiating (51), and setting $p = 0$, we obtain

$$\frac{\tau'_-(0)}{\tau_-(0)} = \frac{1}{2\pi i} \int_{-\beta-i\infty}^{-\beta+i\infty} \frac{1}{w^2} \ln \tau(w) \, dw.$$

Integrating by parts, and using the fact that $(1/w)\ln \tau(w)$ is odd, so that the integrated part vanishes, we find

$$\frac{\tau'_-(0)}{\tau_-(0)} = \frac{1}{2\pi i} \int_{-\beta-i\infty}^{-\beta+i\infty} \frac{\tau'(w)}{\tau(w)} \frac{dw}{w}. \tag{54}$$

From (43) and the expansion for $f(p)$ in the neighbourhood of the origin

$$\tau(w) = \tfrac{1}{3} - (\tfrac{1}{3} - \tfrac{1}{5})w^2 - (\tfrac{1}{5} - \tfrac{1}{7})w^4 - \dots .$$

The integrand in (54) therefore does not have a singularity at the origin so we set $\beta = 0$, and the path of integration is along the imaginary axis. But $\tau(w)$ is an even function, so that $\tau'(w)$ is odd, and the integrand will therefore be an even function. Hence

$$\frac{\tau'_-(0)}{\tau_-(0)} = \frac{1}{\pi i} \int_{0}^{i\infty} \frac{\tau'(w)}{\tau(w)} \frac{dw}{w}. \tag{55}$$

Now
$$\tau(w) = w^{-2}(w^2 - 1)(1 - (1/w)\tanh^{-1} w),$$

and by logarithmic differentiation we readily find

$$\frac{1}{w} \frac{\tau'(w)}{\tau(w)} = -\frac{3}{w^2} - \frac{2}{1 - w^2} - \frac{1}{(1 - w^2)(1 - (1/w)\tanh^{-1} w)}.$$

Changing to the real variable t, where $w = it$, equation (55) becomes

$$\frac{\tau'_-(0)}{\tau_-(0)} = \frac{1}{\pi} \int_0^\infty \left\{ \frac{3}{t^2} - \frac{2}{1+t^2} - \frac{1}{(1+t^2)(1-(1/t)\tan^{-1}t)} \right\} dt. \qquad (56)$$

Equations (53) and (56) now give

$$q(\infty) = \frac{1}{\pi} \int_0^\infty \left\{ \frac{3}{t^2} - \frac{1}{(1+t^2)(1-(1/t)\tan^{-1}t)} \right\} dt. \qquad (57)$$

By means of the substitution $t = \tan x$, equation (57) reduces to

$$q(\infty) = \frac{6}{\pi^2} + \frac{1}{\pi} \int_0^{\frac{1}{2}\pi} \left(\frac{3}{x^2} - \frac{1}{1-x\cot x} \right) dx. \qquad (58)$$

The integrand in (58) can be expanded as a power series which converges rapidly within the entire range of integration, and then integrated term by term to give
$$q(\infty) = 0{\cdot}71044609.$$

3.42. *The emergent intensity $I(0, \mu)$*

According to equation (27) $I(0, \mu) = (1/\mu)\bar{J}(1/\mu)$, where $\bar{J}$ is given by (50). Hence
$$I(0, \mu) = \sqrt{3}H(1+\mu)\tau_-(1/\mu). \qquad (59)$$

Now $\tau_-(1/\mu)$ is given by equation (51) with $p = 1/\mu$. To evaluate the integral we proceed as in Fig. 8, but the indentation at the origin is not necessary in this case. We obtain

$$\ln\tau_-\left(\frac{1}{\mu}\right) = \frac{\mu}{2\pi i}\left\{ \int_{-i\infty}^{-i0} + \int_{i0}^{i\infty} \right\} \frac{1}{\mu w - 1} \ln\tau(w)\, dw.$$

Since
$$\int_{-i\infty}^{-i0} \frac{1}{\mu w - 1} \ln\tau(w)\, dw = -\int_{i0}^{i\infty} \frac{1}{\mu w + 1} \ln\tau(w)\, dw,$$

we have
$$\ln\tau_-\left(\frac{1}{\mu}\right) = \frac{\mu}{\pi i} \int_{i0}^{i\infty} \frac{1}{\mu^2 w^2 - 1} \ln\tau(w)\, dw,$$

so that
$$\tau_-\left(\frac{1}{\mu}\right) = \exp\left\{ -\frac{\mu}{\pi} \int_0^\infty \frac{1}{1+\mu^2 t^2} \ln\tau(it)\, dt \right\},$$

where
$$\tau(it) = t^{-2}(1+t^2)(1-(1/t)\tan^{-1}t).$$

Put $t = \tan x$, then

$$\tau_-\left(\frac{1}{\mu}\right) = \exp\left\{\frac{\mu}{\pi} \int_0^{\frac{1}{2}\pi} \frac{\ln[\sin^2 x/(1-x\cot x)]}{\cos^2 x + \mu^2 \sin^2 x}\,dx\right\}. \tag{60}$$

From equations (59) and (60) we obtain the desired result

$$I(0,\mu) = \sqrt{3}H(1+\mu)\exp\left\{\frac{\mu}{\pi} \int_0^{\frac{1}{2}\pi} \frac{\ln[\sin^2 x/(1-x\cot x)]}{1-(1-\mu^2)\sin^2 x}\,dx\right\} \tag{61.1}$$

$$= \frac{\sqrt{3}H}{(1+\mu^2)^{\frac{1}{2}}} \exp\left\{\frac{1}{\pi} \int_0^{\frac{1}{2}\pi} \frac{x\tan^{-1}(\mu\tan x)}{1-x\cot x}\,dx\right\}, \tag{61.2}$$

which is the Wiener–Hopf expression for the emergent intensity. The alternative form (61.2) is more suited to numerical evaluation, and is due to Placzek† who tabulates the function $\varphi(\mu) = \dfrac{I(0,\mu)}{2\sqrt{3}H}$. Equation (61.2) shows more readily than does (61.1) that for very small values of μ the intensity is given asymptotically by

$$I(0,\mu) = \sqrt{3}H(1-\tfrac{1}{2}\mu\ln\mu) \quad (\mu \ll 1).$$

The derivative of the intensity has a logarithmic infinity at $\mu = 0$ which is directly related to the fact that the derivative of the source function at the boundary is logarithmically infinite.

3.5. *Mark's exact solution for $q(\tau)$*

From the Laplace transform $\bar{J}(p)$ of the source function $J(\tau)$, the source function itself may be obtained by inverting its Laplace transform. According to the Fourier–Mellin inversion theorem

$$J(\tau) = \frac{1}{2\pi i} \int_{\gamma-i\infty}^{\gamma+i\infty} e^{\lambda\tau} \bar{J}(\lambda)\,d\lambda, \tag{62}$$

where γ is a constant greater than the real part of all the singularities of $\bar{J}(\lambda)$. From equation (42)

$$\bar{J}(p) = g(p)/f(p), \tag{63}$$

where

$$f(p) = -p^2 \int_0^1 \frac{\mu^2}{1-\mu^2 p^2}\,d\mu, \qquad g(p) = -\frac{1}{2} \int_0^1 \frac{\mu}{1-\mu p} I(0,\mu)\,d\mu.$$

Now the function $f(p)$ has a double zero at $p = 0$, and may be shown to have no other zeros in the p-plane cut from $-\infty$ to -1; $f(p)$ has a

† G. Placzek, *Phys. Rev.* **72**, 556 (1947).

branch point at $p = \pm 1$, and is regular in the cut plane. We use the branch for which $f(p)$ is real for $-1 < p < 1$. The function $g(p)$ has a branch point at $p = +1$, and is regular in the p-plane cut from $+1$ to $+\infty$. We take that branch of $g(p)$ which is real for real $p < 1$. The function $\bar{J}(\lambda)$ is therefore regular in the λ-plane cut from $-\infty$ to -1, except for a double pole at the origin.

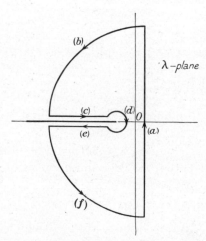

FIG. 9. Contour for evaluating the line integral in the Fourier–Mellin inversion formula for $J(\tau)$.

To evaluate the line integral in equation (62) we consider the closed contour shown in Fig. 9, and apply the calculus of residues. From equations (35) and (36) the Laurent expansion at the origin is

$$\bar{J}(\lambda) = 3H\left[\frac{1}{\lambda^2} + \frac{q(\infty)}{\lambda} + \cdots\right],$$

so that the residue of $e^{\lambda\tau}\bar{J}(\lambda)$ at the only pole within the contour C is $3H[\tau + q(\infty)]$, and we have

$$\frac{1}{2\pi i}\int_C e^{\lambda\tau}\bar{J}(\lambda)\,d\lambda = 3H[\tau + q(\infty)].$$

Since $\bar{J}(\lambda)$ is of order $1/|\lambda|$ as $|\lambda| \to \infty$, the integrals over (b) and (f) tend to zero as $R \to \infty$. The small circular path (d) around the branch point gives no contribution to the integral since $\lambda = -1$ is a zero of the integrand. We now have

$$J(\tau) = 3H[\tau + q(\infty)] - \frac{1}{2\pi i}\left\{\int_{(c)} + \int_{(e)}\right\}e^{\lambda\tau}\bar{J}(\lambda)\,d\lambda. \qquad (64)$$

Along the path (c) where $-\infty < \lambda < -1$

$$f(\lambda) = 1 + \frac{1}{2\lambda}\ln\frac{\lambda-1}{\lambda+1} - \frac{i\pi}{2\lambda} = 1 - \frac{1}{\lambda}\coth^{-1}\lambda - \frac{i\pi}{2\lambda}, \qquad (65)$$

and along (e) $\qquad f(\lambda) = 1 - \frac{1}{\lambda}\coth^{-1}\lambda + \frac{i\pi}{2\lambda}. \qquad (66)$

Using (65) and (66) in (64), and setting $\lambda = -t$, we find

$$J(\tau) = 3H[\tau + q(\infty)] + \frac{1}{2}\int_1^\infty \frac{g(-t)e^{-t\tau}\,dt}{t[(1-(1/t)\coth^{-1}t)^2 + \pi^2/4t^2]}. \qquad (67)$$

Now equations (47) and (50) give

$$g(-t) = -\frac{\sqrt{3}H\tau_+(-t)}{1+t},$$

and it may be shown from (51) and a similar form for $\tau_+(p)$ that $\tau_+(-t) = 1/\tau_-(t)$, and from (59) we then obtain

$$g(-t) = -\frac{3H^2}{tI(0,1/t)}. \tag{68}$$

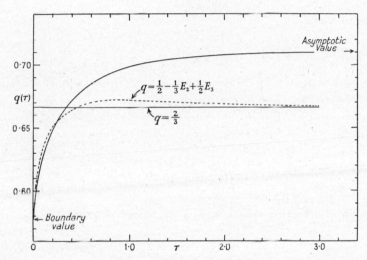

FIG. 10. The function $q(\tau)$ according to Mark compared with the approximation $q = \frac{2}{3}$, and the improved value given by $\tau+q(\tau) = \Lambda(t+\frac{2}{3})$, that is,
$$q(\tau) = \frac{2}{3} - \frac{1}{3}E_2(\tau) + \frac{1}{2}E_3(\tau).$$

Substituting (68) in (67), and changing the variable to μ, where $t = 1/\mu$, we find

$$J(\tau) = 3H[\tau+q(\infty)] - \frac{3H^2}{2} \int_0^1 \frac{e^{-\tau/\mu}\,d\mu}{I(0,\mu)[(1-\mu\tanh^{-1}\mu)^2+\mu^2\pi^2/4]}. \tag{69}$$

Since $J(\tau) = 3H[\tau+q(\tau)]$, equation (69) may be written in the form

$$q(\tau) = q(\infty) - \frac{1}{2}H \int_0^1 \frac{e^{-\tau/\mu}\,d\mu}{I(0,\mu)[(1-\mu\tanh^{-1}\mu)^2+\mu^2\pi^2/4]}, \tag{70}$$

a result due to Mark.† The integral in equation (70) involves the emergent intensity. This is given by the extensive and accurate calculations of Placzek.

† C. Mark, *Phys. Rev.* **72**, 558 (1947).

4. A comparison of solutions

If the method of successive approximation is applied to equation (8), namely

$$q(\tau) = \Lambda(q) + \tfrac{1}{2}E_3(\tau),$$

an approximate solution $q_0(\tau)$ will be improved by the Λ-operation to give the next approximation

$$q(\tau) = \Lambda(q_0) + \tfrac{1}{2}E_3(\tau).$$

Let $q_0 = \tfrac{2}{3}$ then, since $\Lambda(1) = 1 - \tfrac{1}{2}E_2(\tau)$, we have

$$q(\tau) = \tfrac{2}{3} - \tfrac{1}{3}E_2(\tau) + \tfrac{1}{2}E_3(\tau).$$

Now

$$J(\tau) = 3H[\tau + q(\tau)]$$
$$= 3H[\tau + \tfrac{2}{3} - \tfrac{1}{3}E_2(\tau) + \tfrac{1}{2}E_3(\tau)],$$

which is identical with Eddington's second approximation, equation (31) of Chapter I. The application of the Λ-operator now gives a boundary value $q(0) = \tfrac{7}{12}$ but leaves the solution unchanged at $\tau = \infty$, where $q(\tau)$ still has the value $\tfrac{2}{3}$. But $q(\infty) = K(0)/H$, and from equation (33) of Chapter I we have

$$K(\tau) = H[\tau + \tfrac{2}{3} - E_4(\tau) + \tfrac{3}{2}E_5(\tau)],$$

so that $q(\infty) = \tfrac{17}{24}$. This is the asymptotic value for large τ in Eddington's second approximation to $q(\tau)$, given by equation (36) of Chapter I.

TABLE III.

	$q(\tau)$		
τ	Mark's solution	Eddington's approximation	Chandrasekhar's 4th approx.
0·0	0·5773$_{50}$	0·5833	0·5774
0·05	0·6107	0·6183	0·5974
0·1	0·6279	0·6347	0·6139
0·2	0·6495	0·6538	0·6386
0·3	0·6634	0·6652	0·6557
0·4	0·6731	0·6730	0·6676
0·5	0·6803	0·6787	0·6761
0·6	0·6858	0·6831	0·6823
0·7	0·6901	0·6866	0·6870
0·8	0·6935	0·6894	0·6905
0·9	0·6963	0·6918	0·6933
1·0	0·6985	0·6938	0·6954
1·2	0·7019	0·6970	0·6987
1·5	0·7051	0·7004	0·7017
2·0	0·7079	0·7038	0·7044
2·5	0·7092	0·7057	0·7056
3·0	0·7098	0·7068	0·7065
∞	0·7104$_{46}$	0·7083	0·7069

Table III gives the exact values of $q(\tau)$ according to Mark, together with Eddington's solution, and Chandrasekhar's fourth approximation. Other approximations† are available from variational and operational methods which give $q(\tau)$ to a high degree of accuracy.

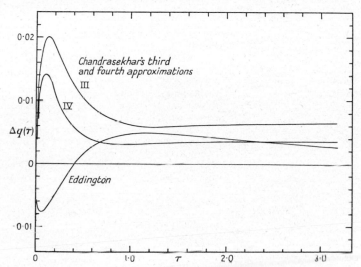

FIG. 11. Corrections $\Delta q(\tau) = q_{\text{exact}} - q_{\text{approx}}$ to Eddington's approximation, and the third and fourth approximations of Chandrasekhar.

To put in evidence the role of $q(\tau)$ in determining the darkening of the limb, we write

$$I(0,\mu) = 3H \int_0^\infty [\tau + q(\tau)] e^{-\tau/\mu} \, d\tau/\mu$$

$$= 3H\Big[\mu + \int_0^\infty q(\mu t) e^{-t} \, dt\Big].$$

Owing to the decaying exponential factor under the integral sign, errors in the adopted $q(\tau)$ for large values of τ are of no serious consequence in calculating the limb darkening. Table IV gives the exact values for the limb darkening, and Fig. 12 shows the limb-darkening errors $\Delta I(0,\mu)$ in the approximate solutions considered.

The variation of temperature with depth is given by

$$T^4 = \tfrac{3}{4} T_e^4 [\tau + q(\tau)],$$

so that the boundary temperature follows from the relation

$$(T_0/T_e)^4 = \tfrac{3}{4} q(0).$$

† R. E. Marshak, *Phys. Rev.* **71**, 688 (1947); J. le Caine, ibid. **72**, 564 (1948); V. Kourganoff, *Ann. d'Ap.* **12**, 169 (1949); D. H. Menzel and H. K. Sen, *Ap. J.* **110**, 1 (1949).

Table IV

Limb Darkening. Exact Values from the Wiener–Hopf Solution according to Placzek

μ	$\varphi(\mu)$	$I(0, \mu)/\mathfrak{F}$
0	0·5000 000	0·4330 13
0·1	0·6236 751	0·5401 18
0·2	0·7251 757	0·6280 20
0·3	0·8212 611	0·7112 33
0·4	0·9146 378	0·7921 00
0·5	1·0063 894	0·8715 59
0·6	1·0970 665	0·9500 87
0·7	1·1869 875	1·0279 61
0·8	1·2763 522	1·1053 53
0·9	1·3652 938	1·1823 79
1·0	1·4539 053	1·2591 19

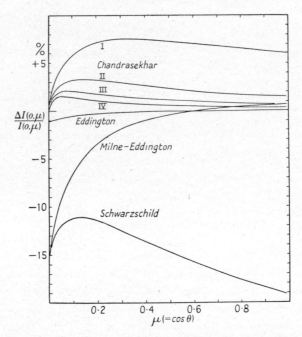

Fig. 12. Corrections $\Delta I(0, \mu)$ to approximate solutions for limb darkening expressed as percentage departures (exact minus approx.) from the exact values given by the Wiener–Hopf solution.

Table V compares the boundary values $q(0)$ and T_e/T_0 in the Milne–Eddington approximation, and in Eddington's second approximation, with the exact values of Hopf and Bronstein.

TABLE V

Relation between Boundary and Effective Temperature

	First approximation	Second approximation	Exact
$q(0)$	$\frac{2}{3} = 0\cdot6667$	$\frac{7}{12} = 0\cdot5833$	$\dfrac{1}{\sqrt{3}} = 0\cdot5773$
T_e/T_0	$1\cdot189$	$1\cdot211$	$1\cdot233$

THE CONTINUOUS SPECTRUM

1. Monochromatic radiative transfer with the absorption co-efficient a function of frequency

CONSIDER the transfer of radiation in a semi-infinite plane-parallel atmosphere in which the coefficient of absorption k_ν is a function of the frequency of the radiation. As before, we take the normal to the boundary of the atmosphere as the axis of x, with the positive direction outwards. Let $I_\nu(\theta)\,d\nu d\omega$ be the flow of radiation in frequencies from ν to $\nu+d\nu$ within the solid angle $d\omega$ in a direction making an angle θ with the outward normal, and let $4\pi j_\nu\,d\nu$ be the rate of emission within ν to $\nu+d\nu$ by unit mass of the atmosphere assuming the emission to be isotropic. The equation of monochromatic radiative transfer is then given by equation (1) of Chapter I which may be written as

$$\cos\theta\,\frac{dI_\nu(\theta)}{k_\nu\rho\,dx} = -I_\nu(\theta)+j_\nu/k_\nu. \tag{1}$$

We now define J_ν, H_ν, and K_ν by the relations

$$J_\nu = \frac{1}{4\pi}\int I_\nu(\theta)\,d\omega, \qquad H_\nu = \frac{1}{4\pi}\int I_\nu(\theta)\cos\theta\,d\omega,$$

$$K_\nu = \frac{1}{4\pi}\int I_\nu(\theta)\cos^2\theta\,d\omega$$

as in Chapter I. Multiplying (1) by $d\omega/4\pi$, also by $(d\omega/4\pi)\cos\theta$, and integrating, we get

$$\frac{dH_\nu}{\rho\,dx} = -k_\nu J_\nu+j_\nu, \tag{2}$$

$$\frac{dK_\nu}{\rho\,dx} = -k_\nu H_\nu. \tag{3}$$

We assume that the outer layers are in *local thermodynamic equilibrium*. In other words, the matter in an element of volume at temperature T behaves as it would in an enclosure at temperature T. The emission is given by Kirchhoff's law, equation (15) of Chapter I, namely

$$j_\nu = k_\nu B(\nu, T), \tag{4}$$

where $B(\nu, T)$ is Planck's function for the intensity of equilibrium radiation at temperature T. Writing $d\tau_\nu = -k_\nu \rho \, dx$ and making use of (4), equations (2) and (3) become

$$\frac{dH_\nu}{d\tau_\nu} = J_\nu - B(\nu, T), \tag{5}$$

$$\frac{dK_\nu}{d\tau_\nu} = H_\nu. \tag{6}$$

When k_ν is independent of ν, the transfer problem is the same as in Chapter I, and (6) leads to the result

$$J = H(2+3\tau). \tag{7}$$

On account of the constancy of the integrated net flux, equation (5) integrated with respect to ν gives

$$J = \int B(\nu, T) \, d\nu = B(T), \tag{8}$$

so that $B(T)$ is a linear function of τ. It does not follow that $B(\nu, T)$ is also a linear function of τ, even in the special case of k_ν independent of ν, but a linear expansion of $B(\nu, T)$ as a function of τ_ν, namely

$$B(\nu, T) = a_\nu + b_\nu \tau_\nu, \tag{9}$$

is likely to be a fairly good approximation for small values of τ_ν. If we use the geometrical approximation $K_\nu = \frac{1}{3}J_\nu$ in equation (6) and differentiate with respect to τ_ν, then

$$\frac{d^2 J_\nu}{d\tau_\nu^2} = 3\frac{dH_\nu}{d\tau_\nu}. \tag{10}$$

From the approximate formula (9) we have $d^2(B(\nu, T))/d\tau_\nu^2 = 0$, hence equations (5) and (10) give

$$\frac{d^2}{d\tau_\nu^2}\{J_\nu - B(\nu, T)\} = 3\{J_\nu - B(\nu, T)\}. \tag{11}$$

The solution of (11) is

$$J_\nu - B(\nu, T) = A_\nu e^{-\sqrt{3}\tau_\nu} + B_\nu e^{+\sqrt{3}\tau_\nu}. \tag{12}$$

As we go into the interior of a star the intensity of radiation will not diverge exponentially from the intensity in thermodynamic equilibrium, so that we must have $B_\nu = 0$ and $J_\nu \to B(\nu, T)$ as $\tau_\nu \to \infty$. At the surface we have $J_\nu = 2H_\nu$ from Section 3 of Chapter I, giving

$$A_\nu(1+2/\sqrt{3}) = \frac{2}{3}b_\nu - a_\nu.$$

Hence equation (12) becomes

$$J_\nu = B(\nu, T) + \frac{2b_\nu - 3a_\nu}{3 + 2\sqrt{3}} e^{-\sqrt{3}\tau_\nu}. \tag{13}$$

We now verify that, when k_ν is independent of ν, equation (13) gives $J = B(T)$. From equation (9) $a_\nu = B(\nu, T_0)$ and

$$b_\nu = \left\{ \frac{\partial}{\partial \tau} B(\nu, T) \right\}_{\tau=0} = \left\{ \frac{\partial}{\partial T} B(\nu, T) \frac{dT}{d\tau} \right\}_{\tau=0}.$$

When k_ν is independent of ν we have $T^4 = T_0^4(1 + \frac{3}{2}\tau)$ according to equation (18) of Chapter I, so that $4T^3(dT/d\tau) = \frac{3}{2}T_0^4$ and $(dT/d\tau)_{\tau=0} = \frac{3}{8}T_0$.

Accordingly $b_\nu = \frac{3}{8}T_0 \left\{ \frac{\partial}{\partial T} B(\nu, T) \right\}_{\tau=0}$.   We now have

$$2b_\nu - 3a_\nu = \frac{3}{4}T_0 \left\{ \frac{\partial}{\partial T} B(\nu, T) \right\}_{\tau=0} - 3B(\nu, T_0),$$

and therefore

$$\int (2b_\nu - 3a_\nu) \, d\nu = 3 \int \left[\frac{1}{4}T_0 \left\{ \frac{\partial}{\partial T} B(\nu, T) \right\}_{\tau=0} - B(\nu, T_0) \right] d\nu.$$

But

$$\int B(\nu, T) \, d\nu = bT^4,$$

so that

$$\int \frac{\partial}{\partial T} B(\nu, T) \, d\nu = 4bT^3.$$

Accordingly

$$\int (2b_\nu - 3a_\nu) \, d\nu = 0,$$

and with τ_ν independent of ν, equation (13), integrated with respect to ν, gives $J = B(T)$.

1.1. *Mean coefficients of absorption—the straight mean and Rosseland's mean*

In the absence of any source or sink of radiant energy in the outer layers the integrated net flux of radiation is constant from one layer to another. However, the net flux in particular frequency ranges is not constant, as there is a net transfer of energy to longer wave-lengths on going outwards, as is shown by the distribution in frequency of the net flux of radiation at various optical depths in a grey atmosphere (k_ν independent of ν) given in Table VI.

Let $J = \int J_\nu \, d\nu,$ $H = \int H_\nu \, d\nu,$ $K = \int K_\nu \, d\nu.$

Integrating (3) with respect to the frequency

$$\frac{dK}{\rho \, dx} = -\int k_\nu H_\nu \, d\nu. \tag{14}$$

We now define a mean coefficient of absorption

$$\bar{k} = \frac{1}{H} \int k_\nu H_\nu \, d\nu, \tag{15}$$

TABLE VI

Monochromatic Flux F_α/F in a Grey Atmosphere

τ	$\alpha = h\nu/RT_e$							
	1	2	3	4	6	8	10	12
0	0·0864	0·1837	0·2074	0·1772	0·0856	0·0314	0·0101	0·0030
0·1	0·0784	0·1732	0·2027	0·1791	0·0911	0·0346	0·0114	0·0034
0·2	0·0719	0·1640	0·1981	0·1801	0·0961	0·0376	0·0126	0·0039
0·3	0·0663	0·1556	0·1933	0·1804	0·1005	0·0406	0·0139	0·0043
0·4	0·0615	0·1480	0·1886	0·1802	0·1044	0·0435	0·0152	0·0048
0·5	0·0571	0·1407	0·1835	0·1793	0·1078	0·0462	0·0165	0·0053
0·6	0·0532	0·1342	0·1789	0·1783	0·1110	0·0489	0·0178	0·0058
0·7	0·0498	0·1282	0·1745	0·1772	0·1138	0·0515	0·0192	0·0064
0·8	0·0466	0·1225	0·1699	0·1755	0·1163	0·0539	0·0205	0·0069
0·9	0·0439	0·1174	0·1656	0·1740	0·1186	0·0563	0·0218	0·0075
1·0	0·0413	0·1128	0·1616	0·1724	0·1207	0·0586	0·0231	0·0081
1·2	0·0370	0·1042	0·1540	0·1688	0·1240	0·0628	0·0257	0·0092
1·4	0·0335	0·0968	0·1470	0·1651	0·1268	0·0667	0·0282	0·0105
1·6	0·0305	0·0906	0·1406	0·1614	0·1289	0·0702	0·0307	0·0117
1·8	0·0280	0·0850	0·1349	0·1578	0·1306	0·0735	0·0331	0·0129
2·0	0·0259	0·0803	0·1295	0·1543	0·1319	0·0764	0·0353	0·0142

After S. Chandrasekhar, *Ap. J.* **101**, 344 (1945).

so that $\bar{k}$ is the arithmetic mean of the k_ν with the associated fluxes as weight factors. With the optical depth τ measured in terms of this mean coefficient of absorption we have $d\tau = -\bar{k}\rho\,dx$, and equation (3) becomes

$$\frac{dK}{d\tau} = H, \tag{16}$$

for which the solution is

$$K = H\tau + \text{constant.} \tag{17}$$

Equations (16) and (17) are formally the same as equations (6) and (8) of Chapter I for the case k_ν independent of ν. But $K = \frac{1}{3}J$, and with the boundary condition $J = 2H$ at $\tau = 0$, we then have

$$J = H(2 + 3\tau).$$

Now in the case k_ν independent of ν we had $J = B$, and hence

$$T^4 = T_0^4(1 + \tfrac{3}{2}\tau).$$

But the condition of radiative equilibrium is really

$$\int k_\nu B_\nu\,d\nu = \int k_\nu J_\nu\,d\nu, \tag{18}$$

and this does not necessarily reduce to $J = B$ unless k_ν is independent of ν. The point is discussed by Chandrasekhar† who shows that $J = B$

† S. Chandrasekhar, *Ap. J.* **101**, 328 (1945). See also *Radiative Transfer* (Oxford), chap. xi.

is a good approximation if the variation of k_ν with ν is reasonably small. Let $k_\nu/\bar{k} = 1+\delta_\nu$, then from equation (18) we have

$$\int (1+\delta_\nu)B_\nu \, d\nu = \int (1+\delta_\nu)J_\nu \, d\nu.$$

Hence
$$B-J = \int \delta_\nu(J_\nu-B_\nu) \, d\nu. \tag{19}$$

From the equation of transfer,

$$\cos\theta \frac{dI_\nu(\theta)}{d\tau_\nu} = I_\nu(\theta)-B_\nu,$$

we find
$$\delta_\nu(J_\nu-B_\nu) = \frac{1}{4\pi}\int \delta_\nu \frac{dI_\nu(\theta)}{d\tau_\nu}\cos\theta \, d\omega = \delta_\nu \frac{dH_\nu}{d\tau_\nu}.$$

Equation (19) may now be written

$$B-J = \int \delta_\nu(dH_\nu/d\tau_\nu) \, d\nu.$$

Since
$$\bar{k}H = \int k_\nu H_\nu \, d\nu = \bar{k}\int (1+\delta_\nu)H_\nu \, d\nu,$$

we have
$$\int \delta_\nu H_\nu \, d\nu = 0. \tag{20}$$

Accordingly $\int \delta_\nu(dH_\nu/d\tau_\nu) \, d\nu$ will be a small quantity, and $J = B$ is a good approximation even in a non-grey atmosphere. The result is, in fact, exact if δ_ν is independent of τ_ν. We then have

$$T^4 = T_0^4(1+\tfrac{3}{2}\tau),$$

provided that $d\tau = -\bar{k}\rho \, dx$, and $\bar{k}$ is defined by equation (15). Equivalent definitions of this mean coefficient are

$$\frac{1}{\bar{k}}\int \frac{dK_\nu}{dT} \, d\nu = \int \frac{1}{k_\nu}\frac{dK_\nu}{dT} \, d\nu, \tag{21}$$

$$\frac{1}{\bar{k}}\int \frac{dJ_\nu}{dT} \, d\nu = \int \frac{1}{k_\nu}\frac{dJ_\nu}{dT} \, d\nu. \tag{22}$$

The relation (22) follows from (21) by means of the geometrical approximation $K_\nu = \tfrac{1}{3}J_\nu$. It should be noted that the mean coefficient of absorption as defined by (15), (21), and (22) is not the geometrical mean of Rosseland, as originally defined for the stellar interior, namely

$$\frac{1}{\bar{k}}\int \frac{dB_\nu}{dT} \, d\nu = \int \frac{1}{k_\nu}\frac{dB_\nu}{dT} \, d\nu. \tag{23}$$

The use of equation (15), and the distinction between (22) and (23) were first pointed out by Krook.†

† M. Krook, *M.N.* **98**, 204 (1938).

2. A microscopic analysis of the hypothesis of local thermodynamic equilibrium

The theory of radiative equilibrium of the outer layers makes use of laws representing certain kinds of equilibrium. Two main types of equilibrium are considered, local thermodynamic equilibrium and monochromatic radiative equilibrium. Local thermodynamic equilibrium is defined as a state in which the emission of radiation is the same as the emission from matter in an equilibrium enclosure at temperature T. This gives $j_\nu = k_\nu B(\nu, T)$, where $B(\nu, T) = (2h\nu^3/c^2)(e^{h\nu/RT}-1)^{-1}$. On the other hand, material is said to be in monochromatic radiative equilibrium with respect to ν-radiation when it emits just as much radiation as it absorbs. In other words, the emission is the absorption averaged over all directions, and we have the equation of monochromatic radiative equilibrium

$$4\pi j_\nu = k_\nu \int I_\nu(\theta)\, d\omega = 4\pi k_\nu J_\nu.$$

Material in the outer layers of a star might be in one of these two types of equilibrium, or a mixture of the two, or it might be in neither. As we shall see, the hypothesis that the outer layers of the Sun are substantially in local thermodynamic equilibrium gives a darkening of the limb which is in very satisfactory agreement with observation. The close agreement of the observations with theory may be taken as a justification of the hypothesis. But there is another way in which the equilibrium assumption may be justified, that is, by making an analysis of the absorbing atmosphere in terms of its constituent particles. We now attempt to establish the type of equilibrium by a study of the interaction between the elementary particles themselves in the presence of radiation.

Consider an atmosphere in which only one kind of absorbing atom is present, and let us suppose that the absorption process is one in which the electron transition involves a bound state and the continuum, so that the absorption of a quantum in the frequency range ν to $\nu+d\nu$ results in the liberation of a free electron having a velocity within v to $v+dv$. In the interval of time dt unit mass of the atmosphere absorbs an amount of energy $k_\nu I_\nu(\theta)\, d\nu d\omega dt$ from the radiation field within $d\omega$ in the direction θ. The absorption summed over all directions is equal to $4\pi k_\nu J_\nu\, d\nu dt$, and the number of quanta absorbed by unit mass will be $4\pi k_\nu J_\nu\, d\nu dt/h\nu$. Let $f(v)\, dv$ be the rate of liberation of electrons with velocities in the range v to $v+dv$ when $J_\nu = B_\nu$, then

$$f(v)\, dv = 4\pi k_\nu B_\nu\, d\nu/h\nu. \qquad (24)$$

When $J_\nu \neq B_\nu$, the velocity distribution of the liberated electrons deviates from $f(v)$. Let

$$g_0(v)\, dv = 4\pi k_\nu J_\nu\, dv/h\nu \qquad (25)$$

be the rate of liberation of electrons having velocities within v to $v+dv$.

Consider an ideal experiment in which one gramme of matter at a given temperature and electron pressure is thrust at time t_0 into an atmosphere of free electrons (at the same temperature and pressure) having a Maxwellian distribution of velocities, but in which there is a radiation field of intensity $J_\nu \neq B_\nu$. Let the gramme be withdrawn at time t_0+dt. The number of electrons with velocities v to $v+dv$ is increased on account of photo-ionization of the absorbing atoms in the gramme by the amount $g_0(v)\, dvdt$, and decreased on account of electron capture by $f(v)\, dvdt$. After the gramme of matter is withdrawn, collisions will ultimately restore the original Maxwellian distribution of velocities, and if $\phi(v) = g(v)-f(v)$ is the disturbance at time t, then

$$\phi = \phi_0 e^{-\lambda(t-t_0)},$$

where ϕ_0 is the initial deviation.† The quantity λ^{-1} is referred to as 'the time of relaxation', and is a measure of the rate at which deviations from Maxwell's law subside. Hence

$$g(v) = f(v)-\{f(v)-g_0(v)\}e^{-\lambda(t-t_0)}. \qquad (26)$$

Having established the result (26), we now consider matter left permanently in the atmosphere. Consider first the subsequent history of the electrons liberated from one gramme between t_0 and t_0+dt. To take into account the effect of recombinations we suppose that the fraction μdt of electrons present at any time t are lost during the subsequent interval dt by recombination. When the process has been operating for a time $t-t_0$, the initial electron population is reduced by the factor $e^{-\mu(t-t_0)}$, so that of the electrons initially liberated the number remaining at time t and having velocities within v to $v+dv$ will be $g(v)\, dvdt_0\, e^{-\mu(t-t_0)}$. The number which recombine during the interval dt is therefore

$$g(v)\, dvdt_0\, \mu e^{-\mu(t-t_0)}\, dt. \qquad (27)$$

Since each recombination gives rise to the emission of a quantum of energy $h\nu$, the emission per gramme in time dt at any given instant t is given by the expression (27) summed for all t_0 from $-\infty$ to t. Hence

$$4\pi j_\nu\, dv/h\nu = \mu \int_{-\infty}^{t} g(v)\, dv\, e^{-\mu(t-t_0)}\, dt_0. \qquad (28)$$

Substituting for $f(v)$ and $g_0(v)$ from (24) and (25), equation (26) gives

$$g(v)\, dv = 4\pi k_\nu\, (dv/h\nu)[B_\nu+(J_\nu-B_\nu)e^{-\lambda(t-t_0)}]. \qquad (29)$$

† J. H. Jeans, *Dynamical Theory of Gases* (Cambridge), 2nd ed., p. 260.

Put $t' = t-t_0$ so that $dt' = -dt_0$. Equations (28) and (29) now give

$$j_\nu/k_\nu = \mu \int [B_\nu + (J_\nu - B_\nu)e^{-\lambda t'}]e^{-\mu t'}\, dt'$$

$$= \frac{\mu}{\lambda+\mu} J_\nu + \frac{\lambda}{\lambda+\mu} B_\nu. \tag{30}$$

Hence $\lambda \gg \mu$ is a necessary and sufficient condition for local thermodynamic equilibrium. The values of λ and μ depend upon the probability that an electron will collide with another electron, and the probability that an electron will be captured.

Consider an electron moving with velocity v relative to another electron, close to which it will pass, and suppose that as a result of the collision it loses energy between Q and $Q+dQ$. The (annular) cross-section for this collision† is

$$\frac{2\pi e^4}{mv^2}\frac{dQ}{Q^2},$$

so that the cross-section for all collisions in which Q is not less than Q_0 is

$$\frac{2\pi e^4}{mv^2}\frac{1}{Q_0}. \tag{31}$$

Accordingly, if a fast electron moves with a velocity v among n_e slower electrons per cubic centimetre, it will experience $N\, dt$ collisions in time dt, each collision removing at least $1/\alpha$ of the excess energy of the fast electron, where

$$N = n_e v\alpha 4\pi \left(\frac{e^2}{mv^2}\right)^2.$$

The average energy of the electrons with a Maxwellian velocity distribution is $\frac{3}{2}RT$. Let the fast electron have β times the mean energy: then $mv^2 = 3\beta RT$, and

$$N = n_e v\alpha\beta^{-2}\frac{4\pi}{9}\left(\frac{e^2}{RT}\right)^2.$$

To compare the probability of an α, β collision with the probability of capture by an ion (or neutral atom, if the recapture process is $H+e \rightarrow H^- + h\nu$), we note that if there are n capturing particles per cubic centimetre and the cross-section is S cm.^{2}, the number of captures in time dt is $N'\, dt = nvS\, dt$. Accordingly

$$\frac{N}{N'} = \frac{n_e}{n}\frac{4\pi\alpha}{9\beta^2 S}\left(\frac{e^2}{RT}\right)^2.$$

For example, in an atmosphere at $T = 6{,}000°$ K., and $n_e/n = 10^{-4}$

† N. F. Mott and H. S. W. Massey, *The Theory of Atomic Collisions* (Oxford), 2nd ed., p. 369.

(conditions appropriate to the Sun), with $\alpha = 2$ and $\beta = 3$, and $S = 2 \cdot 5 \times 10^{-22}$ cm.^{2} (the maximum value for negative hydrogen ions), there are approximately 10^4 electron-electron collisions to every capture. The average fast electron liberated from a negative ion therefore experiences many collisions with other electrons before it is recaptured. We therefore conclude that $\lambda \gg \mu$.

It is of some interest to inquire whether this inequality persists when the pressure becomes very small, since early theory[†] suggested that local thermodynamic equilibrium existed in the middle of the photosphere, but gave way to monochromatic radiative equilibrium near the surface. This would be so if $\lambda \gg \mu$ for moderate values of the pressure p, and if $\lambda/\mu \to 0$ as $p \to 0$. But λ is proportional to n_e^2. Thus if negative ions are the main source of opacity, the recapture process is $H + e \to H^- + h\nu$, and we have $\mu \propto n_e n$, $\lambda/\mu \propto n_e/n$ and the ratio λ/μ does not tend to zero with the electron pressure. Accordingly local thermodynamic equilibrium persists even at very low pressures. This result is quite general, for if the hydrogen were mainly ionized and the recapture process is $H^+ + e \to H + h\nu$, then λ/μ is independent of electron pressure and local thermodynamic equilibrium will again persist at low pressure.

3. Physical nature of the continuous absorption coefficient

According to the early work of Kramers,[‡] and later work by Gaunt,[§] the absorption coefficient of a hydrogen-like atom of atomic number Z in its bound-free continuum is

$$\left. \begin{aligned} \kappa_\lambda &= \frac{64\pi^4}{3\sqrt{3}} \frac{me^{10}Z^4}{c^4 h^6 n^5} g(\lambda)\lambda^3 \\ &= 0 \cdot 0104 g(\lambda) Z^4 \lambda^3 / n^5 \end{aligned} \right\}, \tag{32}$$

where $g(\lambda)$ is a slowly varying factor whose numerical value is close to unity, hc/λ_0 is the energy required to remove the electron from the atom, and n is the principal quantum number of the state of the atom. By 'hydrogen-like' we mean that the field in which the outermost electron of the atom moves is a Coulomb field (varying with the inverse square of the distance), and by bound-free continuum we mean that when the absorption takes place, this electron (bound, because it moves in an elliptical orbit and has not enough energy to escape from the Coulomb field) receives enough energy to escape altogether from the atom (that is, becomes free, and moves off in a hyperbolic orbit). Although the

† E. A. Milne, *M.N.* **88**, 493 (1928).
‡ H. A. Kramers, *Phil. Mag.* **46**, 836 (1923).
§ J. A. Gaunt, *Phil. Trans. Roy. Soc.* A, **229**, 163 (1930).

fields of most nuclei are not exactly Coulomb fields, and the absorption coefficient is not observed to fall off as the cube of the wave-length, as given by (32), the Kramers–Gaunt formula illustrates the matters of principle involved in a study of solar continuous absorption.

In the first place there is no absorption at all if $\lambda > \lambda_0$ because the absorbed quantum has not enough energy to set the bound electron free. Considering at first only the ground states of atoms, hc/λ_0 is equal to the ionization potential of the atom. The values for typical atoms are as follows:

Element				H	Fe	Na
Ionization potential (volts)	.			13·59	7·89	5·14
λ_0 (angstroms)	.	.	.	912	1,570	2,412

Visible light of wave-length, say, 5,000 A is not absorbed at all by these atoms in their ground states. However, when the atoms are in their excited states they can absorb light in the visible wave-lengths. In the case of hydrogen, equation (32) with the Gaunt factor $g(\lambda)$ omitted, may be written as
$$\kappa_\lambda = 7\cdot9 \times 10^{-18} n(\lambda/\lambda_0)^3.$$

The continua are called Balmer (excitation potential 10·19 volts, energy required to free the electron 13·59—10·19 volts, or 3·40 volts, so that $\lambda_0 = 3,646$ A), Paschen (E.P. 12·09 volts, $\lambda_0 = 8,208$ A), and other higher continua in the infra-red. The metals also have excited states. Since hydrogen is by far the most abundant constituent of the solar atmosphere it was thought that the excited H atoms which form the Paschen series of hydrogen must make a very important contribution to the solar absorption coefficient. In this continuum alone the absorption coefficient is proportional to $(\lambda/8,208)^3$ and therefore decreases markedly in the visible spectrum. However, many abundant metals have excited states so disposed as to contribute to the absorption of visible light, and as we proceed from red to violet more of these states are able to absorb the light so that the absorption coefficient due to metals increases from red to violet. In fact it was thought for many years that the approximate constancy of the solar absorption coefficient from red to violet, suggested by Milne's theoretical limb darkening, was due to the combination of hydrogen absorption decreasing from red to violet and metallic absorption increasing in that direction. There were, however, certain difficulties: no absorption edges had been observed, and on the basis of theoretical absorption coefficients the calculated ratio of hydrogen to metals required to bring about a constant photospheric opacity could not easily be reconciled with the absence of metal absorption edges.

This balance was later found to be unnecessary when Wildt† drew attention to the negative hydrogen ion as possibly the dominant source of opacity in the outer layers of the Sun.

3.1. *The negative hydrogen ion*

In a mixture of atoms differing greatly in ionization potential—say sodium and hydrogen—the electrons released from the atoms of low ionization potential at comparatively low temperatures may readily attach themselves to the hydrogen atoms to form negative hydrogen ions, H^-. The electron affinity of the H^- ion being only 0·747 volts, a hydrogen-metal mixture is necessary for ion formation in appreciable quantities since an assembly consisting only of hydrogen atoms could not release enough electrons at the low radiation temperature required to allow many electrons to remain so loosely attached to neutral hydrogen atoms. The conditions required for the formation of negative hydrogen ions are realized in the outer layers of stars of medium or late spectral type.

The concentration of negative ions is given exactly in thermodynamic equilibrium, and with a good degree of approximation in the solar photosphere, by Saha's relation. If there are N_H hydrogen atoms, N_{H^-} negative ions and N_e electrons per unit volume, according to this relation we have

$$N_H N_e / N_{H^-} = 2(2\pi m R T)^{\frac{3}{2}} \varpi h^{-3} e^{-\chi/RT}, \tag{33}$$

where ϖ depends on the statistical weights of the particles (and has the value 2 in this case) and χ is the detachment potential of the negative ion. For a typical photospheric region in the Sun $T = 6,000$ K., $N_e = 10^{14}$ and with $\chi = 0·747$ volts equation (33) gives $N_{H^-}/N_H = 10^{-7}$. On the other hand the number of hydrogen atoms in the third quantum state, capable of absorbing in the Paschen continuum, is given by Boltzmann's relation

$$\frac{N_{H'}}{N_H} = \frac{q_3}{q_1} e^{-\chi_3/RT}. \tag{34}$$

Now $q_3/q_1 = 9$, $\chi_3 = 12·09$ volts, and with $T = 6,000°$ equation (34) gives $N_{H'}/N_H = 6 \times 10^{-10}$. Accordingly, negative ions, although rare compared with hydrogen atoms in the ground state, are much more abundant than excited hydrogen atoms capable of absorbing in the visible spectrum. If the absorption coefficient of the negative ion is comparable with that of the excited hydrogen atom, the ion will then contribute far more to absorption in this region of the spectrum than the atom itself.

† R. Wildt, *Ap. J.* **89**, 295 (1939).

Since the detachment potential of the H⁻ ion is 0·747 volts, the continuous absorption due to photo-detachment of electrons from negative ions extends from λ 16,730 A, in the infra-red, towards shorter wave-

TABLE VII

Negative Hydrogen Ion Bound-free Absorption Coefficient

$\lambda(A)$	Multiply by 10^{-17}	$\lambda(A)$	Multiply by 10^{-17}
505	0·0657	5,875	3·87
1,066	0·333	6,280	4·06
1,642	0·740	7,283	4·41
2,249	1·231	8,275	4·52
2,987	1·84	8,069	4·50
3,572	2·32	9,102	4·44
3,960	2·62	10,111	4·13
4,443	2·97	12,131	2·96
5,059	3·39	13,994	1·50

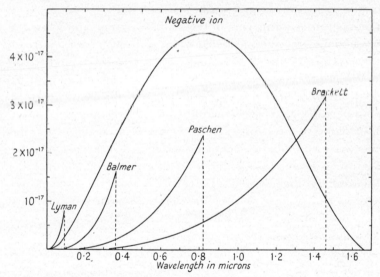

Fig. 13. The continuous absorption coefficient of the negative hydrogen ion compared with the absorption continua shown by neutral hydrogen per atom in the ground state, and per atom in each of the excited states according to Kramers' formula. For an assembly of H atoms the absorption in each continuum is to be weighted by the population in the excited state from which the absorption takes place.

lengths. Theoretical calculations show that the absorption coefficient for the ion does not vary with λ^3, as does that of the atom, but is more or less constant over a comparatively wide spectral range. The values of κ_λ per negative hydrogen ion, according to Chandrasekhar,[†] are given in Table VII and are illustrated in Fig. 13 together with the continuous

† S. Chandrasekhar, ibid. **102**, 395 (1945).

absorption coefficient for an excited H atom in the various absorption continua calculated from the Kramers–Gaunt formula (32). The absorption per cubic centimetre of atmosphere by the neutral hydrogen atoms themselves will be the sum of the absorption coefficients weighted by the number of atoms in the appropriate excited state from which the absorption occurs. Under photospheric conditions the absorption due to H$^-$ ions is far superior to that due to H atoms except in the Lyman continuum. With $T = 6,000°$ and $N_e = 10^{14}$ the ratio of the concentration of ions to the excited atoms producing the various absorption continua are as follows: $N_{H^-}/N_{H'} = 10$ (Balmer), 160 (Paschen), and 310 (Brackett). But the atoms which give rise to the Lyman continuum outnumber the negative ions by a factor of 10^7.

Bound-free and free-free processes. In addition to bound-free absorption another kind of absorption can occur which is called free-free absorption.† In this process a free electron moving in the field of an atom momentarily forms part of the atomic system, and when the atom absorbs a quantum there is a change in the hyperbolic orbit of the electron around the atom.‡ Free-free absorption is inferior to bound-free absorption in the visible part of the spectrum, but rises superior to it in the infra-red region. There is a variety of circumstances in which free-free absorption can take place. In addition to free-free absorption when electrons move in the strong attractive fields of positive ions, there is a free-free spectrum due to electrons moving in the field of a negative ion, also free-free absorption in the weak attractive field in the vicinity of a neutral hydrogen atom. In this last case the attraction of the positive nucleus (a proton) is incompletely cancelled at small distances by the repulsion due to the bound electron.

In the photosphere of the Sun the radiative transitions of free electrons in the field of neutral hydrogen atoms is the most important free-free absorption process, on account of the great abundance of neutral atoms in comparison with ions. The contribution of free-free absorption to the continuous absorption coefficient of the negative hydrogen ion according to Chandrasekhar and Breen§ is given in Table VIII. The free-free absorption coefficient is evaluated for an assembly in which there is a

---

† Eddington (*Internal Constitution of the Stars* (Cambridge), pp. 229, 375) refers to this process as 'switches of electron orbits'.

‡ One might consider the astronomical analogy of comets to free electrons and planets to bound electrons, and think of a bound-free transition as similar to an impulse applied to a planet giving it a velocity greater than the velocity of escape, a free-free transition being likened to a perturbation in the hyperbolic orbit of a comet.

§ S. Chandrasekhar and F. Breen, *Ap. J.* **104**, 430 (1946).

TABLE VIII

Continuous Absorption Coefficient of the Negative Hydrogen Ion

Bound-free and free-free absorption† per neutral H atom per unit electron pressure

$\theta = 5{,}040/T$ $\lambda(\text{Å})$	0·5	0·6	0·7	0·8	0·9	1·0	1·2	1·4	1·6	1·8	2·0
						κ'_λ Multiply by 10^{-26}					
4,050	0·454	0·865	1·52	2·54	4·05	6·27	13·98	29·04	57·27	108·5	199·6
	0·081	0·106	0·13	0·16	0·20	0·23	0·30	0·37	0·45	0·56	0·62
4,556	0·509	0·974	1·72	2·87	4·50	7·12	15·89	33·00	65·09	123·4	226·8
	0·100	0·132	0·17	0·20	0·24	0·28	0·36	0·46	0·55	0·65	0·76
5,063	0·556	1·070	1·90	3·18	5·10	7·90	17·64	36·66	72·32	137·1	252·1
	0·121	0·160	0·20	0·24	0·29	0·34	0·44	0·55	0·66	0·78	0·91
5,695	0·603	1·171	2·09	3·51	5·63	8·75	19·58	40·73	80·36	152·3	280·1
	0·150	0·198	0·25	0·30	0·36	0·42	0·54	0·67	0·81	0·96	1·11
6,509	0·644	1·261	2·26	3·82	6·16	9·60	21·53	44·85	88·57	168·0	308·8
	0·191	0·252	0·32	0·39	0·46	0·53	0·69	0·85	1·02	1·20	1·39
7,594	0·659	1·306	2·37	4·02	6·52	10·20	22·99	48·03	94·98	180·3	331·6
	0·252	0·334	0·42	0·51	0·61	0·70	0·91	1·12	1·34	1·57	1·81
9,113	0·612	1·229	2·25	3·86	6·31	9·92	22·57	47·38	94·00	178·8	329·1
	0·352	0·466	0·59	0·71	0·85	0·98	1·26	1·56	1·86	2·18	2·50
10,130	0·544	1·100	2·03	3·50	5·74	9·07	20·76	43·76	87·03	165·8	305·6
	0·427	0·565	0·71	0·87	1·03	1·19	1·53	1·89	2·25	2·63	3·02
11,390	0·431	0·879	1·63	2·83	4·68	7·42	17·12	36·27	72·40	138·3	255·3
	0·529	0·702	0·88	1·08	1·27	1·48	1·90	2·24	2·79	3·26	3·73
13,020	0·265	0·545	1·02	1·79	2·97	4·74	11·02	23·52	47·19	90·46	167·4
	0·677	0·897	1·13	1·38	1·63	1·89	2·44	3·00	3·53	4·16	4·76
15,190	0·071	0·148	0·28	0·49	0·82	1·32	3·12	6·72	13·56	26·13	48·55
	0·902	1·04	1·50	1·83	2·17	2·52	3·25	3·99	4·76	5·54	6·33
18,230	1·57	1·68	2·11	2·57	3·05	3·54	4·56	5·62	6·70	7·79	8·91
22,780	1·94	2·56	3·22	3·91	4·64	5·38	6·94	8·54	10·2	11·9	13·6
30,380	3·38	4·44	5·57	6·77	8·01	9·29	12·0	14·7	17·6	20·5	23·4
36,450	4·81	6·32	7·93	9·61	11·4	13·2	16·9	20·9	24·9	29·0	33·2
45,560	7·45	9·77	12·2	14·8	17·5	20·3	26·1	32·1	38·3	44·6	51·0
60,750	13·1	17·2	21·5	26·0	30·7	35·5	45·6	56·1	66·9	77·9	89·1
91,130	29·3	38·4	48·0	57·9	68·3	79·0	101	124	148	172	197
182,300	117	153	191	230	271	313	401	491	585	680	777

† For $\lambda < 15{,}190$ the upper entry for each wave-length gives the bound-free absorption whilst the lower entry gives the free-free contribution.

Maxwellian distribution of velocities corresponding to a given temperature. Averaging over the distribution of initial velocities of the electrons, the free-free atomic absorption coefficient is then expressed as *per unit electron pressure*. Table VIII gives both the bound-free and free-free absorption coefficients, the bound-free contribution having been reduced to the same system (cm.^{4}/dyne) as the free-free absorption coefficient by multiplying the absorption per negative hydrogen ion by the number of H$^-$ ions present per neutral H atom at unit electron pressure, namely

$$\phi(\theta) = 4 \cdot 158 \times 10^{-10}\theta^{5/2}e^{1 \cdot 726\theta},$$

where $\theta = 5{,}040/T$. The coefficients given in the table are corrected for stimulated emission, which reduces the absorption by the factor $1 - e^{-hc/\lambda RT}$.

3.2. *The mass coefficient of absorption*

We write κ'_λ for the absorption coefficient per neutral H atom at unit electron pressure due to negative hydrogen ion absorption and free-free absorption, whilst k_λ refers to the absorption per gramme of the stellar atmosphere. Let x_H be the degree of ionization of hydrogen at a given depth at temperature T ($= 5{,}040/\theta$) and electron pressure p_e. If N is the concentration of H atoms, the number of neutral H atoms present is $N(1-x_H)$, and the absorption per cubic centimetre is equal to $\kappa'_\lambda N(1-x_H)p_e$. Assuming a predominant abundance of hydrogen, so that the mass per unit volume may be taken as Nm_H, the absorption per unit mass of the atmosphere will then be given by

$$k_\lambda = \kappa'_\lambda (1-x_H)p_e/m_H. \tag{35}$$

The mean coefficient $\bar{k}$ is defined by equation (15), but to carry out an actual evaluation of this mean it is necessary to know the flux in various frequencies. This is not known until $\bar{k}$ itself has already been found. It has been proposed by Chandrasekhar† that a first approximation to $\bar{k}$ should be found by weighting the values of k_λ with the fluxes F^1_λ in a grey atmosphere (Chandrasekhar shows that the approximation is a good one if the variation of k_λ with λ is not severe). The mean absorption coefficient for an atmosphere in which a number of absorbing processes contribute to the total absorption is the sum of the mean absorption coefficients due to each process. The mean coefficient due to H$^-$ absorption alone will be given by

$$\bar{k}(\mathrm{H}^-) = \frac{1}{m_H}(1-x_H)p_e \int_0^\infty \kappa'_\lambda(\mathrm{H}^-)(F_\lambda/F)\,d\lambda. \tag{36}$$

† S. Chandrasekhar, *Ap. J.* **101**, 328 (1945); *Radiative Transfer* (Oxford), chap. xi.

Let
$$a(\mathrm{H}^-) = \int_0^\infty \kappa'_\lambda(\mathrm{H}^-)(F_\lambda/F)\,d\lambda,$$

then from equations (35) and (36) we find

$$k_\lambda/\bar{k}(\mathrm{H}^-) = \kappa'_\lambda/a(\mathrm{H}^-). \tag{37}$$

Table IX shows that the ratio $k_\lambda/\bar{k}(\mathrm{H}^-)$ is fairly constant with depth for wave-lengths in the visible spectrum, but in the infra-red it is an increasing function of the depth.

TABLE IX

Variation of $k_\lambda/\bar{k}(\mathrm{H}^-)$ with Optical Depth

λ \ τ	0	0·1	0·2	0·4	0·6	0·8	1·0	1·2	1·4
4,050	0·801	0·785	0·780	0·773	0·777	0·783	0·787	0·803	0·817
4,556	0·896	0·889	0·878	0·875	0·894	0·906	0·920	0·928	0·936
5,063	0·989	0·978	0·977	0·978	0·991	1·009	1·023	1·035	1·036
5,695	1·107	1·099	1·089	1·088	1·104	1·112	1·128	1·147	1·155
6,509	1·228	1·214	1·212	1·198	1·221	1·233	1·256	1·272	1·286
7,594	1·313	1·296	1·298	1·294	1·314	1·331	1·346	1·367	1·380
9,113	1·324	1·315	1·305	1·293	1·318	1·331	1·359	1·379	1·383
10,130	1·244	1·237	1·226	1·227	1·240	1·248	1·276	1·303	1·319
11,390	1·058	1·057	1·057	1·069	1·104	1·118	1·143	1·162	1·190
13,020	0·786	0·793	0·798	0·818	0·858	0·875	0·910	0·936	0·965
15,190	0·417	0·445	0·469	0·508	0·554	0·591	0·638	0·679	0·717
18,230	0·341	0·393	0·433	0·504	0·573	0·633	0·695	0·751	0·801
22,780	0·519	0·597	0·662	0·771	0·875	0·971	1·059	1·150	1·229

The contribution of neutral H atoms to the absorption coefficient may be found from the Kramers–Gaunt formula (32) together with Boltzmann's relation
$$N_n/N_{\mathrm{H}} = n^2 e^{-\chi_n/RT} \tag{38}$$

with $\chi_n = \chi_{\mathrm{H}}(1 - 1/n^2)$, χ_{H} being the ionization potential of the H atom by excitation from its ground state ($\chi_{\mathrm{H}} = 13\cdot59$ volts). Since only the fraction $n^2 e^{-\chi_n/RT}$ of neutral atoms present in a given volume absorb from the nth quantum state, the absorption coefficient at wave-length λ per neutral H atom in the ground state will be the expression

$$\frac{64\pi^4}{3\sqrt{3}} \frac{me^{10}}{c^4 h^6} \frac{\lambda^3}{n^3} e^{-\chi_n/RT}$$

summed over all the absorption continua involved, in other words over all n for which $\lambda_n > \lambda$, where λ_n is the wave-length at the absorption edge corresponding to ionization from the lowest level in the nth quantum state. Multiplying by the stimulated emission factor $1-e^{-hc/\lambda RT}$ the absorption coefficient per neutral atom is

$$\kappa'_\lambda = \frac{64\pi^4}{3\sqrt{3}} \frac{me^{10}}{c^4 h^6} \lambda^3 (1-e^{-hc/\lambda RT}) e^{-\chi_H/RT} D, \tag{39}$$

where
$$D = \sum_{\lambda_n > \lambda} \frac{1}{n^3} e^{\chi_H/n^2 RT}.$$

The contribution of the higher absorption continua in the infra-red may be found by means of an integral corresponding to the summation. Thus

$$\sum_{\lambda_n > \lambda} \frac{1}{n^3} e^{\chi_H/n^2 RT} = \sum_{\lambda_n > \lambda}^{4} \frac{1}{n^3} e^{\chi_H/n^2 RT} + \frac{RT}{2\chi_H} e^{\chi_H/5^2 RT}.$$

The summation D is a constant between any two adjacent absorption edges, and is a function of the temperature.

Since the number of neutral H atoms in the ground state per gramme of atmosphere is approximately $\dfrac{1}{m_H}(1-x_H)$, the mass coefficient of absorption will be

$$k_\lambda(H) = \frac{1}{m_H}(1-x_H)\kappa'_\lambda(H). \tag{40}$$

From equations (35) and (40) we have $k_\lambda(H^-)/k_\lambda(H) = p_e \kappa'_\lambda(H^-)/\kappa'_\lambda(H)$, where $\kappa'_\lambda(H^-)$ comes from Table VIII and $\kappa'_\lambda(H)$ is given by (39). For the electron pressures which exist in the photospheric layers of the Sun, and stars of similar spectral type, $k_\lambda(H^-) \gg k_\lambda(H)$. The ratio $k_\lambda(H^-)/k_\lambda(H)$ decreases with increasing depth, but for the outermost layers, the H$^-$ ion dominates the continuous absorption in the visible and infra-red wave-lengths.

The mean coefficient due to both neutral H atom absorption, and H$^-$ ions is

$$\bar{k} = \bar{k}(H) + \bar{k}(H^-) = \frac{1}{m_H}(1-x_H)[a(H) + p_e a(H^-)], \tag{41}$$

where
$$a(H) = \int k_\lambda(H)(F_\lambda/F)\,d\lambda.$$

According to equation (41), $a(H^-)$ has to be multiplied by the electron pressure in order to compare the mean absorption contributions of H with H$^-$. Table X gives the electron pressure according to Münch[†] for $\log A = 3\cdot 8$ (where A is the hydrogen to metal ratio). The theoretical values of $\bar{k}(H^-)/\bar{k}(H)$ given in the table show the extent to which the

† G. Münch, *Ap. J.* **106**, 217 (1947).

mean coefficient of absorption in the outermost layers of the Sun is
dominated by the negative ion absorption.

TABLE X

Theoretical Mean Coefficients of Absorption in the Solar Atmosphere

τ	0	0·1	0·2	0·4	0·6	0·8	1·0	1·2	1·4
θ	1·083	1·026	0·986	0·929	0·887	0·854	0·827	0·804	0·783
p_e	..	3·16	5·13	9·12	14·1	20·9	30·2	43·6	60·3
$a(\text{H}^-)$ multiply by 10^{-26}	11·74	9·447	8·082	6·320	5·235	4·470	3·901	3·460	3·109
$a(\text{H})$ multiply by 10^{-26}	..	..	0·05	0·22	0·70	1·69	3·48	6·42	11·20
$\bar{k}(\text{H}^-)/\bar{k}(\text{H})$	..	..	830	263	106	55·3	33·9	23·4	16·8

The mean coefficients shown in Tables IX and X have been calculated by Chandrasekhar's approximation

$$\bar{k}^{(1)} = \int k_\lambda (F_\lambda^{(1)}/F)\, d\lambda, \tag{42}$$

where $F_\lambda^{(1)}$ is the flux in a grey atmosphere. A more accurate value of
$\bar{k}$ can be obtained by successive approximation. If T_{t_λ} is the temperature at optical depth t_λ then the monochromatic flux F_λ ($= \pi \mathfrak{F}_\lambda$) in
an atmosphere in local thermodynamic equilibrium is given by

$$\mathfrak{F}_\lambda = 2 \int_{\tau\lambda}^{\infty} B(\lambda, T_{t_\lambda}) E_2(t_\lambda - \tau_\lambda)\, dt_\lambda - 2 \int_0^{\tau\lambda} B(\lambda, T_{t_\lambda}) E_2(\tau_\lambda - t_\lambda)\, dt_\lambda, \tag{43}$$

which is the non-grey analogue of equation (3.1) of Chapter III. The
only difficulty in applying (43) is lack of knowledge of $k_\lambda/\bar{k}$ (and
therefore of τ_λ/τ). But this may be taken from (42). Let the values
be $n_\lambda^{(1)}$; then inserting these in (43) we get a second approximation
to F_λ, or

$$\mathfrak{F}_\lambda^{(2)} = 2 \int_{\tau}^{\infty} B(\lambda, T_t) E_2\{n_\lambda^{(1)}(t-\tau)\} n_\lambda^{(1)}\, dt - 2 \int_0^{\tau} B(\lambda, T_t) E_2\{n_\lambda^{(1)}(\tau-t)\} n_\lambda^{(1)}\, dt. \tag{44}$$

This leads to a new approximation to $\bar{k}$, namely

$$\bar{k}^{(2)} = \int k_\lambda (F_\lambda^{(2)}/F)\, d\lambda. \tag{45}$$

THE VARIATION OF ABSORPTION COEFFICIENT WITH WAVE-LENGTH IN THE SOLAR ATMOSPHERE

1. Limb darkening in monochromatic light

WHEN the outer layers are in local thermodynamic equilibrium, the emission is given by equation (4) of Chapter IV, namely $j_\nu = k_\nu B(\nu, T)$, where $B(\nu, T) = (2h\nu^3/c^2)(e^{h\nu/RT}-1)^{-1}$, and the equation of monochromatic radiation transfer is

$$\cos \theta \, \frac{dI_\nu(\theta)}{d\tau_\nu} = I_\nu(\theta) - B(\nu, T). \tag{1}$$

According to equation (25) of Chapter I, the solution of (1) for the emergent intensity is

$$I_\nu(0, \theta) = \int_0^\infty e^{-\tau_\nu \sec \theta} B(\nu, T) \sec \theta \, d\tau_\nu. \tag{2}$$

Let τ be the optical depth measured in terms of the mean coefficient of absorption $\overline{k}$. If $\overline{k}$ is the straight mean defined by equation (15) of Chapter IV, the temperature distribution in the outer layers will be given by Milne's equation $T^4 = T_0^4(1+\frac{3}{2}\tau)$. Since $d\tau_\nu = (k_\nu/\overline{k}) \, d\tau$,

$$T^4 = T_0^4[1+\tfrac{3}{2}\tau_\nu(\overline{k}/k_\nu)].$$

Let $x = \tau_\nu \sec \theta$, $\alpha = h\nu/RT_0$, $p = \frac{3}{2}(\overline{k}/k_\nu)\cos \theta$; then $T^4 = T_0^4(1+px)$ and equation (2) may be written

$$I_\nu(0, \theta) = \frac{2h\nu^3}{c^2} \int_0^\infty \frac{e^{-x} \, dx}{e^{\alpha(1+px)^{-\frac{1}{4}}}-1}. \tag{3}$$

Define the function

$$f(\alpha, p) = \alpha^5 \int_0^\infty \frac{e^{-x} \, dx}{e^{\alpha(1+px)^{-\frac{1}{4}}}-1},$$

then

$$I_\nu(0, \theta) = (2h\nu^3/c^2)\alpha^{-5}f(\alpha, p). \tag{4}$$

If $\overline{k}/k_\nu$ were known, we should then be able to calculate the emergent intensity at any frequency by means of equation (4). Assuming for the moment that $\overline{k}/k_\nu$ does not differ much from unity, we see that for a given value of p, that is, for a given distance from the centre of the disk, the limb-darkening ratio $I_\nu(0, \theta)/I_\nu(0, 0)$ depends only on α, and hence on the product λT_0. If the boundary temperature, or the effective temperature, is increased by a factor n the law of darkening is then the same as it was in the wave-length λ/n. Furthermore, it may be shown that $I_\nu(0,\theta)/I_\nu(0,0)$ decreases with increasing α, so that for a given temperature the darkening decreases with decreasing wave-length. Hence an increase in temperature will bring about a decrease in the darkening ratio at each wave-length, a result which differs from that for integrated radiation, for which the law of darkening is independent of T_0. It may seem to be a paradox that the darkening in every wave-length should decrease with increasing temperature whilst the darkening in integrated light remains constant. But it should be noted that an increase in temperature gives an increased flow of radiation in the shorter wave-lengths, where the contrast is greatest. Thus it appears that the integrated darkening, being the weighted sum of the darkening in each wave-length, will not change with the temperature.

1.1. *Milne's calculation of the darkening of the limb in a grey atmosphere*

The function $f(\alpha, p)$ has been discussed and tabulated by Milne and Lindblad. Milne[†] has given a comparison of Abbot's[‡] observed values of the darkening of the limb of the Sun with the theoretical values obtained from (4), taking $\bar{k}/k_\nu = 1$, that is, assuming k_ν to be independent of ν. This gives $p = \frac{3}{2}\cos\theta$, and from equation (4) the darkening ratio is

$$\frac{I_\nu(0,\theta)}{I_\nu(0,0)} = \frac{f(\alpha, \frac{3}{2}\cos\theta)}{f(\alpha, \frac{3}{2})}. \tag{5}$$

The limb darkening given by (5), and Abbot's observations, are given in Table XI which is abstracted from Milne's classical paper.

The general agreement between the observed and calculated values in Table XI suggests that the hypothesis of local thermodynamic equilibrium is justified, and that the variation of the absorption coefficient with wave-length is not large.

1.2. *The blanketing effect*

The presence of absorption lines in a stellar spectrum raises difficulties. The lines prevent the escape of an appreciable fraction of the energy in late type stars, and modify the behaviour of the continuous spectrum between the lines. Milne[§] originally treated the question by considering a model in which the layers giving rise to the absorption lines were

† E. A. Milne, *Phil. Trans. Roy. Soc.* A, **223**, 201 (1922).
‡ C. G. Abbot, *Ann. Ap. Obs. Smithsonian Inst.* **3**, 157 (1913).
§ E. A. Milne, *Observatory*, **51**, 88 (1928); *Handbuch d. Ap.* III/1, p. 144.

TABLE XI

Milne's Calculated Values of Solar Limb Darkening Compared with Observation

Wave-length	sin θ	0	0·4	0·65	0·75	0·875	0·920	0·956
3,230 A	Abbot	1·000	0·897	0·775	0·690	0·530	0·452	0·382
	Milne	1·000	0·908	0·737	0·637	0·469	0·393	0·332
4,810 A	Abbot	1·000	0·944	0·840	0·771	0·638	0·566	0·499
	Milne	1·000	0·942	0·828	0·757	0·629	0·563	0·507
5,340 A	Abbot	1·000	0·950	0·856	0·792	0·672	0·605	0·548
	Milne	1·000	0·946	0·854	0·780	0·664	0·601	0·548
6,700 A	Abbot	1·000	0·961	0·887	0·838	0·740	0·680	0·629
	Milne	1·000	0·958	0·876	0·824	0·724	0·669	0·618
8,600 A	Abbot	1·000	0·969	0·911	0·871	0·792	0·744	0·699
	Milne	1·000	0·967	0·903	0·860	0·775	0·727	0·685
10,310 A	Abbot	1·000	0·977	0·925	0·889	0·816	0·772	0·730
	Milne	1·000	0·970	0·917	0·875	0·798	0·756	0·716

relatively transparent to the radiation between the lines, but 'act as a blanket, keeping the photosphere warmer than it would be if the photosphere were the actual boundary'.

1.21. *Milne's theory*

Suppose the reversing layer returns a fraction n of the radiation incident on it from the photosphere. The distribution of temperature in the photosphere will then be approximately the same as in the case where there is no blanketing, provided we suppose it to terminate at some place $\tau = \tau_0$, instead of at $\tau = 0$. Now, in the absence of blanketing, the outward and inward flow at a depth τ_0 are given by equations (9) and (10) of Chapter I, or

$$I_1(\tau_0) = H(4+3\tau_0), \qquad I_2(\tau_0) = 3H\tau_0.$$

Set $I_2(\tau_0)/I_1(\tau_0) = n$, then

$$\tau_0 = \frac{4}{3}\frac{n}{1-n}.$$

The outward flow is given by equation (25) of Chapter I,

$$I(\tau_0, \theta) = \int_{\tau_0}^{\infty} e^{-(\tau-\tau_0)\sec\theta} J(\tau)\sec\theta \, d\tau,$$

where $J(\tau) = (\sigma/\pi)T^4 = (\sigma/\pi)T_0^4(1+\tfrac{3}{2}\tau)$. This gives

$$I(\tau_0, \theta) = H\left(2\frac{1+n}{1-n}+3\cos\theta\right),$$

and the boundary temperature is T_0', where

$$T_0'^4 = T_0^4 \frac{1+n}{1-n}.$$

Now
$$T^4 = T_0^4(1+\tfrac{3}{2}\tau) = T_0'^4\left\{1+\tfrac{3}{2}(\tau-\tau_0)\frac{1-n}{1+n}\right\},$$

so that the emergent intensity $I_\nu(\tau_0, \theta)$ is given by the following analogue of equation (4):
$$I_\nu(\tau_0, \theta) = (2h\nu^3/c^2)\alpha'^{-5}f(\alpha', p'), \qquad (4a)$$

where $\alpha' = h\nu/RT_0'$, and $p' = \dfrac{3}{2}\dfrac{1-n}{1+n}\dfrac{\bar{k}}{k_\nu}.$

1.22. *An alternative theory*

It may be objected to Milne's theory of the blanketing effect that the separation between photosphere and reversing layer is artificial, as the lines are, in fact, formed throughout the photosphere. To work out a theory of blanketing without using Milne's separation, it is necessary to anticipate some of the results of Chapter VII. It is there shown that equation (1) of the present chapter contains extra terms on account of line absorption coefficients. Omitting the collision terms, that is, setting $\epsilon = 0$, we have

$$\cos\theta\frac{dI_\nu(\theta)}{\rho\, dx} = -k_\nu I_\nu(\theta) - l_\nu I_\nu(\theta) + k_\nu B(\nu, T) + l_\nu J_\nu,$$

which, of course, becomes identical with equation (1) at frequencies where the line absorption coefficient l_ν becomes zero. Treating this equation exactly as in Chapter IV, the analogues of equations (5) and (6) of that chapter are

$$\frac{dH_\nu}{\rho\, dx} = -k_\nu\{J_\nu - B(\nu, T)\},$$

and
$$\frac{dK_\nu}{\rho\, dx} = -(k_\nu + l_\nu)H_\nu.$$

Now, if we adopt the definition

$$\bar{k} = \frac{1}{H}\int (k_\nu + l_\nu)H_\nu\, d\nu$$

instead of the definition by equation (15) of Chapter IV, and set $d\tau = -\bar{k}\rho\, dx$ we recover the result $K = H\tau + \text{constant}$: and with Eddington's approximation $K = \tfrac{1}{3}J$ and the boundary condition $J_\nu = 2H_\nu$ (so that by integration $J = 2H$), we get

$$J = H(2+3\tau).$$

This is exactly the same as in Chapter IV, except that the absorption lines have increased the value of the mean absorption coefficient. Since the condition of radiative equilibrium is still

$$\int k_\nu J_\nu \, d\nu = \int k_\nu B(\nu, T) \, d\nu,$$

we have, as before, $J = B$ if k_ν is independent of ν, and the argument about $J = B$ approximately if k_ν does not vary greatly with ν still stands. We have therefore

$$B = H(2 + 3\tau),$$

just as if there were no absorption lines, but with a changed meaning of τ.

We now calculate the increase in $\bar{k}$ due to absorption lines for the case k independent of ν. Let $B(\nu, T) = a_\nu + b_\nu t$, where t is the optical depth outside the lines, then from equations (17) and (19) of Chapter VII we have

$$H_\nu = \frac{1}{3(1+\eta)}\left\{b_\nu + \frac{a_\nu(1+\eta) - \frac{2}{3}b_\nu}{1+\eta+\frac{2}{3}q} qe^{-qt}\right\},$$

where $\eta = l_\nu/k$, and $q^2 = 3(1+\eta)$. Setting

$$f(a_\nu, b_\nu, \eta) = \frac{a_\nu(1+\eta) - \frac{2}{3}b_\nu}{1+\eta+\frac{2}{3}q},$$

we have the following results:

$$H = \int H_\nu \, d\nu = \frac{1}{3}\int \frac{b_\nu}{1+\eta} \, d\nu + \frac{1}{3}\int f(a_\nu, b_\nu, \eta) \frac{qe^{-qt}}{1+\eta} \, d\nu,$$

$$(\bar{k}/k)H = \int (1+\eta)H_\nu \, d\nu = \tfrac{1}{3}\int b_\nu \, d\nu + \tfrac{1}{3}\int f(a_\nu, b_\nu, \eta)qe^{-qt} \, d\nu,$$

$$\frac{dH}{dt} = -\frac{1}{3}\int f(a_\nu, b_\nu, \eta)\frac{q^2 e^{-qt}}{1+\eta} \, d\nu.$$

In these integrals the quantities η and q vary rapidly with the frequency as it passes through a line, but the quantities a_ν and b_ν only vary slowly. If the lines are well distributed in the spectrum, we may replace the rapidly varying quantities qe^{-qt}, etc., by their average values before performing the spectrum integral, that is, we may write

$$\int f(a_\nu, b_\nu, \eta)qe^{-qt} \, d\nu = \overline{qe^{-qt}}\int f(a_\nu, b_\nu, \eta) \, d\nu, \quad \text{etc.}$$

Then since $dH/dt = 0$, we must have $\int f(a_\nu, b_\nu, \eta) \, d\nu = 0$. Hence

$$H = \frac{1}{3}\int \frac{b_\nu}{1+\eta} \, d\nu.$$

Further, $$(\bar{k}/k)H = \tfrac{1}{3}\int b_\nu \, d\nu = \tfrac{1}{3}b,$$

a result which also follows from $B = a + bt$ and $B = H(2+3\tau)$, since $\tau = (\bar{k}/k)t$. We now have

$$\bar{k}/k = \left\{1 - \frac{1}{b} \int \frac{\eta}{1+\eta} b_\nu \, d\nu\right\}^{-1}.$$

Since b_ν is practically constant over the width of each line, the integral in this expression may be written as

$$\sum b_\nu \int \frac{\eta}{1+\eta} \, d\nu,$$

where the integration extends over the profile of each line, and the summation over all lines in the spectrum. The integration over each line may be easily evaluated if we use the approximation

$$\eta = (\nu_1 - \nu_0)^2/(\nu - \nu_0)^2,$$

for then

$$\int_0^\infty \frac{\eta}{1+\eta} \, d\nu = \pi(\nu_1 - \nu_0),$$

and we have

$$\bar{k}/k = \{1 - \pi \sum (\nu_1 - \nu_0)b_\nu/b\}^{-1}.$$

The summation over all lines is related to the weighted sum of the equivalent widths of the lines, the equivalent width W_ν of a strong line being equal to $(\nu_1 - \nu_0)w^*$, where $w^* = 2\sqrt{3}\ln\sqrt{3} = 1 \cdot 903$ (see Chapter IX, Section 5.3).

The sum of the equivalent widths of lines in the solar spectrum weighted with the solar energy curve has been determined by several authors,[†] the result being about $0 \cdot 09$. Although the weights in this case are not identical with b_ν/b, we may assume that the result is not much affected by the weighting, and thus set

$$\sum (\nu_1 - \nu_0)b_\nu/b = 0 \cdot 09/1 \cdot 903.$$

Accordingly, for the Sun we have $\bar{k}/k = 1 \cdot 18$.

2. Connexion between limb darkening and the variation of absorption coefficient with wave-length

The darkening of the limb in various wave-lengths and the solar energy curve are both connected with the variation of the continuous absorption coefficient with wave-length and with the temperature distribution in the photosphere.

We define the limb-darkening function by the relation

$$\varphi_\lambda(\theta) = I_\lambda(\theta)/I_\lambda(0), \tag{6}$$

† For example, J. Wempe, *A.N.* **275**, 107 (1947). R. Michard, *B.A.N.* **11** (No. 416), 227 (1950), suggests a much greater value of the blanketing constant.

where $I_\lambda(\theta) \equiv I_\lambda(0,\theta)$ is the intensity of monochromatic radiation emerging from the Sun at a point on the disk where the angular distance from the centre of the disk is θ. The theoretical value of the energy distribution at the centre of the disk may be found as follows. Equation (2) may be written in the form

$$I_\lambda(\theta) = \int_0^\infty e^{-(k_\lambda/\bar{k})\tau \sec\theta} B(\lambda, T)(k_\lambda/\bar{k}) \sec\theta \, d\tau, \qquad (7)$$

where $B(\lambda, T) = (2hc^2/\lambda^5)(e^{hc/\lambda RT}-1)^{-1}$, and with $\theta = 0$ equation (4) becomes

$$I_\lambda(0) = 2hc^2\left(\frac{RT_0}{hc}\right)^5 f(\alpha, p_0), \qquad (8)$$

where $p_0 = \frac{3}{2}(\bar{k}/k_\lambda)$. Equation (8) gives the theoretical solar energy curve for the centre of the Sun. The darkening ratio defined by equation (6) is

$$\phi_\lambda(\theta) = f[\alpha, \tfrac{3}{2}(\bar{k}/k_\lambda)\cos\theta]/f[\alpha, \tfrac{3}{2}(\bar{k}/k_\lambda)], \qquad (9)$$

where $\alpha = hc/\lambda RT_0$.

We have assumed that $T^4 = T_0^4(1+\frac{3}{2}\tau)$, a result which we shall see later is not a good approximation at certain optical depths if an appreciable fraction of the solar flux is carried by convection. But any theory or hypothesis that proposes definite values of T as a function of τ can be introduced into equation (4). In practice it is not desirable to construct a modified function to replace $f(\alpha, p)$ but to resort to numerical integration of equation (2). A formal reconstruction of the function may readily be made. If we set $T_0/T = \phi(\frac{3}{2}\tau)$, then from equation (2)

$$I_\lambda(\theta) = 2hc^2\left(\frac{RT_0}{hc}\right)^5 F(\alpha, p), \qquad (10)$$

where

$$F(\alpha, p) = \alpha^5 \int_0^\infty \frac{e^{-x} \, dx}{e^{\alpha\phi(px)}-1}. \qquad (11)$$

Chandrasekhar and Breen[†] have computed a modification of $f(\alpha, p)$ which is very conveniently tabulated. Their first function $\mathscr{I}(\alpha', \beta)$ only differs from $f(\alpha, p)$ because they used the fourth approximation to the temperature distribution. They also tabulated a second function $\mathscr{F}(\alpha', \beta)$ which is related to the flux, while $\mathscr{I}(\alpha', \beta)$ is related to the intensity. The quantity α' is not the same as α, but is equal to $hc/\lambda RT_e$, where T_e may be taken as $2^{\frac{1}{4}}T_0$.

A method of determining the energy distribution of radiation from the centre of the disk from the observed monochromatic fluxes (from

† S. Chandrasekhar and F. H. Breen, *Ap. J.* **105**, 461 (1947); *Radiative Transfer* (Oxford), chap. xi, section 80.1.

all parts of the disk) and the limb darkening is as follows. The mono-chromatic flux received from all parts of the Sun outside the atmosphere of the Earth at its mean distance r from the Sun is $(a/r)^2 F_\lambda$, where a is the radius of the Sun, and F_λ is the flux at the boundary of the photo-sphere. According to equation (12) of Chapter I,

$$F_\lambda = \int_0^{\frac{1}{2}\pi} 2\pi I_\lambda(\theta)\sin\theta\cos\theta \; d\theta. \tag{12}$$

Dividing this by $I_\lambda(0)$, and inverting we get

$$I_\lambda(0) = F_\lambda \Big/ \int_0^{\frac{1}{2}\pi} 2\pi\varphi_\lambda(\theta)\sin\theta\cos\theta \; d\theta. \tag{13}$$

2.1. Lundblad's analysis

The following theorem, which is due to Lundblad,[†] has been used to deduce the variation of k_λ with λ from the observed limb darkening, without supposing that the variation of temperature with optical depth is known. If

$$B(\lambda, T)/I_\lambda(0) = a_\lambda + b_\lambda \tau_\lambda + \tfrac{1}{2} c_\lambda \tau_\lambda^2, \tag{14}$$

then from equation (2)

$$I_\lambda(\theta)/I_\lambda(0) = a_\lambda + b_\lambda \cos\theta + c_\lambda \cos^2\theta. \tag{15}$$

This theorem can be extended to higher powers of τ_λ and $\cos\theta$, but an expansion to two terms suffices to illustrate the principle involved.

Now $I_\lambda(0)$ is known from the observed monochromatic flux and the limb darkening according to equation (13), and if a_λ, b_λ, c_λ are derived from an analysis of the observed darkening of the limb then for any pair of values of λ and T the ratio $B(\lambda, T)/I_\lambda(0)$ can be computed, and the quadratic equation (14) solved for τ_λ. This gives

$$\tau_\lambda = -\frac{b_\lambda}{c_\lambda} \pm \sqrt{\left\{ \left(\frac{b_\lambda}{c_\lambda}\right)^2 - \frac{2}{c_\lambda}[a_\lambda - B(\lambda, T)/I_\lambda(0)] \right\}}, \tag{16}$$

the physically significant root being real and positive. The combina-tion of mathematical approximation in (14) and observational analysis according to equation (15) could give imaginary roots; indeed, one finds in practice that for certain values of λ and T the roots given by (16) are imaginary: but let us suppose that for a given T there is one real, positive value of τ_λ for all λ. Then, if T is so close to the boundary temperature T_0 that $4\pi H_\lambda$ is practically equal to the surface flux F_λ, the straight mean value of τ can be found from

$$\tau = \int \tau_\lambda F_\lambda \; d\lambda \Big/ \int F_\lambda \; d\lambda. \tag{17}$$

† R. Lundblad, *Ap. J.* **58**, 113 (1923).

Further, if the depth is reasonably small, so that the distribution of k_λ with λ is substantially the same throughout the interval from the surface $\tau = 0$ to the level in question, then

$$k_\lambda/\bar{k} = \tau_\lambda/\bar{\tau}. \tag{18}$$

The method therefore yields a determination of the variation of k_λ with λ without appeal to a theoretical temperature distribution, since τ in equation (17) is found for a particular value of T.

3. Comparison between theory and observation

3.1. *Relative absorption coefficients $k_\lambda/\bar{k}$*

3.11. *Determination from the energy curve*

The emergent intensity of the centre of the disk $I_\lambda(0)$ being connected with k_λ by the relation (8), namely

$$I_\lambda(0) = 2hc^2\left(\frac{RT_0}{hc}\right)^5 f\left(\frac{hc}{\lambda RT_0}, \frac{3}{2}\frac{\bar{k}}{k_\lambda}\right), \tag{19}$$

it is possible to deduce values of $k_\lambda/\bar{k}$ from observed values of $I_\lambda(0)$ with the help of a table of values of $f(\alpha, p)$, provided that the boundary temperature is known. Instead of measuring $I_\lambda(0)$ directly, using light from the centre of the disk only, it is possible to use the energy curve of solar radiation as a whole, F_λ, if values of the limb-darkening ratios $\varphi_\lambda(\theta)$ are available from observation, $I_\lambda(0)$ being then determined from equation (13).

A complication is introduced by the Fraunhofer lines. In the neighbourhood of these lines $I_\lambda(0)$ varies rapidly and attention must be paid to whether the observer measures $I_\lambda(0)$ in a region free from absorption lines, or whether his apparatus samples a spectral region which has some lines in it. The latter course was actually adopted by Abbot, who made the most extensive series of observations secured so far; and Mulders† applied a correction to bring Abbot's (and other observers') values up to 'the spectrum between the lines'. But now the question arises whether the theory which supposes that there are no absorption lines refers to the spectrum between the lines, or whether some correction should be applied on their account. The effect is the 'blanketing' of Section 1.2. Mulders not only applied a correction to the observed values of $I_\lambda(0)$ to bring them up to the spectrum between the lines, but amended T_0 to T_0' as in Section 1.21, so that he calculated $k_\lambda/\bar{k}$ from (4 a) instead of (4).

† G. Mulders, *Zs. f. Ap.* **11**, 143 (1936).

Another series of calculations of $k_\lambda/\bar{k}$ has been made by Münch,[†] who used $I_\lambda(0)$ from Mulders but discarded the blanketing correction to the boundary temperature. Using F_λ as well as $I_\lambda(0)$, Münch obtained two series of values of $k_\lambda/\bar{k}$ which agree well with one another but which are systematically lower than Mulders's by 20 per cent. These values are reproduced in Table XII, and illustrated in Fig. 14, together with the original determinations of Milne, who used Abbot's values of $I_\lambda(0)$ without any correction for Fraunhofer lines.

TABLE XII

Collected Values of $k_\lambda/\bar{k}$

Mulders		Münch			
$\lambda(A)$	$k_\lambda/\bar{k}$	$\lambda(A)$	$k_\lambda/\bar{k}$		Mean
3,000	1·46	3,000	1·34	1·32	1·33
3,500	1·20	3,230	1·41	1·36	1·38
4,000	0·80	3,400	1·38	1·32	1·35
4,500	0·79	3,737	0·94	1·02	0·98
5,000	0·84	3,800	0·80	0·91	0·86
5,500	0·87	3,900	0·72	0·76	0·74
6,000	0·91	4,000	0·67	0·66	0·66
6,500	0·95	4,265	0·65	..	(0·65)
7,000	1·01	4,500	0·66	0·64	0·65
7,500	1·08	5,000	0·72	0·67	0·70
8,000	1·16	5,062	0·72	..	(0·72)
8,500	1·23	5,500	0·73	0·70	0·72
9,000	1·37	5,955	0·77	..	(0·77)
10,000	1·27	6,000	0·78	0·75	0·76
11,000	0·99	6,500	0·82	0·79	0·80
12,000	0·85	6,702	0·83	..	(0·83)
13,000	0·64	7,000	0·84	0·80	0·82
14,000	0·63	7,500	0·86	0·87	0·86
15,000	0·51	8,000	0·98	0·96	0·97
16,000	0·36	8,500	1·00	1·00	1·00
17,000	0·18	8,580	1·02	..	(1·02)
18,000	0·21	9,000	1·12	1·07	1·10
19,000	0·18	9,500	1·09	1·04	1·16
20,000	0·21	10,000	1·03	0·93	0·98
21,000	0·45	10,080	0·99	..	(0·99)
22,000	1·06	10,500	0·91	0·82	0·86
23,000	1·27	11,000	0·79	0·73	0·76

3.12. Determination from limb darkening

Turning to the method which does not assume a temperature distribution in the atmosphere, but which analyses the darkening of the limb in each wave-length as a power series in $\cos\theta$, very complete calculations were made by the originator of the method, Lundblad, whose series

[†] G. Münch, *Ap. J.* **102**, 385 (1945).

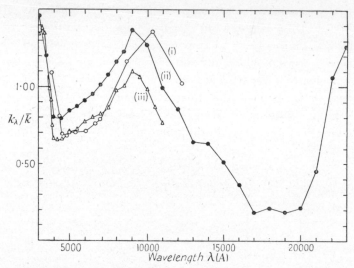

FIG. 14. Variation of the absorption coefficient with wave-length in the solar
atmosphere according to Milne (i), Mulders (ii), and Münch (iii).

TABLE XIII

Analysis of Limb-darkening Observations†

(Chalonge and Kourganoff)

$\lambda(A)$	a_λ	b_λ	c_λ	$\lambda(A)$	a_λ	b_λ	c_λ
3,230	0·1216	0·8273	+0·0361	5,960 R	0·3959	0·7271	−0·1244
3,737	0·1435	0·9481	−0·0921	6,040	0·3668	0·7743	−0·1422
3,860	0·1610	0·8106	+0·0267	6,700	0·4088	0·7633	−0·1736
4,260 R	0·1754	0·9740	−0·1525	6,702 R	0·4511	0·6873	−0·1398
4,265	0·1752	0·8788	−0·0534	6,702	0·4215	0·7603	−0·1816
4,330	0·2006	0·7900	+0·0064	6,990	0·4218	0·7525	−0·1761
4,560	0·1837	0·9638	−0·1482	8,580	0·5289	0·6353	−0·1648
4,810	0·2277	0·9178	−0·1465	8,660	0·5141	0·6497	−0·1657
5,010	0·2593	0·8724	−0·1336	10,080	0·5630	0·5995	−0·1634
5,060 R	0·2615	0·8895	−0·1530	10,310	0·5534	0·6254	−0·1777
5,062	0·2671	0·8870	−0·1538	12,250	0·5969	0·5667	−0·1646
5,340	0·3018	0·8275	−0·1302	16,550	0·6894	0·4563	−0·1472
5,955	0·3591	0·8115	−0·1712	20,970	0·7249	0·4100	−0·1360

† Wave-length entries marked R denote observations by Raudenbusch (S. Raudenbusch, *A.N.* **263**, 300 (1938)); all other entries are from Abbot's observations.

included a term in $\cos^3\theta$. His values of τ_λ (relative to the values at
$\lambda\,4{,}810\,A$) are nearly proportional to the values found in later calculations
by Chalonge and Kourganoff,‡ but he used Abbot's values of $I_\lambda(0)$
without Mulders's corrections, which were introduced more than ten

‡ D. Chalonge and V. Kourganoff, *Ann. d'Ap.* **9**, 69 (1946).

years later. Chalonge and Kourganoff went no farther than $\cos^2\theta$, and an analysis by Barbier[†] includes a term in $\cos^3\theta$. However, it is remarkable that the observed darkening in all wave-lengths can be represented very closely by the three terms $a_\lambda + b_\lambda \cos\theta + c_\lambda \cos^2\theta$, indeed, so closely that the introduction of further terms. is scarcely justified, on account of errors of observation.

Using Mulders's values of $I_\lambda(0)$, Chalonge and Kourganoff calculate the values of τ_λ for various values of T from equation (16). Their results are shown in Table XIV and Fig. 15. Values in italics have been supplied. The general agreement between the two methods of studying the opacity of the photospheric layers may be seen by comparing Tables XII and XIV by means of equation (18).

TABLE XIV

Optical Depth in the Photosphere

$\lambda(A)$	$I_\lambda(0)$ (Mulders) multiply by 10^{14}	Temperature				
		5,500°	6,000°	6,500°	7,000°	7,500°
3,200	2·18	*0·44*	*0·95*	*1·70*	*2·80*	*4·40*
3,600	3·20	*0·32*	*0·73*	*1·38*	*2·40*	*4·40*
4,000	4·40	*0·26*	*0·57*	*1·02*	*1·62*	*2·44*
4,560	4·538	0·27	0·57	0·98	1·54	2·33
4,810	4·340	0·27	0·59	1·02	1·61	2·49
5,010	4·151	0·28	0·62	1·07	1·68	2·51
5,060	4·106	0·28	0·61	1·07	1·68	2·54
5,062	4·104	0·28	0·61	1·07	1·68	2·56
5,340	3·854	0·30	0·65	1·14	1·77	2·64
5,955	3·346	0·31	0·68	1·17	1·85	2·89
5,960	3·342	0·32	0·70	1·23	1·93	2·91
6,040	3·280	0·32	0·70	1·20	1·86	2·80
6,700	2·780	0·34	0·73	1·23	1·92	3·04
6,702	2·780	0·31	0·73	1·28	2·02	3·16
6,702	2·780	0·32	0·71	1·23	1·94	3·20
6,990	2·568	0·36	0·75	1·26	1·95	3·13
8,580	1·632	0·43	0·88	1·48	2·39	imaginary
8,660	1·593	0·45	0·90	1·48	2·34	,,
10,080	1·154	0·42	0·85	1·40	2·19	,,
10,310	1·108	0·41	0·81	1·31	2·02	,,
12,250	0·754	0·26	0·60	1·00	1·51	2·23
16,550	0·372	negative	0·23	0·55	0·92	1·37
20,970	0·162	0·01	0·31	0·66	1·07	1·61

3.13. *Comparison with the coefficient of the negative hydrogen ion*

The analysis of observations only yields values of k_λ relative to the mean coefficient $\bar{k}$. We are now in a position to collect relative values

† D. Barbier, ibid. 173 (1946).

from various sources. With the exception of some of the longer wave-lengths the results agree in a very satisfactory manner. They are shown in Table XV, where they are reduced by appropriate factors to make $k_\lambda = 0.939$ for $\lambda\,5,000$ A.

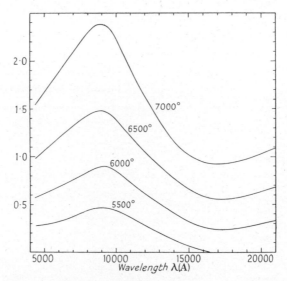

FIG. 15. Variation with wave-length of the opacity of the solar atmosphere. The ordinate τ_λ gives the optical depth down to a level where the temperature has the prescribed value T as shown on the curves.

The mean solar coefficient shows a wave-length variation which is similar to that of the negative hydrogen ion, in its bound-free and free-free absorption spectra, as calculated by Chandrasekhar and Breen.† Relative values are shown in Fig. 16. In producing this similarity between theoretical and observed variation with wave-length of the absorption coefficient, the theory of radiative equilibrium applied to the solar atmosphere achieves its greatest success, and we shall see in later sections of this chapter that the agreement is not quite so good when other tests are applied. Some of these difficulties may perhaps be explained by blanketing, and others by convection, which modifies the temperature distribution from the form $T^4 = T_0^4(1+\tfrac{3}{2}\tau)$ given by radiative equilibrium. It must be repeated that the observations described in this chapter only fix the variation of k_λ with λ, and say nothing about the actual value of $\bar{k}$.

† S. Chandrasekhar and F. H. Breen, *Ap. J.* **104**, 430 (1946).

TABLE XV

Relative Absorption Coefficients

$\lambda(A)$	3,000	3,500	4,000	4,500	5,000	5,500	6,000	7,000	8,000	9,000	10,000
From τ_λ for $T = 6,000°$ K.	..	1·19	0·91	0·83	0·94	1·00	1·06	1·20	1·33	1·41	1·33
From τ_λ for $T = 6,500°$ K.	..	1·31	0·90	0·83	0·94	0·98	1·05	1·16	1·27	1·34	1·25
Mulders	1·63	1·34	0·89	0·88	0·94	0·97	1·01	1·13	1·30	1·53	1·42
Münch	1·80	1·63	0·90	0·88	0·94	0·97	1·03	1·11	1·31	1·48	1·32
Mean k_λ	1·72	1·37	0·90	0·85	0·94	0·98	1·04	1·15	1·30	1·44	1·33

$\lambda(A)$	11,000	12,000	13,000	14,000	15,000	16,000	17,000	18,000	19,000	20,000	21,000
From τ_λ for $T = 6,000°$ K.	1·15	0·97	0·82	0·66	0·52	0·42	0·36	0·36	0·42	0·45	0·52
From τ_λ for $T = 6,500°$ K.	1·08	0·93	0·81	0·68	0·58	0·51	0·48	0·50	0·54	0·55	0·60
Mulders	1·11	0·95	0·71	0·70	0·57	0·40	0·20	0·23	0·20	0·23	0·51
Mean k_λ	1·11	0·95	0·78	0·68	0·55	0·44	0·35	0·37	0·38	0·41	0·54

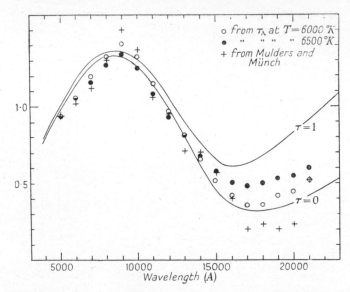

FIG. 16. Relative values of k_λ from observations compared with theoretical values of $k_\lambda/\bar{k}$ derived from negative hydrogen ion bound-free absorption and free-free absorption. The upper curve gives the variation of $k_\lambda/k(\mathrm{H}^-)$ with wave-length at $\tau = 1$, whilst the lower curve corresponds to $\tau = 0$ (see Table IX).

3.14. *A check on the relative coefficients*

A check that can be applied to the values of $k_\lambda/\bar{k}$ is that

$$\int (k_\lambda/\bar{k})(F_\lambda/F)\, d\lambda$$

should be equal to unity. Neither Mulders's values, nor those of Münch, satisfy this check. The relative values collected in Table XV have been normalized so as to satisfy it—that is to say that numerical integration of $\int k_\lambda F_\lambda\, d\lambda$ from $\lambda 3{,}000$ A to $\lambda 21{,}000$ A divided by $\int F_\lambda\, d\lambda$ between the same limits, is equal to unity. The values of k_λ from limb darkening are only relative, but the determinations from $I_\lambda(0)$ are determinations of $k_\lambda/\bar{k}$, so that the adjustment from Table XII to Table XV must somehow be accounted for. Mulders's values have to be increased by 10 per cent., and Münch's by 30 per cent., to satisfy the check.

The increase could be due to uncounted contributions to $\bar{k}$ from regions $\lambda < 3{,}000$ A and $\lambda > 21{,}000$ A. In this connexion it should be noted that the flux from wave-lengths shorter than $3{,}000$ A is $\frac{1}{24}$ of the total flux of a black body at $6{,}000°$, and is $\frac{1}{36}$ of the total flux at $5{,}000°$. Accordingly, if the solar flux at $\lambda 3{,}000$ A is equal to that of a black body at $6{,}000°$, and if the average value of k_λ is $2\bar{k}$ for $\lambda < 3{,}000$ A, the relative values of k_λ in the table should be divided by $1\cdot04$: if $k_\lambda = 5\bar{k}$, by $1\cdot16$, etc. But if the absorption is much higher than $\bar{k}$ the flux will be closer to that of a black body at $5{,}000°$, and, assuming that the visible spectrum corresponds to $6{,}000°$, the weight is $\frac{1}{36} \times (\frac{5}{6})^4$ or $\frac{1}{76}$. In this case the value $k_\lambda = 10\bar{k}$ in the ultra-violet reduces the tabular values of k_λ in Table XV by 10 per cent., and in fact brings about reasonable agreement with Mulders's values. Since Mulders used Milne's theory of the blanketing effect, this supposition about k_λ in the far ultra-violet supports Milne's blanketing theory: but that theory can hardly be regarded as completely satisfactory as the division between photosphere and reversing layer is too artificial. The theory of Section 1.22, however, suggests an 18 per cent. increase to Münch's values of $k_\lambda/\bar{k}$, on account of blanketing. If to this is added another 10 per cent. increase on account of far ultra-violet contributions, the agreement between theory and observation then becomes very good.

The discrepancy between Tables XII and XV could also be due to errors in the adopted values of $I_\lambda(0)$, which are used in equation (19); and since the correction to Abbot's values are substantial, there may be some errors in Mulders's values of $I_\lambda(0)$. That there are some such errors are indicated by the negative values which occur in some wavelengths in the solutions for τ_λ. (Only one negative value is shown in Table XIV, but there would have been more if the results for lower T had been shown.)

3.2. *The temperature distribution*

Lundblad's method of analysis of limb darkening leads to values of τ_λ at which various temperatures are reached (Table XIV) and if we combine these results with values of $k_\lambda/\bar{k}$ we can find empirically the values of τ at which the temperatures occur. When this has been done we shall be able to test the relation $T^4 = T_0^4(1 + \frac{3}{2}\tau)$. Since the quadratic approximation [equation (14)]

$$B(\lambda, T)/I_\lambda(0) = a_\lambda + b_\lambda\tau_\lambda + \tfrac{1}{2}c_\lambda\tau_\lambda^2$$

breaks down for large values of T (as is shown by the occurrence of imaginary values of τ_λ in Table XV) it is of some interest to apply the quadratic analysis to a theoretical model.

Consider an atmosphere in which $T^4 = T_0^4(1 + \frac{3}{2}\tau)$, $T_0 = 4{,}830°$, and $k_\lambda = \bar{k}$ at the three wave-lengths $\lambda\,3{,}860$ A, $\lambda\,6{,}690$ A, and $\lambda\,10{,}310$ A. The corresponding values of α are $7\cdot68$, $4\cdot24$, and $2\cdot87$ respectively. The darkening of the limb in each of these wave-lengths is given by

$$\varphi_\lambda(\theta) = f(\alpha, \tfrac{3}{2}\cos\theta)/f(\alpha, \tfrac{3}{2}),$$

and may be extracted directly from Milne's tables of $f(\alpha, p)$. The representation of these values by quadratic formulae in $\cos\theta$ can be made very close.

TABLE XVI

$\cos\theta$	1·000	0·916	0·760	0·565	0·392	0·312
$\varphi_\lambda(\theta) = f(\alpha, \tfrac{3}{2}\cos\theta)/f(\alpha, \tfrac{3}{2})$	1·000	0·960	0·883	0·778	0·680	0·632
$0·431 + 0·675\cos\theta - 0·106\cos^2\theta$	1·000	0·960	0·883	0·779	0·679	0·631

Representation of Milne's theoretical limb darkening in the wave-length 6,990 A by a quadratic formula in $\cos\theta$.

For any value of τ_λ ($= \tau$ in the three wave-lengths under discussion) we may calculate $B(\lambda, T)/I_\lambda(0)$ from (14) and compare the results with the theoretical value, namely

$$B(\lambda, T)/I_\lambda(0) = [\alpha^5 f(\alpha, \tfrac{3}{2})\{e^{hc/\lambda RT} - 1\}]^{-1}. \qquad (20)$$

The results of this comparison are shown in Table XVII, and in graphical form in Fig. 17. The quadratics used for the theoretical limb darkening ratio were:

$$\lambda\, 3{,}860 \text{ A}; \quad 0·171 + 0·720\cos\theta + 0·109\cos^2\theta,$$

$$6{,}990 \text{ A}; \quad 0·431 + 0·675\cos\theta - 0·106\cos^2\theta,$$

$$10{,}310 \text{ A}; \quad 0·541 + 0·610\cos\theta - 0·151\cos^2\theta.$$

The results of this test show that the quadratic approximation (14) is quite good for optical depths $\tau_\lambda < 1$, reasonably reliable for $1 < \tau_\lambda < 3$, and inadequate for $\tau_\lambda > 3$ in the cases examined.

Now if we divide values of τ_λ for a particular temperature by the mean values of $k_\lambda/\bar{k}$ we get a number of determinations of the mean optical depth at which the temperature occurs. Table XVIII shows determinations of τ obtained in this way,† the entry τ observed being an average over suitable values of τ_λ (that is to say, imaginary and negative entries in Table XIV are discarded). These optical depths are shown compared with τ from $T^4 = T_0^4(1 + \tfrac{3}{2}\tau)$ (no blanketing), and with $t = \tau/1·18$, after Section 1.22. The last line shows a reduction of 10 per cent. in t to allow for possible ultra-violet correction; the agreement between these entries and the observed values of τ is tolerably good.

Since $I_\lambda(0)$ enters into equation (16), any errors in the adopted value of this quantity will produce errors in the values of τ_λ deduced from the

† Cf. D. Barbier, *Ann. d'Ap.* **9**, 173 (1946).

TABLE XVII

Optical depth τ		0	0·5	1·0	1·5	2·0	4·0	6·0	8·0
$\dfrac{B(\lambda, T)}{I_\lambda(0)}$, $\lambda\,3{,}860\ A$	Approximate (14)	0·196	0·536	0·950	1·40	1·87	3·82	5·74	7·58
	Theoretical (20)	0·171	0·544	0·946	1·37	1·83	3·93	6·47	9·45
$\dfrac{B(\lambda, T)}{I_\lambda(0)}$, $\lambda\,6{,}990\ A$	Approximate (14)	0·436	0·765	1·06	1·32	1·56	2·37	3·03	3·58
	Theoretical (20)	0·431	0·755	1·05	1·32	1·57	2·28	2·57	2·44
$\dfrac{B(\lambda, T)}{I_\lambda(0)}$, $\lambda\,10{,}310\ A$	Approximate (14)	0·543	0·812	1·03	1·21	1·37	1·87	2·25	2·56
	Theoretical (20)	0·541	0·827	1·08	1·29	1·46	1·77	1·48	0·59

TABLE XVIII

Temperature Distribution in the Solar Photosphere

T	5,500°	6,000°	6,500°	7,000°	7,500°
τ, observed	0·31	0·65	1·12	1·77	2·70
τ, no blanketing	0·45	0·92	1·52	2·28	3·21
t, Section 1.22	0·38	0·78	1·28	1·93	2·73
t, less $u-v$ correction	0·34	0·70	1·16	1·76	2·48

equation. Table XIX, which is due to Chalonge and Kourganoff, shows the proportional errors in τ_λ (that is, $d\tau_\lambda/\tau_\lambda$) arising from a 10 per cent. error in the adopted value of $I_\lambda(0)$.

TABLE XIX

Errors arising out of a 10 per cent. Error in the Adopted Value of $I_\lambda(0)$

$\lambda(A)$	$d\tau_\lambda/\tau_\lambda$ from Chalonge and Kourganoff		
	$T = 5{,}590°$ K.	6,500°	7,000°
4,560	0·16	0·13	0·13
8,660	0·28	0·20	0·27
12,250	0·47	0·27	0·27
16,550	..	0·44	0·35
20,970	3·00	0·46	0·38

Variations in $I_\lambda(0)$ from the values adopted by Mulders will, in general, disturb the relative values of $k_\lambda/\overline{k}$, but it is hardly likely that the errors are such that they have altered this quantity proportionately in a manner equivalent to a simple variation in $\bar{k}$. The agreement of the relative values of k_λ with the wave-length variation of the coefficient of absorption of the negative hydrogen ion is therefore an argument against the existence of very serious errors in $I_\lambda(0)$.[†]

We now turn to the rather puzzling fact that if Münch's values of $k_\lambda/\bar{k}$ are fed into equation (9) and the darkening of the limb calculated, the values agree with observation less closely than do Milne's original calculations with k_λ independent of λ. The fact is puzzling since Münch's $k_\lambda/\bar{k}$ agrees so well (in its variation with λ) with the relative values actually determined from the darkening.

Lastly we may satisfy ourselves that no changes in $\bar{k}$ and $I_\lambda(0)$, that is to say in $k_\lambda/\bar{k}$, will enable equation (9) to represent the observed darkening faithfully. This is shown by the values of c_λ in the formula (15), namely

$$I_\lambda(\theta)/I_\lambda(0) = a_\lambda + b_\lambda \cos\theta + c_\lambda \cos^2\theta.$$

According to Chalonge and Kourganoff the values of c_λ are well represented by

$$c_\lambda = -0 \cdot 1069 - 0 \cdot 1112\lambda + 0 \cdot 0480\lambda^2, \qquad 0 \cdot 45\mu < \lambda < 2 \cdot 1\mu,$$

so that the greatest negative value of c_λ is $-0 \cdot 1713$ at $\lambda\, 11{,}580$ A. According to another solution by Allen (who imposes the condition

$$a_\lambda + b_\lambda + c_\lambda = 1,$$

which Chalonge and Kourganoff do not), c_λ takes still larger negative values, the average value between $\lambda\, 5{,}000$ A and $\lambda\, 15{,}000$ A being $-0 \cdot 25$. But if one fits a quadratic in $\cos\theta$ to values calculated from $f(\alpha, p)$, one finds that the greatest negative value of c_λ is $-0 \cdot 151$ at $\lambda\, 10{,}310$ A, with an average of c_λ equal to $-0 \cdot 103$ between $\lambda\, 5{,}010$ A and $\lambda\, 12{,}550$ A. This feature cannot be eliminated by likely variations of $k_\lambda/\bar{k}$. (For example, Münch's values at $\lambda\, 5{,}955$ A with $k_\lambda/\bar{k} = 0 \cdot 75$ give

$$I_\lambda(\theta)/I_\lambda(0) = 0 \cdot 331 + 0 \cdot 683 \cos\theta - 0 \cdot 014 \cos^2\theta.)$$

The experimental evidence that c_λ is more negative than the values given by $f(\alpha, p)$ shows that no likely values of $k_\lambda/\bar{k}$ will enable the observations to be represented well by equation (9).

But the equation $T^4 = T_0^4(1 + \frac{3}{2}\tau)$, on which equation (9) is founded, has been challenged by Plaskett[‡] and later by de Jager.[§] Both of these

[†] Mulders's values of $I_\lambda(0)$ are supported by recent determinations by R. Peyturaux, *C.R.* **232**, 931 (1951).

[‡] H. H. Plaskett, *M.N.* **96**, 418 (1936).

[§] C. de Jager, *Kon. Ned. Akad. Wet.* **51**, 731 (1948).

authors put forward temperature distributions which differ from the radiative formula, Plaskett's being empirical, and de Jager's semi-empirical, guided by the theory of convection. Since convection carries

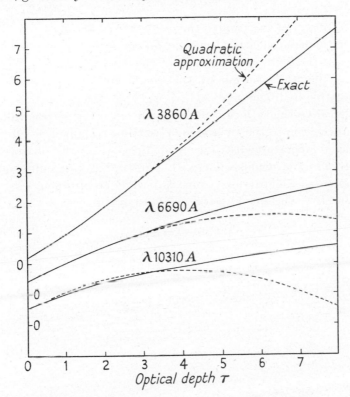

FIG. 17. Theoretical values of $B(\lambda, T)/I_\lambda(0) = [\alpha^5 f(\alpha, \frac{3}{2})\{e^{hc/\lambda RT}-1\}]^{-1}$ plotted as a function of optical depth for three wave-lengths $\lambda\lambda\, 3{,}860$, $6{,}690$, and $10{,}310$ A (full lines) and compared with the approximation $B(\lambda, T)/I_\lambda(0) = a+b\tau_\lambda+\frac{1}{2}c\tau_\lambda^2$, where a, b, and c are coefficients which represent Milne's theoretical darkening $f(\alpha, \frac{3}{2}\cos\theta)/f(\alpha, \frac{3}{2})$ in the form $a+b\cos\theta+c\cos^2\theta$. It is assumed that $T^4 = T_0^4(1+\frac{3}{2}\tau)$, and that $\tau = \tau_\lambda$ at these three wave-lengths.

part of the energy flux, the radiation flux is reduced in the convection zone. Hence $dT/d\tau$ is reduced, and T, as a function of τ, falls below $T_0'(1+\frac{3}{2}\tau)^{\frac{1}{4}}$ at depths below $\tau = 2$. Now de Jager adopts $k_\lambda/\bar{k} = 0{\cdot}70$ for $\lambda\,5{,}010$ A, so that his coefficient closely resembles that of Münch: yet de Jager finds $\varphi(\theta) = 0{\cdot}227+1{\cdot}027\cos\theta-0{\cdot}254\cos^2\theta$,

nearly. The high negative value of c_λ is accounted for by a decrease beyond $\tau = 2$, of the temperature gradient, consistent with convection. There is a suggestion of support for this in Table XVIII.

3.3. *Summary*

To sum up this section on the comparison between the theory of radiative equilibrium and the observed darkening of the solar limb, we may say that

(1) The observed variation of the coefficient of absorption with wave-length, deduced either from the energy curve, or from the darkening of the limb, with the help of the theory, agrees well with the wave-length variation of the coefficient of absorption of the negative hydrogen ion.

(2) The wave-length mean of the coefficient of absorption demands a correction to the theory such as Milne's blanketing effect.

(3) The temperature distribution deduced from the observed limb darkening is inconsistent with pure radiative equilibrium, and supports a departure from radiative equilibrium, at certain depths, consistent with the presence of convection.

VI
THE PHYSICAL NATURE OF LINE ABSORPTION

1. Introduction

Two important aspects of the mechanism of line absorption and emission were considered by Kirchhoff, and Sir George Stokes in the year 1860. In Kirchhoff's view line absorbing atoms have a greater coefficient of absorption and emission than surrounding matter. This amounts to assuming that thermodynamic equilibrium applies to a line frequency, the energy absorbed from the radiation field by the atoms being converted into heat by collisions with neighbouring particles. But, according to Stokes, the atoms may be considered as *oscillators* which absorb and re-emit the incident radiation without interaction with other atoms. In the interior of a star, where both the temperature and density are large, radiation from excited atoms is completely quenched by collisions and Kirchhoff's mechanism applies. But in the outer layers the number of collisions is much smaller and most of the radiation absorbed by the atoms is returned to the radiation field in accordance with Stokes's view. Indeed it will appear in the following chapters on the formation of absorption lines that the model of Stokes gives the better description of Fraunhofer lines in the solar spectrum, although it is necessary to introduce a small amount of Kirchhoff's process in order to account for the intensity of radiation at the centre of the lines. The present chapter deals with the mechanism of the absorption and emission by atoms in a stellar atmosphere and provides a physical basis for later discussions on the formation of absorption lines.

2. The classical oscillator

The harmonic oscillator is a mechanism which absorbs and emits radiation in a line spectrum; it is in fact the only mechanism in the classical theory which does so. We suppose that a classical oscillator in a radiation field behaves like an atom taking part in the formation of an absorption line in a stellar atmosphere.

The oscillator consists of an electron of charge $-e$ and mass m executing motion in a straight line about a centre of force, with a frequency $\nu_0 = \omega_0/2\pi$. In the absence of any frictional forces the equation of motion of the oscillating particle will be

$$\ddot{x} = -\omega_0^2 x.$$

But according to classical electrodynamics an accelerating charge radiates energy and thus introduces a quasi-frictional force equal to $(2e^2/3c^3)\dddot{x}$. The equation of the damped motion of the electron is then

$$\ddot{x} = -\omega_0^2 x - \frac{2e^2}{3mc^3}\dddot{x}. \tag{1}$$

If we set $x = x_0 e^{i\sigma t}$ in equation (1) we obtain

$$\sigma^2 = \omega_0^2 + i\frac{2e^2}{3mc^3}\sigma^3. \tag{2}$$

Let $\sigma = \omega_0 + i\gamma_0$, and assume that γ_0 is small compared with ω_0. From equation (2) we then find $\gamma_0 = (e^2/3mc^3)\omega_0^2$. We now define the damping constant γ by the relation

$$\gamma = 2\gamma_0 = \frac{8\pi^2 e^2 \nu_0^2}{3mc^3}, \tag{3}$$

so that equation (1) takes the form

$$\ddot{x} + \gamma\dot{x} + \omega_0^2 x = 0, \tag{4}$$

the frictional term being proportional to the velocity of the electron. The solution of equation (4) is the damped vibration

$$x = x_0 e^{-\frac{1}{2}\gamma t}\cos(\omega_0 t - \phi). \tag{5}$$

Since the total energy of the oscillator is proportional to the square of the amplitude of the vibration, the energy will decrease to e^{-1} of its initial value in the time $\tau = 1/\gamma$, a quantity referred to as the *time of decay*.

2.1. *Absorption*

In the presence of radiation the oscillator electron executes forced vibrations under the influence of the electric vector of the light wave. Energy is removed from the radiation field in forcing the oscillator to perform in this way, thereby giving rise to absorption. Consider a region containing N classical oscillators per unit volume and suppose that the radiation in the region consists of plane polarized electromagnetic waves. The equation of motion of the oscillator is

$$\ddot{x} + \gamma\dot{x} + \omega_0^2 x = -\frac{e}{m}E, \tag{6}$$

where $E = E_0 e^{i\omega t}$, the direction of the electric vector defining the x-axis. The solution of equation (6) is made up of two parts, a natural vibration given by the complementary function, and a forced vibration described by the particular integral. In the steady state the natural vibrations in equation (5) are damped out and the motion of the oscillator is given by the particular integral, namely

$$x = \frac{-eE/m}{\omega_0^2 - \omega^2 + i\omega\gamma}. \qquad (7)$$

The electron therefore oscillates with the frequency of the radiation with a phase difference between the displacement of the electron and the electric field. If ω does not differ very much from ω_0 we may write $\omega_0^2 - \omega^2 \doteq 2\omega(\omega_0 - \omega)$, and equation (7) becomes

$$x = \frac{-eE/2m\omega}{\omega_0 - \omega + \frac{1}{2}i\gamma}, \qquad (8)$$

and the current density due to the motion of the electrons will be

$$\mathbf{J} = -Ne\dot{x} = \frac{Ne^2/2m\omega}{\omega_0 - \omega + \frac{1}{2}i\gamma} \frac{\partial \mathbf{E}}{\partial t}. \qquad (9)$$

The electromagnetic field in the region is given by Maxwell's equations:

$$\operatorname{curl} \mathbf{H} = \frac{1}{c}\frac{\partial \mathbf{E}}{\partial t} + \frac{4\pi}{c}\mathbf{J}, \qquad \operatorname{div} \mathbf{H} = 0,$$

$$\operatorname{curl} \mathbf{E} = -\frac{1}{c}\frac{\partial \mathbf{H}}{\partial t}, \qquad \operatorname{div} \mathbf{E} = -4\pi Ne.$$

Since $\operatorname{curl}\operatorname{curl} \mathbf{E} = \operatorname{grad}\operatorname{div} \mathbf{E} - \nabla^2 \mathbf{E},$

we have for N constant (i.e. $\operatorname{grad} N = 0$)

$$\nabla^2 \mathbf{E} = \frac{1}{c}\frac{\partial}{\partial t}\operatorname{curl} \mathbf{H} = \frac{1}{c^2}\frac{\partial}{\partial t}\left\{\frac{\partial \mathbf{E}}{\partial t} + 4\pi \mathbf{J}\right\}. \qquad (10)$$

Substituting for $\mathbf{J}$ from equation (9) we obtain the wave motion equation

$$\nabla^2 \mathbf{E} = \frac{1}{c^2}\left\{1 + \frac{2\pi Ne^2/m\omega}{\omega_0 - \omega + \frac{1}{2}i\gamma}\right\}\frac{\partial^2 \mathbf{E}}{\partial t^2} \qquad (11)$$

which represents a damped wave. Let z be in the direction of the wave motion so that plane-wave solutions are of the form

$$\mathbf{E} = \tilde{n}E_0 e^{-\frac{1}{2}kz}\cos\omega(t - z/v),$$

$\tilde{n}$ being a unit vector along the x-axis, k the coefficient of absorption, and v the wave velocity. The factor $\frac{1}{2}k$ is introduced into the damping term as we are usually concerned with the intensity, that is, the energy of the radiation, which is proportional to the square of the amplitude. The intensity of the light wave will then be reduced by the factor e^{-kz} in the distance z. We therefore adopt the variation

$$\exp\{-\tfrac{1}{2}kz + i\omega(t - z/v)\} \quad \text{or} \quad \exp\{i\omega[t - (\mu/c - \tfrac{1}{2}ik/\omega)z]\},$$

where μ is the refractive index given by c/v. Setting $\nabla^2 = \partial^2/\partial z^2$ equation (11) gives

$$(\mu - ick/2\omega)^2 = 1 + \frac{2\pi N e^2/m\omega}{\omega_0 - \omega + \frac{1}{2}i\gamma}. \qquad (12)$$

Separating the real and imaginary parts in equation (12) we find

$$\mu^2 - 1 = \frac{c^2 k^2}{4\omega^2} + \frac{2\pi N e^2}{m\omega} \frac{\omega_0 - \omega}{(\omega_0 - \omega)^2 + (\frac{1}{2}\gamma)^2},$$

$$\mu k = \frac{\pi e^2}{mc} N \frac{\gamma}{(\omega_0 - \omega)^2 + (\frac{1}{2}\gamma)^2}.$$

Now if N is small, μk is also small; but μ^2 is then $1 + O(k^2)$ so that μ is of order unity. The absorption coefficient per unit volume will now be

$$k = \frac{\pi e^2}{mc} \frac{N}{\pi} \frac{\gamma/4\pi}{(\nu - \nu_0)^2 + (\gamma/4\pi)^2}.$$

Let $\alpha(\nu)$ be the line-absorption coefficient per oscillator, then

$$\alpha(\nu) = \frac{\pi e^2}{mc} \frac{1}{\pi} \frac{\gamma/4\pi}{(\nu - \nu_0)^2 + (\gamma/4\pi)^2} = \frac{\alpha}{\pi} \frac{\gamma/4\pi}{(\nu - \nu_0)^2 + (\gamma/4\pi)^2}, \qquad (13)$$

where $\alpha = \int_0^\infty \alpha(\nu)\, d\nu = \pi e^2/mc$. The coefficient $\alpha(\nu)$ has a maximum at $\nu = \nu_0$, and decreases rapidly to half the maximum value when

$$\Delta\nu = |\nu - \nu_0| = \gamma/4\pi.$$

We refer to $2\Delta\nu$ as the *width* of the absorption profile so that $\Delta\nu$ is the *half-width*.

2.2. *Emission*

According to the classical theory the rate of emission of radiant energy by an accelerating electron is given by

$$S = \frac{2e^2}{3c^3} \ddot{x}^2. \qquad (14)$$

From equation (6) the motion of the oscillator electron in the absence of the perturbing field is

$$\ddot{x} + \gamma\dot{x} + \omega_0^2 x = 0. \qquad (15)$$

The emission from the classical oscillator will therefore be in the form of a wave train of frequency $\nu_0 = \omega_0/2\pi$, the amplitude decreasing exponentially with the time. A spectroscopic analysis of such a wave train breaks the radiation up into an infinite number of homogeneous wave trains with different frequencies and amplitudes.

Consider an oscillator which begins to radiate at $t = 0$, the displacement of the electron being zero for $t < 0$. The solution of equation (15) for the displacement at time t will be

$$x = Ae^{-(\frac{1}{2}\gamma - i\omega_0)t} + Be^{-(\frac{1}{2}\gamma + i\omega_0)t}.$$

Now if $A = \alpha + i\beta$, the condition that the displacement x is real gives $B = \alpha - i\beta = A^*$, where A^* denotes the complex conjugate of A. Hence

$$x = Ae^{-(\frac{1}{2}\gamma - i\omega_0)t} + A^*e^{-(\frac{1}{2}\gamma + i\omega_0)t}. \tag{16}$$

Let the first member of equation (16) be denoted by $g(t)$. The Fourier integral representation of this function is

$$g(t) = \int_{-\infty}^{\infty} a(\omega)e^{i\omega t}\, d\omega.$$

Multiplying both sides by $e^{-i\mu t}$ and integrating with respect to t from $-\tau$ to $+\tau$ we obtain

$$\int_{-\tau}^{\tau} g(t)e^{-i\mu t}\, dt = \int_{-\infty}^{\infty} a(\omega)\, d\omega \int_{-\tau}^{\tau} e^{i(\omega - \mu)t}\, dt.$$

In the limit as $\tau \to \infty$ the right-hand side gives

$$\lim_{\tau \to \infty} \int_{-\infty}^{\infty} a(\omega)\frac{2\sin(\omega - \mu)\tau}{\omega - \mu}\, d\omega = \lim_{\tau \to \infty} \int_{-\infty}^{\infty} a\left(\mu + \frac{\xi}{\tau}\right)\frac{2\sin\xi}{\xi}\, d\xi.$$

Hence

$$\int_{-\infty}^{\infty} g(t)e^{-i\mu t}\, dt = 2\pi a(\mu).$$

But $g(t) = 0$ for $t < 0$ so that

$$a(\mu) = \frac{1}{2\pi} \int_{0}^{\infty} g(t)e^{-i\mu t}\, dt = \frac{1}{2\pi}\frac{A}{\frac{1}{2}\gamma - i(\omega_0 - \mu)}.$$

Equation (16) may now be written in the form

$$x = \frac{1}{2\pi} \int_{-\infty}^{\infty} \left\{\frac{A}{\frac{1}{2}\gamma - i(\omega_0 - \omega)} + \frac{A^*}{\frac{1}{2}\gamma + i(\omega_0 + \omega)}\right\} e^{i\omega t}\, d\omega. \tag{17}$$

Hence

$$\ddot{x} = \int_{-\infty}^{\infty} f(\omega)e^{i\omega t}\, d\omega,$$

where

$$f(\omega) = -\frac{\omega^2}{2\pi}\left\{\frac{A}{\frac{1}{2}\gamma - i(\omega_0 - \omega)} + \frac{A^*}{\frac{1}{2}\gamma + i(\omega_0 + \omega)}\right\}. \tag{18}$$

Taking the complex conjugate in equation (18) we have

$$\ddot{x}^* = \int_{-\infty}^{\infty} f^*(\omega)e^{-i\omega t}\, d\omega = \int_{-\infty}^{\infty} f^*(-\omega)e^{i\omega t}\, d\omega. \tag{19}$$

Since $\ddot{x}^2 = \ddot{x}\ddot{x}^*$ the rate of emission of energy, given by equation (14), will be

$$S = \frac{2e^2}{3c^3} \int_{-\infty}^{\infty} \int_{-\infty}^{\infty} f(\omega)f^*(\mu)e^{i(\omega-\mu)t}\, d\omega d\mu. \tag{20}$$

We now make a spectroscopic analysis of the total energy radiated by the oscillating electron. Let $I(\omega)\, d\omega$ be the intensity of the Fourier component within ω to $\omega + d\omega$ so that

$$\int_{0}^{\infty} I(\omega)\, d\omega = \frac{1}{4\pi} \int_{0}^{\infty} S\, dt, \tag{21}$$

the emission being taken as isotropic. Now $S = 0$ for $t < 0$ so that we may write

$$\frac{3c^3}{2e^2} \int_{0}^{\infty} S\, dt = \lim_{T \to \infty} \int_{-\infty}^{\infty} \int_{-\infty}^{\infty} \int_{-T}^{T} f(\omega)f^*(\mu)e^{i(\omega-\mu)t}\, d\omega d\mu dt$$

$$= \lim_{T \to \infty} \int_{-\infty}^{\infty} \int_{-\infty}^{\infty} f(\omega)f^*(\mu)\frac{2\sin(\omega-\mu)T}{\omega-\mu}\, d\omega d\mu.$$

But $\qquad \displaystyle \lim_{T \to \infty} \int_{-\infty}^{\infty} f^*(\mu)\frac{2\sin(\omega-\mu)T}{\omega-\mu}\, d\mu = 2\pi f^*(\omega).$

Hence

$$\frac{3c^3}{2e^2} \int_{0}^{\infty} S\, dt = 2\pi \int_{-\infty}^{\infty} f(\omega)f^*(\omega)\, d\omega = 2\pi \int_{-\infty}^{\infty} |f(\omega)|^2\, d\omega.$$

From the definition of $f(\omega)$ in equation (18) it follows that

$$|f(\omega)|^2 = |f(-\omega)|^2,$$

so that $\qquad \displaystyle \frac{3c^3}{2e^2} \int_{0}^{\infty} S\, dt = 4\pi \int_{0}^{\infty} |f(\omega)|^2\, d\omega.$

Equation (21) therefore gives

$$I(\omega)\, d\omega = \frac{2e^2}{3c^3} |f(\omega)|^2\, d\omega. \tag{22}$$

Now when $|\omega-\omega_0| \ll \omega_0$, we have from (18)

$$f(\omega) \doteq -\frac{\omega^2}{2\pi}\frac{A}{\tfrac{1}{2}\gamma-i(\omega_0-\omega)},$$

whence
$$|f(\omega)|^2 \doteq \left(\frac{\omega^2}{2\pi}\right)^2 \frac{AA^*}{(\tfrac{1}{2}\gamma)^2+(\omega-\omega_0)^2}.$$

Changing to ordinary frequency units, equation (22) becomes

$$I(\nu)\,d\nu = \frac{4\pi e^2 \nu^4}{3c^3}\frac{AA^*}{(\nu-\nu_0)^2+(\gamma/4\pi)^2}\,d\nu. \tag{23}$$

In the slowly varying factor involving ν^4 in equation (23) we set $\nu = \nu_0$. This leads to

$$I(\nu) = \frac{I}{\pi}\frac{\gamma/4\pi}{(\nu-\nu_0)^2+(\gamma/4\pi)^2}, \tag{24}$$

where $I = \int I(\nu)\,d\nu$. The emission (24) is of the same form as equation (13) for the absorption coefficient. This is required by Kirchhoff's principle of balancing between emission and absorption in thermodynamic equilibrium, since the variation of intensity of full radiation is small over the width of a line.

3. Collision damping

The effect of collisions on the form of the emission coefficient as a function of frequency can be studied by making a Fourier analysis of the disturbed wave train. The simplest supposition is that a monochromatic wave train is started in some manner, and that it is completely stopped by the first effective collision which the emitting atom experiences, all other collisions having no effect. This supposition—the quenching of radiation by collisions—is adopted in the following treatment which avoids the actual application of a Fourier analysis.

3.1. *Impact broadening*

Consider an assembly of atoms and let τ be the mean free time between collisions with other atoms so that N/τ collisions occur per unit interval of time. If we suppose that the effect of collisions is to redistribute the vector displacements and velocities of the oscillator electrons in a random fashion then, on the average, both x and $\dot{x}$ are zero for the group of atoms which collide at any time t'. Now the complete solution of equation (6) for the motion of the bound electron may be written in the form

$$x = x_0 e^{i\omega t}+(Ae^{i\omega_0 t}+Be^{-i\omega_0 t})e^{-\frac{1}{2}\gamma t}, \tag{25}$$

H

the amplitude of the oscillation in the steady state being

$$x_0 = \frac{-eE_0/m}{\omega_0^2 - \omega^2 + i\omega\gamma}. \tag{26}$$

Introducing the boundary condition $x = \dot{x} = 0$ at $t = t'$, equation (25) gives

$$A = -\frac{x_0}{2\omega_0}(\omega_0 + \omega - \tfrac{1}{2}i\gamma)e^{[-i(\omega_0 - \omega) + \frac{1}{2}\gamma]t'},$$

$$B = -\frac{x_0}{2\omega_0}(\omega_0 - \omega + \tfrac{1}{2}i\gamma)e^{[i(\omega_0 + \omega) + \frac{1}{2}\gamma]t'}.$$

Hence the displacement at time t for oscillators disturbed by collisions at time t' in the manner described will be given by

$$x_\theta(t) = x_0 e^{i\omega t}\left\{1 - \frac{1}{2\omega_0}(\omega_0 + \omega - \tfrac{1}{2}i\gamma)e^{[i(\omega_0 - \omega) - \frac{1}{2}\gamma]\theta} - \right.$$
$$\left. -\frac{1}{2\omega_0}(\omega_0 - \omega + \tfrac{1}{2}i\gamma)e^{-[i(\omega_0 + \omega) + \frac{1}{2}\gamma]\theta}\right\}, \tag{27}$$

where $\theta\ (= t - t')$ is the time interval since the last collision.

The fraction $f(\theta)$ of atoms having free times within θ to $\theta + d\theta$ is given by the probability law

$$f(\theta) = \frac{1}{\tau}e^{-\theta/\tau}\, d\theta. \tag{28}$$

The average value of the oscillator amplitude at time t may be determined by considering the atoms in groups having times $\theta = t - t'$ since their last collision and integrating over all values of θ. Thus the mean displacement at time t will be

$$\bar{x}(t) = \int_0^\infty f(\theta)x_\theta(t)\, d\theta.$$

The integration is straightforward, and after some reduction we find

$$\bar{x}(t) = \frac{\omega_0^2 - (\omega - \tfrac{1}{2}i\gamma)^2}{\omega_0^2 - [\omega - i(\tfrac{1}{2}\gamma + 1/\tau)]^2}x_0 e^{i\omega t}. \tag{29}$$

Since $\omega \gg \gamma$ the coefficient of $e^{i\omega t}$ may be written as

$$\bar{x}_0 = \frac{x_0(\omega_0^2 - \omega^2 + i\omega\gamma)}{\omega_0^2 - \omega^2 + i\omega(\gamma + 2/\tau)} = \frac{-eE_0/m}{\omega_0^2 - \omega^2 + i\omega(\gamma + 2/\tau)}. \tag{30}$$

Comparing equations (26) and (30) we see that the statistical effect of collisions is to make the atoms in the assembly behave like oscillators with damping constant $\gamma + 2/\tau$ instead of γ.

Since the damping constant determines the width of the absorption and emission profile of the oscillator, the width in the presence of collisions is made up of two parts: the natural width and the collision width. Now the quantity $1/\tau$ is the collision frequency, and according to the kinetic theory

$$\frac{1}{\tau} = \sigma_0 \bar{v} n,$$

where σ_0 $(= \pi \rho_0^2)$ is the collision cross-section, $\bar{v}$ is the mean relative velocity, whilst n is the concentration of colliding atoms, which is proportional to the pressure. The mean free time being inversely proportional to the pressure, the width due to collisions increases linearly with pressure. The half width of the line being $(\gamma + 2/\tau)/4\pi$, the half width due to collisions is

$$\frac{\gamma_c}{4\pi} = \frac{1}{2\pi\tau} = \tfrac{1}{2}\rho_0^2 \bar{v} n. \tag{31}$$

The absorption profile of the oscillator will therefore be considerably broadened if collisions occur sufficiently frequently, that is if the effective cross-section for collisions is sufficiently large or the density sufficiently high.

The kind of collision considered above causes the oscillator motion to cease at the moment of impact, the radiation being thereby quenched. Since the energy of the oscillator is converted into kinetic energy of the particles, the process of broadening by impact is really the same as Kirchhoff's process mentioned in Section 1.

3.2. *Phase collisions*

For a more detailed treatment of collision damping we must consider more carefully the physical effect of a collision on the emitting atom. A collision can, in general, change either the amplitude or the phase of the radiated wave, or both. The appearance of a change in amplitude would imply an exchange of kinetic energy between the disturbing atom and the radiator, and would tend to set up or maintain thermal equilibrium. If changes of phase occur at constant amplitude, the interaction between the disturbing atom and the radiator only takes the form of a time dependent perturbation in the frequency of the radiation emitted by the atom.

The manner in which a passing foreign atom modifies the frequency of the emitted radiation is illustrated in Fig. 18, which shows the perturbation of the upper and lower energy levels of a radiating atom as a function of the distance between the perturber and radiator. The effect is more pronounced for the higher than for the lower energy level. The frequency of the radiation emitted or absorbed by the atom will therefore change as the separation varies. At the low pressures in the outer layers (roughly equal to 0·01 atmospheres in the case of the Sun), small values of r are much less likely than large values so that we are concerned mainly with the portion BC of the $U(r)$ curve shown.

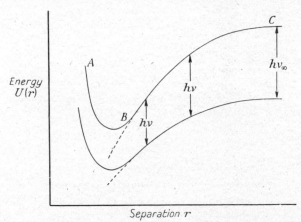

Fig. 18. Perturbation of the upper and lower energy levels of a radiating atom by a foreign atom (diagrammatic only).

Let the frequency of the radiation from the atom at infinite separation from the perturber be ν_∞. On the average the frequency absorbed or emitted in the presence of foreign atoms will be less than ν_∞, and the line is shifted towards the red. The disturbance in the frequency is given by

$$\Delta\nu = \frac{C}{r^6},$$

where C is a constant† which depends on the radiating atom and the perturber. The forces which operate between the two atoms at the large distances under consideration are the so-called van der Waals forces. (For the Stark effect, see section 4.4.)

In order to calculate the total change in phase at a collision we assume that the motion of the perturbing particle relative to the radiating atom is along a straight line path traversed with the mean relative velocity $\bar{v}$. Although the assumption of rectilinear motion is only true for a short interval of time, there is some justification for its use in the fact that the *optical collision cross-section* is much greater than the cross-section for particle impact. Thus, if the impact cross-section be taken as vanishingly small compared with the optical cross-section we may then reasonably neglect the impacts which alter direction.

Let the frequency of the oscillator at any instant during the disturbance be

$$\omega(t) = \omega_0 - \Delta\omega,$$

† The evaluation of C is dealt with in Chapter IX, section 5.

the total phase change being

$$\eta = \int \Delta\omega \, dt,$$

where the integration extends over the collision time. For the sake of generality we write $\Delta\omega = 2\pi C / r^n$. Then since

$$r = \sqrt{(\rho^2 + \bar{v}^2 t^2)},$$

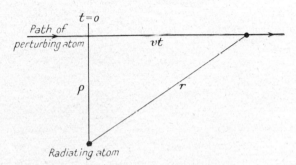

$t = 0$

Path of
perturbing atom

vt

ρ r

Radiating atom

FIG. 19. Geometry of a phase collision.

the total phase change is given by

$$\eta = 2\pi C \int_{-\infty}^{\infty} \frac{dt}{(\rho^2 + \bar{v}^2 t^2)^{\frac{1}{2}n}} = \frac{4\pi C}{\bar{v}\rho^{n-1}} \int_{0}^{\frac{1}{2}\pi} \cos^{n-2}\theta \, d\theta. \qquad (32)$$

With $n = 6$ equation (32) gives

$$\eta = \frac{3\pi^2 C}{4\bar{v}\rho^5}. \qquad (33)$$

Consider an oscillator which begins to radiate at $t = 0$. Let the oscillations be subject to phase disturbances from time to time, the total change in phase at time t being

$$\Delta(t) = \sum_{0}^{t} \eta, \qquad (34)$$

where η is the phase change at any one of the collisions which takes place in the time interval t. The amplitude of the oscillations may be modified by the collisions in addition to being dependent upon the time on account of natural damping. For simplicity we consider an oscillator without natural decay, undergoing phase disturbances at constant amplitude. We therefore represent the disturbed oscillations by the expression

$$x(t) = x_0 \, e^{i[\omega_0 t - \Delta(t)]}. \qquad (35)$$

The Fourier integral representation of equation (35) gives

$$x(t) = \int_{-\infty}^{\infty} a(\omega)e^{i\omega t}\, d\omega, \tag{36}$$

where

$$a(\omega) = \frac{1}{2\pi} \int_{-\infty}^{\infty} x(t)e^{-i\omega t}\, dt.$$

Since $x(t) = 0$ for $t < 0$ we may write

$$a(\omega) = \frac{1}{2\pi} \int_{0}^{\infty} x_0\, e^{i(\omega_0-\omega)t - i\Delta(t)}\, dt. \tag{37}$$

Now the intensity of the ω-component radiated by the oscillator is given by

$$I(\omega) = \text{const } a(\omega)a^*(\omega), \tag{38}$$

where $a^*(\omega)$ is the complex conjugate of $a(\omega)$. By means of equation (37) we write (38) in the form

$$I(\omega) = \text{const } \int_{0}^{\infty} \int_{0}^{\infty} e^{i(\omega-\omega_0)(t''-t') + i[\Delta(t'')-\Delta(t')]}\, dt'dt''. \tag{39}$$

We introduce the following change of variable in the double integral:

$$t' = t', \qquad t'' = t+t'.$$

Since the Jacobian of the transformation is unity, equation (39) becomes

$$I(\omega) = \text{const } \int_{-\infty}^{\infty} e^{i(\omega-\omega_0)t}\, dt \int_{0}^{\infty} e^{i[\Delta(t+t')-\Delta(t')]}\, dt'. \tag{40}$$

Now

$$\Delta(t+t') - \Delta(t') = \sum_{t'}^{t+t'} \eta, \tag{41}$$

which is the total phase change due to collisions in the interval t at time t'. This phase change is subject to a statistical fluctuation with t'. According to Lenz[†] the second integral in equation (40) may be regarded as a statistical time average, so that the integral itself may be replaced by the time mean value of the integrand.

Following Lindholm[‡] we assume in the first instance that the collisions produce only three different phase changes η_a, η_b, and η_c for which the corresponding differential cross-sections are σ_a, σ_b, and σ_c, the total cross-section being

$$\sigma = \sigma_a + \sigma_b + \sigma_c. \tag{42}$$

Let τ be the mean free time between collisions; then the probability that

---

[†] W. Lenz, *Zs. f. Phys.* **80**, 430 (1933).

[‡] E. Lindholm. Dissertation 'Über die Verbreiterung und Verschiebung von Spektrallinien' (Uppsala, 1942).

z collisions occur in time t ($= t'' - t'$) will be

$$\frac{1}{z!}\left(\frac{t}{\tau}\right)^z e^{-t/\tau}. \tag{43}$$

In addition, the probability that amongst $n+m+l$ collisions there are n a-collisions, m b-collisions, and l c-collisions is

$$\left(\frac{\sigma_a}{\sigma}\right)^n\left(\frac{\sigma_b}{\sigma}\right)^m\left(\frac{\sigma_c}{\sigma}\right)^l \frac{(n+m+l)!}{n!\,m!\,l!}. \tag{44}$$

The compound probability for $n+m+l$ collisions in the time t of which n are a-collisions, m are b-collisions and l are c-collisions will be the product of the probabilities (43) and (44):

$$\left(\frac{\sigma_a}{\sigma}\right)^n\left(\frac{\sigma_b}{\sigma}\right)^m\left(\frac{\sigma_c}{\sigma}\right)^l \frac{1}{n!\,m!\,l!}\left(\frac{t}{\tau}\right)^{n+m+l} e^{-t/\tau}. \tag{45}$$

Since $$\sum_{t'}^{t+t'} \eta = n\eta_a + m\eta_b + l\eta_c,$$

the required time average value of the t' integrand in equation (40) will be the exponential factor $e^{i[n\eta_a + m\eta_b + l\eta_c]}$

weighted by the probability (45) and summed over all statistical variation of n, m, and l with l'. Hence we write

$$\overline{\exp\left(i\sum_{t'}^{t+t'}\eta\right)}$$

$$= \sum_n \sum_m \sum_l \left(\frac{\sigma_a}{\sigma}\right)^n\left(\frac{\sigma_b}{\sigma}\right)^m\left(\frac{\sigma_c}{\sigma}\right)^l \frac{1}{n!\,m!\,l!}\left(\frac{t}{\tau}\right)^{n+m+l} e^{-t/\tau}e^{i[n\eta_a + m\eta_b + l\eta_c]}. \tag{46}$$

If we extend each summation from 0 to ∞ the use of the series expansion $e^x = \sum_0^\infty x^n/n!$ enables us to reduce the summations in equation (46) to the simple form

$$\exp\left\{\frac{t}{\tau\sigma}(\sigma_a e^{i\eta_a} + \sigma_b e^{i\eta_b} + \sigma_c e^{i\eta_c} - \sigma)\right\}.$$

Hence $$\overline{\exp\left(i\sum_{t'}^{t+t'}\eta\right)} = \exp\left\{\frac{l}{\tau\sigma}\sum_a (e^{i\eta_a} - 1)\sigma_a\right\}. \tag{47}$$

If we let

$$\alpha = \frac{1}{\tau\sigma}\sum_a \sigma_a(1 - \cos\eta_a), \tag{48}$$

$$\beta = \frac{1}{\tau\sigma}\sum_a \sigma_a \sin\eta_a, \tag{49}$$

the mean value in equation (47) is simply $e^{t(-\alpha+i\beta)}$. This only applies to positive values of $t\ (=t''-t')$. When t is negative the phase changes η_a must be considered as negative, and the mean value is then $e^{-t(-\alpha-i\beta)}$. Equation (40) may now be written in the form

$$I(\omega) = \text{const} \int_0^\infty e^{-\alpha t} \cos(\omega-\omega_0+\beta)t\ dt.$$

This gives the following formula for the line profile:

$$I(\omega) = \frac{\text{const}}{(\omega-\omega_0+\beta)^2+\alpha^2}.$$

Changing to ordinary frequency units,

$$I(\nu) = \frac{I}{\pi} \frac{\alpha/2\pi}{(\nu-\nu_0+\beta/2\pi)^2+(\alpha/2\pi)^2}, \tag{50}$$

where I is the total intensity of the spectral line. The line has a half width

$$\delta_c = \frac{\alpha}{2\pi}, \tag{51}$$

the position of the maximum being displaced to the red side of the frequency ν_0 by an amount

$$\nu_0-\nu_m = \frac{\beta}{2\pi}. \tag{52}$$

Since σ is the total collision cross-section, the total number of collisions per second is given by

$$\frac{1}{\tau} = \sigma\bar{v}n.$$

Equations (48) and (49) may be written as follows:

$$\alpha = \bar{v}n \sum_a 2\sigma_a \sin^2(\tfrac{1}{2}\eta_a), \tag{53}$$

$$\beta = \bar{v}n \sum_a \sigma_a \sin \eta_a. \tag{54}$$

When the collisions are due to the presence of foreign atoms we have, from equation (33),

$$\eta_a = \frac{3\pi^2 C}{4\bar{v}\rho^5}.$$

Let the collision area corresponding to this phase change be $\sigma_a = 2\pi\rho\ d\rho$, then from equations (51) and (53) the collision half width will be

$$\delta_c = \frac{\bar{v}n}{2\pi} \int_0^\infty \sin^2\left(\frac{3\pi^2 C}{8\bar{v}\rho^5}\right) 4\pi\rho \, d\rho.$$

By means of the substitution $\frac{1}{x^5} = \frac{3\pi^2 C}{8\bar{v}\rho^5}$ we obtain

$$\delta_c = \tfrac{1}{2}(12\pi^2)^{2/5} C^{2/5}(\bar{v})^{3/5} n \int_0^\infty \sin^2\left(\frac{1}{x^5}\right) x \, dx. \tag{55}$$

Similarly for the line displacement given by equations (52) and (54):

$$\nu_0 - \nu_m = \left(\frac{3\pi^2}{8}\right)^{2/5} C^{2/5}(\bar{v})^{3/5} n \int_0^\infty \sin\left(\frac{2}{x^5}\right) x \, dx. \tag{56}$$

Now

$$\int_0^\infty \sin^2\left(\frac{1}{x^5}\right) x \, dx = (\tfrac{1}{2})^{8/5}\Gamma(\tfrac{3}{5})\sin\left(\frac{3\pi}{10}\right),$$

$$\int_0^\infty \sin\left(\frac{2}{x^5}\right) x \, dx = (\tfrac{1}{2})^{3/5}\Gamma(\tfrac{3}{5})\cos\left(\frac{3\pi}{10}\right).$$

Hence the collision half width and the displacement of the line are connected by the expression

$$\delta_c = (\nu_0 - \nu_m)\tan\left(\frac{3\pi}{10}\right). \tag{57}$$

The explicit formula for the collision half width is

$$\delta_c = 1\cdot34\, C^{2/5}(\bar{v})^{3/5} n, \tag{58}$$

the numerical factor being the value of

$$\tfrac{1}{2}(12\pi^2)^{2/5}(\tfrac{1}{2})^{8/5}\Gamma(\tfrac{3}{5})\sin\left(\frac{3\pi}{10}\right).$$

From the kinetic theory we take the following results:

$$\bar{v} = \sqrt{\left\{\frac{8RT}{\pi}\left(\frac{1}{m_1}+\frac{1}{m_2}\right)\right\}}, \tag{59}$$

$$n = p/RT, \tag{60}$$

where m_1 and m_2 are the masses of the colliding atoms and p is the partial pressure due to the foreign atoms. It follows from equations (58), (59), and (60) that

$$\delta_c \propto p/T^{7/10}. \tag{61}$$

We conclude this section by considering briefly the relation between Lindholm's theory and the work of Lorentz† and Weisskopf.‡ In the Lorentz theory the collisions completely interrupt the radiation process so that there is no phase relation between the oscillations before and after each collision. This means that all phase changes are equally likely, in which case equations (48) and (49) reduce to $\alpha = 1/\tau$ and $\beta = 0$. We then have

$$\delta_c = \frac{1}{2\pi\tau} = \tfrac{1}{2}\rho_0^2 \bar{v}n,$$

which is the Lorentz formula (31). In Weisskopf's work the damping constant was taken from the Lorentz theory with a new meaning applied to the collision radius. Now from equation (33) the collision radius for unit change in phase is

$$\rho_0 = \left(\frac{3\pi^2 C}{4\bar{v}}\right)^{1/5}.$$

Weisskopf assumed that collisions for which $\rho \leqslant \rho_0$ (corresponding to phase changes greater than unity) could be regarded as Lorentz collisions in the sense that their spectroscopic effect was the same as for quenching collisions. This gave

$$\delta_c = \tfrac{1}{2}(12\pi^2)^{2/5}(\tfrac{1}{2})^{8/5}C^{2/5}(\bar{v})^{3/5}n,$$

a formula similar to (58) but with a slightly different numerical factor. The Lorentz–Weisskopf theory somewhat arbitrarily neglects collisions which produce phase changes less than unity whilst in Lindholm's more general treatment it is just these more distant collisions which contribute most to the line displacement integral in equation (56).

4. The quantum atom

In the quantum theory line absorption takes place when an atom is excited from one stationary state to another of greater energy by the absorption of a quantum of light, whilst in the reverse process in which an atom in an excited state falls to a state of lower energy a quantum is emitted. The quantum $h\nu$ absorbed or emitted is equal to the energy difference for the two stationary states concerned.

4.1. *Transition coefficients*

Consider the behaviour of an atom in the presence of an isotropic field of radiation. Let E_1 and E_2 be the energy of the atom in two of its stationary states. We define the probability of an upward transition

---

† H. A. Lorentz, *Proc. Amst. Akad.* **8**, 591 (1906).
‡ V. Weisskopf, *Zs. f. Phys.* **75**, 287 (1932).

from state 1 to state 2 as $B_{12} I_\nu$, where B_{12} is an atomic constant† and I_ν the intensity of radiation with frequency ν such that

$$h\nu = E_2 - E_1.$$

The probability that an atom in the upper state will undergo a transition to the lower energy level is defined as

$$A_{21} + B_{21} I_\nu.$$

The coefficient A_{21} gives the probability that the atom will undergo a spontaneous transition from state 2 to state 1 with the emission of a quantum of energy $h\nu$, whilst $B_{21} I_\nu$ is the probability of a downward transition induced by the radiation field. The number of upward transitions per unit time is

$$N_1 B_{12} I_\nu, \qquad\qquad\qquad (62)$$

and the number of downward transitions

$$N_2(A_{21} + B_{21} I_\nu), \qquad\qquad\qquad (63)$$

where N_1 and N_2 are the populations of atoms in state 1 and state 2 respectively. In thermodynamic equilibrium the ratio of the populations in the two states is given by Boltzmann's relation

$$\frac{N_2}{N_1} = \frac{q_2}{q_1} e^{-h\nu/RT}, \qquad\qquad\qquad (64)$$

where q_1 and q_2 are the statistical weights of the two states.

Important relations between the transition coefficients can be deduced from the *Principle of Detailed Balancing* which asserts that every process occurring in a system in thermodynamic equilibrium is capable of direct reversal, and that transformations in the two directions occur with equal frequency. Hence from (62) and (63) we obtain Einstein's relation

$$N_1 B_{12} I_\nu = N_2(A_{21} + B_{21} I_\nu).$$

This gives

$$I_\nu = \frac{A_{21}/B_{21}}{\dfrac{q_1}{q_2} \dfrac{B_{12}}{B_{21}} e^{h\nu/RT} - 1}.$$

But in thermodynamic equilibrium we have $I_\nu = B(\nu, T)$, where

$$B(\nu, T) = \frac{2h\nu^3/c^2}{e^{h\nu/RT} - 1}.$$

† Following Milne the Einstein B-coefficients are here defined in terms of the intensity of the radiation rather than its energy density.

Hence

$$B_{12} = \frac{q_2}{q_1} B_{21},$$ (65)

$$A_{21} = \frac{2h\nu^3}{c^2} B_{21}.$$ (66)

Mean life in an excited state. Consider the decay of the population of atoms in the excited state 2 by transitions to state 1 in the absence of external radiation. By the definition of the coefficient A_{21} in (63) we have

$$\frac{dN_2}{dt} = -N_2 A_{21}.$$ (67)

Let $(N_2)_0$ be the initial population; then the number of atoms in the excited state at any subsequent time is

$$N_2 = (N_2)_0 e^{-A_{21}t}.$$

Let τ be the mean life of an atom in the excited state; then

$$\tau = \frac{1}{(N_2)_0} \int_0^\infty t A_{21} N_2 \, dt = \frac{1}{A_{21}}.$$

To generalize the treatment consider an excited state of energy E_i with $i > 2$. Equation (67) now becomes

$$\left. \begin{aligned} \frac{dN_i}{dt} &= -\gamma_i N_i \\ \gamma_i &= \sum_j A_{ij} \end{aligned} \right\}.$$ (68)

where

The summation for γ_i extends over all levels $j < i$ to which spontaneous transition from the state i are possible. Equation (68) is only strictly true in the absence of external radiation. Two additional terms appear in the presence of radiation due to induced emission and absorption. The quantity γ_i then takes the form

$$\sum_{j=1}^{i-1} [A_{ij} + B_{ij} I(\nu_{ij})] + \sum_{k=i+1}^\infty B_{ik} I(\nu_{ik}).$$

In thermodynamic equilibrium at temperature T equations (65) and (66) apply, and we obtain

$$\gamma_i = \sum_{j=1}^{i-1} \frac{A_{ij}}{1 - e^{-h\nu_{ij}/RT}} + \sum_{k=i+1}^\infty \frac{(N_k/N_i)A_{ki}}{1 - e^{-h\nu_{ik}/RT}}.$$

The additional terms due to the presence of radiation are only of importance when there are strong transitions for which $h\nu/RT < 1$.

4.2. *Oscillator strength*

Let N_1 be the concentration of atoms in the energy state E_1. Neglecting the induced emission term which affects the population when E_1 is not the ground state, the total number of quanta absorbed from the isotropic field per unit volume per second is $N_1 B_{12} I_\nu$. Since each absorption involves a quantum from a definite direction, the amount of energy absorbed in a unit section cylinder with its axis in the s-direction and of length ds will be equal to

$$N_1\, ds \times \frac{d\omega}{4\pi} B_{12}\, I_\nu \times h\nu_{12}. \tag{69}$$

The absorption by the same volume element containing $N\, ds$ classical oscillators having a natural frequency $\nu_0 = \nu_{12}$ will be

$$N\, ds \times \alpha(\nu) I_\nu\, d\nu d\omega$$

integrated over the oscillator absorption profile. Assuming that the intensity of radiation does not vary appreciably within the line the absorption by the volume element may be taken to be

$$N\, ds \times \frac{\pi e^2}{mc} I_\nu\, d\omega. \tag{70}$$

From (69) and (70) the classical oscillators produce the same absorption as the quantum atoms if

$$\frac{N}{N_1} = \frac{mc}{4\pi^2 e^2} B_{12}\, h\nu_{12}. \tag{71}$$

We denote the ratio of the concentrations in (71) by f—the *oscillator strength* of the absorption. Since $N = f N_1$, the absorption due to one quantum atom is equivalent to f classical oscillators. From (65) and (66) we obtain

$$f = \frac{mc}{4\pi^2 e^2} B_{12}\, h\nu_{12} \tag{72}$$

$$= \frac{1}{3} \frac{q_2}{q_1} \frac{A_{21}}{\gamma}, \tag{73}$$

where γ is the classical damping constant, $\dfrac{8\pi^2 e^2 \nu_0^2}{3mc^3}$. It is sometimes convenient to write this oscillator strength (in absorption) as f_{12}, and to define the oscillator strength in emission by the formula

$$f_{21} = \frac{mc}{4\pi^2 e^2} B_{21}\, h\nu_{12}. \tag{74}$$

Substituting for B_{21} from (65), equation (74) becomes

$$f_{21} = \frac{q_1}{q_2} f_{12} = \frac{1}{3} \frac{A_{21}}{\gamma}. \tag{75}$$

The oscillator strengths obey the summation rule due to Thomas† and Kuhn.‡ If we consider all possible transitions from a particular state and form the following sum:

$$\sum_k f_{jk} - \sum_i \frac{q_i}{q_j} f_{ij},$$

the first summation being over all energy states for which $E_k > E_j$ (absorption transitions) and the second summation over all states for which $E_i < E_j$ (stimulated emission transitions), the result is equal to the number of optically active electrons in the atom. If we adopt the convention that oscillator strengths in emission are to be taken as negative, the *f-sum rule* may be written in the form

$$\sum_j f_{ij} = s.$$

In this sum not only bound-bound transitions, but also bound-free transitions must be taken into account, that is transitions to the continuum. We can calculate f_c, the oscillator strength for transition to the continuum, by subtracting the sum of the line oscillator strengths from the number of optical electrons; for a hydrogen-like atom f_c is related to the continuous absorption coefficient by the formula§

$$\kappa_\nu = f_c \frac{2\pi e^2 \nu_0^2}{mc} \frac{1}{\nu^3}.$$

Table XX contains the oscillator strengths for the hydrogen lines in the Lyman, Balmer, and Paschen series.

4.3. *Broadened states*

It follows from the uncertainty principle of Heisenberg that if τ is the mean lifetime of an atom in a given energy state there is an uncertainty ΔE in the determination of the energy of the atom such that

$$\tau \Delta E \sim h/2\pi,$$

where h is Planck's constant. The breadth ΔE of the energy state E varies inversely as the lifetime in that state. Now τ is extremely large for the ground state of an atom and very small (of order 10^{-8} sec.) for

† L. H. Thomas, *Naturwiss.* **13**, 627 (1925).
‡ H. Kuhn, *Zs. f. Phys.* **33**, 408 (1925).
§ R. v. d. R. Woolley, *M.N.* **95**, 101 (1934).

Table XX

Oscillator Strengths for Hydrogen

Initial level i / Final level j	$i = 1$ Lyman	$i = 2$ Balmer	$i = 3$ Paschen
$j = 1$	..	−0·104	−0·0087
2	0·416	..	−0·284
3	0·0791	0·637	..
4	0·0290	0·119	0·841
5	0·0139	0·0443	0·150
6	0·0078	0·0212	0·0554
7	0·0048	0·0122	0·0269
8	0·0032	0·0080	0·0161
9 to ∞	0·0101	0·0237	0·0421
Contribution from lines	0·564	0·762	0·839
Contribution from transitions to continuum f_c	0·436	0·238	0·161
$\sum_j f_{ij}$	1·000	1·000	1·000

excited states. Thus the energy level corresponding to the ground state will be infinitely sharp but excited states will have a natural breadth. The Principal lines in an atomic spectrum are formed by transitions to and from the extremely sharp ground state, but in the case of Subordinate lines the transitions involve two broadened states.

It may be shown† that the proportion of atoms in a broadened state of mean energy E_j having energies within E to $E + dE$ is given by the probability law

$$W_j(E)\,dE = \frac{(\gamma_j/h)\,dE}{(2\pi/h)^2(E-E_j)^2 + (\tfrac{1}{2}\gamma_j)^2},\qquad(76)$$

where γ_j is the reciprocal of the lifetime of the state. The function (76) has a very sharp maximum where $E = E_j$ so that most atoms have energies near the mean energy, and only the fraction $dN_j/N_j = W_j(E)\,dE$ of the N_j atoms in the state j have energies within E to $E + dE$. Equation (76) takes a simpler form if we write $x = (E - E_j)/h$, and $\delta_j = \gamma_j/4\pi$. We then have

$$W_j(x) = \frac{1}{\pi}\frac{\delta_j}{x^2 + \delta_j^2}.\qquad(77)$$

Let E_k be the mean energy of another broadened state of the atom for which $E_k > E_j$. Consider the absorption and emission of radiation by an assembly of atoms containing two and only two broadened energy states between which transitions are possible. Let N_j be the concentration of atoms in the j-state, then in thermodynamic equilibrium at

† V. Weisskopf and E. Wigner, Zs. f. Phys. **63**, 54 (1930). See also R. v. d. R. Woolley M.N. **91**, 977 (1931).

temperature T the number of upward transitions per second per unit volume will be

$$N_j\, B_{jk}\, B(\nu, T),\tag{78}$$

the number of downward transitions being

$$N_k\{A_{kj} + B_{kj}\, B(\nu, T)\},\tag{79}$$

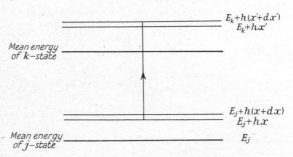

Fig. 20. Transition between two broadened states.

where B_{jk}, A_{kj}, and B_{kj} are the Einstein transition coefficients. The transitions (78) and (79) refer to *all transitions* from state j to state k and the reverse, without distinction as to the sub-states concerned: and we want to inquire about such a subdivision. *We suppose that the probability of a transition ending in a particular sub-state is independent of the particular sub-state from which the transition took place.* Then if $b_{jk}(x, x')B(\nu, T)\,dx\,dx'$ is the number of upward transitions from the sub-state $E_j + hx$ to $E_j + h(x+dx)$ of the j-state to the sub-state $E_k + hx'$ to $E_k + h(x'+dx')$ of k such that $(E_k + hx') - (E_j + hx) = h\nu$, we have

$$b_{jk}(x, x')B(\nu, T)\,dx\,dx' = B(\nu, T)\frac{\delta_j}{x^2 + \delta_j^2} \times \phi(x')\,dx\,dx'.$$

Similarly both $b_{kj}(x, x')B(\nu, T)$ and $a_{kj}(x, x')$ are proportional to $\delta_k/(x'^2 + \delta_k^2)$ multiplied by a function of x, and detailed balancing gives

$$b_{jk}(x, x')B(\nu, T) = a_{kj}(x, x') + b_{kj}(x, x')B(\nu, T).$$

All the quantities are therefore proportional to

$$\frac{\delta_j}{x^2 + \delta_j^2}\,\frac{\delta_k}{x'^2 + \delta_k^2}.\tag{80}$$

The constant of proportionality is determined by

$$\iint b_{jk}(x, x')\,dx\,dx' = B_{jk}.$$

We therefore have

$$b_{jk}(x, x') = B_{jk}\frac{1}{\pi^2}\frac{\delta_j\,\delta_k}{(x^2 + \delta_j^2)(x'^2 + \delta_k^2)}.\tag{81}$$

To find the probability for the absorption of a quantum with frequency between ν and $\nu+d\nu$ per unit intensity of isotropic radiation we set $dx' = d\nu$, and integrate $b_{jk}(x, x')$ over the entire range of the j substates with $x-x'$ constant in keeping with the frequency relation

$$E_k + hx' - (E_j + hx) = h\nu. \tag{82}$$

Let $E_k - E_j = h\nu_0$, then equation (82) gives $x-x' = \nu_0 - \nu = x_0$, say. We have to evaluate

$$\int_{-\infty}^{\infty} b_{jk}(x, x-x_0)\, dx = B_{jk}\frac{1}{\pi^2}\delta_j\,\delta_k \int_{-\infty}^{\infty} \frac{dx}{(x^2+\delta_j^2)[(x-x_0)^2+\delta_k^2]}. \tag{83}$$

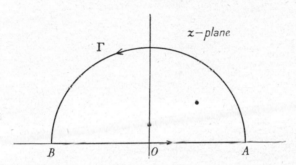

FIG. 21. Path of integration enclosing the two poles $z = i\delta_j$, and $z = x_0 + i\delta_k$.

The integral on the right-hand side is most conveniently evaluated with the help of the calculus of residues. The function

$$f(z) = \frac{1}{(z+i\delta_j)(z-i\delta_j)(z-x_0+i\delta_k)(z-x_0-i\delta_k)} \tag{84}$$

has four poles in the complex plane at $z = \pm i\delta_j$ and $x_0 \pm i\delta_k$. Consider the integral of $f(z)$ around the contour C shown in Fig. 21. By Cauchy's theorem of residues

$$\int_C f(z)\, dz = 2\pi i \times \text{sum of residues at poles within } C. \tag{85}$$

But $\int_\Gamma f(z)\, dz \to 0$ as $R \to \infty$ so that

$$\int_{-\infty}^{\infty} f(x)\, dx = \lim_{R\to\infty} \int_C f(z)\, dz. \tag{86}$$

Let $\mathscr{R}_1$ and $\mathscr{R}_2$ be the residues at the poles $z = i\delta_j$ and $z = x_0 + i\delta_k$ respectively. It readily follows from (84) that

$$\mathscr{R}_1 = \frac{1}{2i\delta_j[i\delta_j - (x_0 - i\delta_k)][i\delta_k - (x_0 + i\delta_k)]},$$

$$\mathscr{R}_2 = \frac{1}{2i\delta_k[x_0 + i(\delta_j + \delta_k)][x_0 - i(\delta_j - \delta_k)]}.$$

After some reduction we obtain

$$\mathscr{R}_1 + \mathscr{R}_2 = \frac{-i}{2\delta_j\,\delta_k} \frac{\delta_j + \delta_k}{x_0^2 + (\delta_j + \delta_k)^2}.$$

Equations (85) and (86) now give

$$\int_{-\infty}^{\infty} f(x)\,dx = \frac{\pi}{\delta_j\,\delta_k} \frac{\delta_j + \delta_k}{x_0^2 + (\delta_j + \delta_k)^2}, \tag{87}$$

and equation (83) for the probability of absorption of a quantum of frequency ν becomes

$$\int_{-\infty}^{\infty} b_{jk}(x, x - x_0)\,dx = B_{jk}\frac{1}{\pi} \frac{\delta_j + \delta_k}{(\nu - \nu_0)^2 + (\delta_j + \delta_k)^2}. \tag{88}$$

Now the line absorption coefficient per atom $\alpha(\nu)$ measures the absorption of radiation of frequency ν and unit intensity incident in a given direction. The total absorption is obtained by summing over all directions. Thus in an isotropic field of unit intensity the number of quanta of frequency ν absorbed per atom, that is the probability of absorption of a quantum of frequency ν, will be $4\pi\alpha(\nu)/h\nu$. Hence

$$\alpha(\nu) = \frac{1}{4\pi} B_{jk} \frac{h\nu}{\pi} \frac{\delta}{(\nu - \nu_0)^2 + \delta^2}, \tag{89}$$

where
$$\delta = \delta_j + \delta_k.$$

According to equation (72), which defines the oscillator strength, we have

$$f = \frac{mc}{4\pi^2 e^2} B_{jk} h\nu_0.$$

Hence, if we write $h\nu_0$ in place of $h\nu$ in equation (89), we obtain

$$\alpha(\nu) = \frac{\pi e^2}{mc} f \frac{\delta}{\pi} \frac{1}{(\nu - \nu_0)^2 + \delta^2}. \tag{90}$$

Integrating over the absorption profile gives

$$\alpha = \int \alpha(\nu)\,d\nu = \frac{\pi e^2}{mc} f,$$

so that equation (90) may be written

$$\alpha(\nu) = \frac{\alpha}{\pi}\frac{\delta}{(\nu-\nu_0)^2+\delta^2}.$$

Comparing the quantum formula (90) with equation (13) for the classical oscillator the results, although formally the same, are seen to differ in some important details. In the first place the classical damping constant is replaced in the quantum treatment by the sum of the decay constants for the two energy states involved in the absorption, and whereas in the classical theory δ depends only on the central frequency of the line, in the quantum theory δ is determined by the energy states themselves and not by their mean energy difference. In addition, the scale of the absorption by the quantum atom is f times the total absorption on the classical theory.

4.4. *Stark effect*

In a uniform electric field a spectral line may be split up into a number of components. The number of components and their separation depends on the strength of the field and on the particular line under consideration: unless the field is very strong, the displacement of any particular component is proportional to the field strength. In a stellar atmosphere charged particles in thermal motion set up local electric fields which, although constantly changing, have a permanent statistical effect.

Let N be the number of charged particles per c.c., and r_0 their average separation, then $\frac{4}{3}\pi r_0^3 = 1/N$. Now the probability that no charged particle shall be nearer to a radiating atom than the distance r is $\exp\{-(r/r_0)^3\}$. Hence the probability that the nearest ion lies within the distance r to $r+dr$ is

$$W(r)\,dr = \exp\{-(r/r_0)^3\}\,d(r/r_0)^3.$$

At the distance r from a charge e the electric field F is e/r^2, and from the theory of the linear Stark effect the displacement of the components from the original frequency of the line is

$$\Delta\nu = (3hF/8\pi^2 me)n_k,$$

where n_k is a quantum number. Hence $\Delta\nu = C_k/r^2$, where

$$C_k = (3h/8\pi^2 m)n_k,$$

and the probability distribution may be written

$$W(\nu)\,d\nu = \exp\left\{-\left(\frac{\Delta\nu_0}{\Delta\nu}\right)^{\frac{3}{2}}\right\}d\left(\frac{\Delta\nu_0}{\Delta\nu}\right)^{\frac{3}{2}} = \exp\left\{-\left(\frac{\Delta\nu_0}{\Delta\nu}\right)^{\frac{3}{2}}\right\}\frac{3}{2}\left(\frac{\Delta\nu_0}{\Delta\nu}\right)^{\frac{5}{2}}\frac{d\nu}{\Delta\nu_0},$$

where $\Delta\nu_0$ is the shift of the k-component in the Stark pattern for an electric field $F_0 = e/r_0^2 = e(\tfrac{4}{3}\pi N)^{4/3}$. Since each component is spread out according to the distribution $W(\nu)\, d\nu$, the broadened profile of the line itself is the sum of the broadened components weighted by their theoretical intensity. A discussion of the broadening of hydrogen lines in stellar spectra based on statistical broadening of the linear Stark effect patterns has been given by Verwey,[†] who used a probability function derived by Holtsmark,[‡] and which takes into account the effect of all ions in addition to those nearest the radiating atom.

It must be emphasized that the Holtsmark distribution only describes accurately the behaviour of a radiating atom when surrounded by a static configuration of perturbing charges, and that in applications of the statistical theory it has been tacitly assumed that the effect of relative motion between the atom and its perturbers can be neglected. The effect of these relative motions has been discussed by Krogdahl.[§]

5. Excitation by collisions

In section 3 of this chapter we dealt with the effect of *elastic* collisions which momentarily change the frequency of the radiation emitted by an atom without changing the amplitude. We now consider the manner in which collision processes stimulate or quench the radiation from an atom. This involves an actual exchange of energy between the colliding particles, potential energy being converted into kinetic energy of the particles, and in the converse process kinetic energy being converted into potential energy.

The exchange of energy by colliding particles was first recognized in the laboratory phenomenon of the ionization of neutral molecules by fast moving particles. It is now recognized that *inelastic collisions* occur in which a particle with sufficient kinetic energy can either ionize an atom or excite it to a bound state, and also that the converse process of *super-elastic collision* occurs. The super-elastic collisions are of two kinds. In one of these, a three-body collision occurs between a positive ion, an electron, and a third particle, and as a result the positive ion captures the electron and gives off the energy of ionization as extra kinetic energy: and in the other kind of super-elastic collision, an excited atom encounters a second body and in the collision loses some (or all) of its excitation energy which reappears as extra kinetic energy of the

† S. Verwey, *Proc. Amst. Acad.* **38**, No. 5 (1935).

‡ J. Holtsmark, *Ann. d. Phys.* **9**, 338 (1931). See also S. Chandrasekhar, *Proc. Camb. Phil. Soc.* **45**, 219 (1949).

§ M. K. Krogdahl, *Ap. J.* **110**, 355 (1949).

colliding particles. We may represent the collisions symbolically as follows:

$$(a) \quad A + X + \tfrac{1}{2}mv^2 \rightarrow A^+ + e + X,$$

$$(b) \quad A^+ + e + X \rightarrow A + X + \tfrac{1}{2}mv^2,$$

$$(c) \quad A + X + \tfrac{1}{2}mv^2 \rightarrow A' + X,$$

$$(d) \quad A' + X \rightarrow A + X + \tfrac{1}{2}mv^2.$$

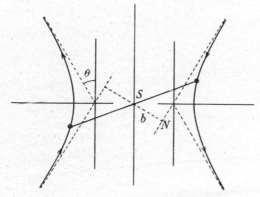

FIG. 22. The hyperbolic orbits of two electrons relative to their centre of mass.

The processes (a) and (c) represent inelastic collisions, (b) and (d) represent the converse process of super-elastic collision. By the Principle of Detailed Balancing, the number of collisions of type (a) which occur in thermodynamic equilibrium is equal to the number of type (b) which occur; similarly collisions of type (c) balance those of type (d) in the thermodynamic equilibrium.

A calculation of the number of ionizations which would occur in given circumstances by collisions of type (a) was made in 1912 by Sir J. J. Thomson.† Consider an electron moving with a velocity v and approaching a second electron at rest which it would pass at a distance d but for the mutual repulsion of the electrons. If they are subject to no other forces the electrons will both describe symmetrical hyperbolic orbits relative to their centre of mass, the asymptotic velocity in both cases being $\tfrac{1}{2}v$. The relative orbits are shown in Fig. 22.

Let 2θ be the angle between the asymptotes of one of these orbits, a being the semi-axis major. The semi-latus rectum p is equal to $a\cot^2\theta$, and the perpendicular distance from the focus S (also the centre of mass of the two particles) to an asymptote is given by $b = a\cot\theta$. If r is the

† J. J. Thomson, *Phil. Mag.* **23**, 419 (1912).

distance between the electrons, the repulsive force will be e^2/r^2, or $e^2/4\rho^2$ where $\rho\ (=\frac{1}{2}r)$ is the distance of either electron from the centre of gravity S. Now the doubled rate of description of area is $h = \frac{1}{2}vb$ so that the planetary relation $h^2 = \mu p$ gives

$$\tfrac{1}{4}v^2 b^2 = \frac{e^2}{4m}\, a \cot^2\theta, \tag{91}$$

an equation for θ in terms of v and b. Writing T for $\frac{1}{2}mv^2$ and setting $b = \frac{1}{2}d$, equation (91) can be written as

$$\sin^2\theta = \frac{1}{1 + T^2 d^2/e^4}. \tag{92}$$

Now the velocity of each electron is changed by $v\sin\theta$. Hence the electron originally at rest has a final velocity $v\sin\theta$, and the energy Q imparted to it is given by

$$Q = T\sin^2\theta. \tag{93}$$

J. J. Thomson argues that if the electron at rest is attached to an atom and requires energy W to escape from it, the atom will be ionized if Q is greater than W. Thus the effective collision diameter for ionization is that value of d which makes Q equal to W. From equations (92) and (93) we then obtain

$$d^2 = \frac{e^4}{T}\left(\frac{1}{W} - \frac{1}{T}\right). \tag{94}$$

It is convenient to express the collision cross-sections in terms of the area πa_0^2, where a_0 is the radius of the first Bohr orbit for the hydrogen atom,

$$a_0 = \frac{e^2}{2Rhc} = 0{\cdot}529 \times 10^{-8} \text{ cm.,}$$

and R is Rydberg's constant. Since the ionization potential $\chi = Rhc$, Thomson's expression for the collision cross-section for the ionization of hydrogen by electrons with energy ϵ is

$$\sigma(\epsilon) = \tfrac{1}{4}\pi d^2 = \pi a_0^2\left(\frac{\chi}{\epsilon} - \frac{\chi^2}{\epsilon^2}\right). \tag{95}$$

Equation (95) is of considerable interest because it represents laboratory measurements (such as they are) reasonably well, and because quantum mechanical calculations of collision cross-sections cannot be made unless ϵ is large compared with χ, which is by no means the case in astrophysical applications.

Consider now the ionization in an assembly of atoms and electrons. Let there be N atoms and N_e electrons per unit volume and let the cross-section for collision ionization by electrons with kinetic energy ϵ be $\sigma(\epsilon)$. If the distribution of kinetic energy amongst the electrons be given by Maxwell's law

$$\mu(\epsilon) = \frac{4\pi}{(2\pi RT)^{\frac{3}{2}}}(2\epsilon)^{\frac{1}{2}}e^{-\epsilon/RT},$$

that is $N_e\,\mu(\epsilon)\,d\epsilon$ gives the number of electrons per unit volume with kinetic energies within ϵ to $\epsilon+d\epsilon$, the total number of ionizations taking place per unit volume per second will be

$$NN_e \int\limits_{\chi}^{\infty} v\mu(\epsilon)\sigma(\epsilon)\,d\epsilon, \tag{96}$$

which we denote by $NN_e\,S(T)$. According to R. H. Fowler† $\sigma(\epsilon)$ is of the same form as that given by Thomson's equation (94). We write

$$\sigma(\epsilon) = b\frac{\pi e^4}{\epsilon}\left(\frac{1}{\chi}-\frac{1}{\epsilon}\right),$$

where b is a constant factor appropriate to the atom considered. The integral in (96) now gives

$$S(T) = \frac{b}{RT}\frac{4\pi e^4}{(2\pi m RT)^{\frac{1}{2}}}\frac{e^{-x}}{x}\{1-xe^x E_1(x)\},$$

where $x = \chi/RT$ and $E_1(x)$ is the first exponential integral.

In the case of excitation of lines by collisions, the oscillator strength can be readily brought into the equations by means of a quantum mechanical formula‡ which applies when the kinetic energy of the incident electron is large compared with the excitation energy for the line. The excitation cross-section $S(\epsilon)$ is defined as follows: let there be N atoms (or ions) of a certain kind per unit volume capable of making a transition in a given line of oscillator strength f, and let there be $N_e\mu(\epsilon)$ electrons per unit volume with kinetic energy between ϵ and $\epsilon+d\epsilon$. Then the number of inelastic collisions in time dt causing upward transitions in the line is $NN_e\mu(\epsilon)S(\epsilon)\,d\epsilon dt$.

According to Mott and Massey, when ϵ is very much greater than $h\nu$ for the line, we have

$$S(\epsilon) = f\frac{3\pi e^4}{h\nu}\frac{1}{\epsilon}\ln\frac{4\epsilon}{h\nu}, \tag{97}$$

† R. H. Fowler, *Phil. Mag.* **47**, 257 (1924).
‡ N. F. Mott and H. S. W. Massey, *The Theory of Atomic Collisions* (Oxford), chap. xi, equation (40) leads to equation (97) above by means of the relation between the matrix element and the oscillator strength of the line.

whereas, according to R. H. Fowler,

$$S(\epsilon) \propto \frac{1}{\epsilon}\left(\frac{1}{h\nu} - \frac{1}{\epsilon}\right). \tag{98}$$

A combination of equation (97), omitting the slowly varying factor $\ln(4\epsilon/h\nu)$, and equation (98) gives

$$S(\epsilon) = 3f \frac{\pi e^4}{\epsilon}\left(\frac{1}{h\nu} - \frac{1}{\epsilon}\right). \tag{99}$$

This probably represents the excitation of bound states as well as is possible. Integrating over all electron energies greater than ϵ ($= h\nu$), the number of excitations per c.c. per sec. is $N N_e S(T)$, where

$$S(T) = \frac{f}{RT}\frac{12\pi e^4}{(2\pi m RT)^{\frac{1}{2}}}\frac{e^{-x}}{x}\{1 - xe^x E_1(x)\}. \tag{100}$$

When x is large $xe^x E_1(x) \sim 1 - 1/x$, and we have

$$S(T) = \frac{f}{RT}\frac{12\pi e^4}{(2\pi m RT)^{\frac{1}{2}}}\left(\frac{RT}{h\nu}\right)^2 e^{-h\nu/RT}. \tag{101}$$

This formula only applies to *permitted transitions*. In the case of *forbidden transitions* the oscillator strength f takes very small values but the collision cross-section remains of order πa_0^2.

We now apply equation (100) to the calculation of the quantity ϵ which Eddington introduced in elaborating the theory of the formation of absorption lines,[†] and which represents the fraction of the energy absorbed by photon capture which is removed from the line frequency by super-elastic collisions. This fraction is converted into kinetic energy and the remaining fraction $1 - \epsilon$ is re-emitted by spontaneous transitions to the lower state of the line. Now the number of spontaneous transitions per atom in the upper state is an atomic constant, and the number of super-elastic collisions depends only on the number of atoms in the upper state, the number of electrons per c.c., and on the temperature (strictly speaking, the temperature parameter of the Maxwellian distribution of electron velocities). It is therefore legitimate to calculate ϵ from considerations involving thermodynamic equilibrium. Now in thermodynamic equilibrium the number of super-elastic collisions balances the number of inelastic collisions. Hence $\epsilon/(1 - \epsilon)$ is the ratio of the number of inelastic collisions to the number of radiative excitations.

Let N_1 be the population of atoms in the lower level of the line; then

† Chapter VII, Section 2.

there are $N_1 N_e S(T)$ inelastic collisions and $N_1 B_{1k} B(\nu, T)$ radiative excitations to the state k per second. We therefore have

$$\frac{\epsilon}{1-\epsilon} = \frac{N_e S(T)}{B_{1k} B(\nu, T)}.$$

From equation (72) the oscillator strength f and the transition coefficient B_{1k} are related as follows:

$$f = \frac{mc}{4\pi^2 e^2} \cdot B_{1k} h\nu.$$

Hence $\qquad \dfrac{\epsilon}{1-\epsilon} = N_e \dfrac{3me^2}{2\pi h^2 c} \dfrac{\lambda^4 RT}{(2\pi m RT)^{\frac{1}{2}}} x(1-e^{-x})\{1-xe^x E_1(x)\}. \qquad (102.1)$

Introducing the electron pressure by the relation $p_e = N_e RT$, and the quantity $\theta\ (= 5{,}040/T)$ we get

$$\frac{\epsilon}{1-\epsilon} = 1 \cdot 2 \times 10^{15} p_e \theta^{\frac{3}{2}} \lambda^4 g(x), \qquad (102.2)$$

where $\qquad\qquad g(x) = x(1-e^{-x})\{1-xe^x E_1(x)\}.$

The function $g(x)$ is a monotonic increasing function of $x\ (= h\nu/RT)$, and $g(x) \sim 1$ for x large. Table XXI gives numerical values of this function.

TABLE XXI

$$g(x) = x(1- e^{-x})\{1-xe^x E_1(x)\}$$

x	$xe^x E_1(x)$	$g(x)$	x	$xe^x E_1(x)$	$g(x)$
0·5	0·4615	0·106	6·0	0·8716	0·768
1·0	0·5964	0·255	7·0	0·8867	0·792
1·5	0·6723	0·382	8·0	0·8984	0·813
2·0	0·7226	0·480	9·0	0·9079	0·828
2·5	0·7586	0·554	10·0	0·9156	0·844
3·0	0·7858	0·611	11·0	0·9220	0·858
3·5	0·8079	0·652	12·0	0·9280	0·864
4·0	0·8253	0·686	13·0	0·9328	0·873
4·5	0·8397	0·713	14·0	0·9372	0·879
5·0	0·8518	0·736	15·0	0·9405	0·893

With $p_e' = 10$ dynes cm.$^{-2}$ and $\theta = 1 \cdot 0$, equation (102.2) gives the following values of ϵ:

TABLE XXII

$\lambda(A)$	3,000	4,000	5,000	6,000	7,000	8,000	9,000
ϵ	0·008	0·024	0·054	0·101	0·166	0·245	0·329

According to this calculation Eddington's ϵ increases with the wavelength.

6. Doppler effect

Consider the absorption of radiation by an assembly of atoms in thermal motion. Let $I_\nu(\theta)$ be the intensity of ν-radiation directed towards a stationary observer. An atom moving with velocity V in a direction making an angle φ with the incident direction receives this radiation as a frequency

$$\nu' = \nu\left(1 - \frac{V}{c}\cos\varphi\right).$$

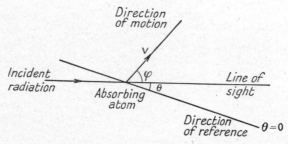

Fig. 23. The absorption of radiation by an atom in motion.

The absorption of ν-radiation by the atom will then be $\alpha'(\nu)I_\nu(\theta)$, where

$$\alpha'(\nu) = \frac{\pi e^2}{mc}f\frac{\delta}{\pi}\frac{1}{(\nu'-\nu_0)^2+\delta^2}.$$

If we write

$$\nu'-\nu_0 = \nu-\nu_0\left(1+\frac{V}{c}\cos\varphi\right)-(\nu-\nu_0)\frac{V}{c}\cos\varphi,$$

and neglect the last term since $V \ll c$ and $\nu \doteq \nu_0$, we obtain

$$\alpha'(\nu) = \frac{\pi e^2}{mc}f\frac{\delta}{\pi}\frac{1}{(\nu-\nu_0')^2+\delta^2},$$

where

$$\nu_0' = \nu_0\left(1+\frac{V}{c}\cos\varphi\right).$$

The behaviour of the atom in the field of ν-radiation is thus the same as a stationary atom with central absorption frequency ν_0'. The absorption profile of the moving atom is thus bodily displaced in frequency, without change in shape, by the amount

$$\Delta\nu = \nu_0\frac{V}{c}\cos\varphi.$$

To obtain the absorption coefficient due to an assembly of atoms we shall have to sum the displaced profiles over all velocities V and directions of motion φ. Alternatively we need only make the summation over all line of sight components $u = V \cos \varphi$. In the following treatment we employ the former procedure.

In thermodynamic equilibrium at temperature T the number of atoms with velocities† between V and $V + dV$ is given by

$$\frac{4N}{\sqrt{\pi}} \left(\frac{M}{2RT} \right)^{\frac{3}{2}} e^{-(M/2RT)V^2} \, V^2 \, dV. \tag{103}$$

The most probable velocity of the atoms is the velocity V_0 for which the velocity distribution (103) has a maximum value, namely

$$V_0 = \left(\frac{2RT}{M} \right)^{\frac{1}{2}}. \tag{104}$$

If the atoms are moving equally in all directions only the fraction $\frac{1}{2} \sin \varphi \, d\varphi$ have directions of motion within φ to $\varphi + d\varphi$. To obtain the absorption coefficient for the assembly of N atoms we have to evaluate

$$\frac{\pi e^2}{mc} Nf \frac{\delta}{\pi} \frac{4}{\sqrt{\pi}} \frac{1}{V_0^3} \int_0^\infty \int_0^\pi \frac{e^{-(V/V_0)^2} \frac{1}{2} V^2 \sin \varphi \, dV d\varphi}{[\nu - \nu_0 \{ 1 + (V/c) \cos \varphi \}]^2 + \delta^2}.$$

The assembly behaves as if each atom had a scattering coefficient

$$\alpha(\nu)_D = \frac{\pi e^2}{mc} f \frac{1}{\pi} \frac{2a}{b\sqrt{\pi}} \int_0^\infty \int_0^\pi \frac{e^{-v^2} y^2 \sin \varphi \, dy d\varphi}{a^2 + (v - y \cos \varphi)^2}, \tag{105}$$

where

$$a = \frac{\delta}{b}, \qquad b = \frac{\nu_0 V_0}{c},$$

$$y = \frac{V}{V_0}, \qquad v = \frac{\nu - \nu_0}{b}.$$

The φ integration may be readily performed. We have

$$a \int_0^\pi \frac{y \sin \varphi \, d\varphi}{a^2 + (v - y \cos \varphi)^2} = \tan^{-1} \frac{v + y}{a} - \tan^{-1} \frac{v - y}{a} = \tan^{-1} \frac{2ay}{a^2 + v^2 - y^2}. \tag{106}$$

Equation (105) may now be written

$$\alpha(\nu)_D = \frac{\pi e^2}{mc} f \frac{1}{\pi} \frac{2}{b\sqrt{\pi}} \int_0^\infty e^{-v^2} y \left(\tan^{-1} \frac{v + y}{a} - \tan^{-1} \frac{v - y}{a} \right) dy. \tag{107}$$

We first evaluate the absorption coefficient at the centre of the line for vanishing damping. With $v = 0$ we have

$$\tan^{-1} \frac{v + y}{a} - \tan^{-1} \frac{v - y}{a} = 2 \tan^{-1} \frac{y}{a}.$$

† The actual velocity V is given by $V^2 = u^2 + v^2 + w^2$.

When the damping is small y/a is large in the range of values of y for which the contribution to the integral is appreciable. Now when x is large

$$\tan^{-1} x = \frac{\pi}{2} - \frac{1}{x}.$$

Hence

$$\int_0^\infty e^{-y^2} 2y \tan^{-1}\frac{y}{a}\, dy = \tfrac{1}{2}\pi - a\sqrt{\pi}.$$

In the limit of vanishing damping ($a = 0$) the absorption coefficient at the centre of the line is

$$\alpha(\nu_0)_D = \frac{\pi e^2}{mc} f \frac{1}{b\sqrt{\pi}}. \tag{108}$$

From equations (107) and (108) we obtain the result

$$\frac{\alpha(\nu)_D}{\alpha(\nu_0)_D} = \frac{2}{\pi}\int_0^\infty e^{-y^2} y\left(\tan^{-1}\frac{v+y}{a} - \tan^{-1}\frac{v-y}{a}\right) dy. \tag{109}$$

Integrating by parts we obtain

$$\frac{\alpha(\nu)_D}{\alpha(\nu_0)_D} = \frac{a}{\pi}\left\{\int_0^\infty \frac{e^{-y^2}\, dy}{a^2+(v+y)^2} + \int_0^\infty \frac{e^{-y^2}\, dy}{a^2+(v-y)^2}\right\} = \frac{a}{\pi}\int_{-\infty}^\infty \frac{e^{-y^2}\, dy}{a^2+(v-y)^2}, \tag{110}$$

which is a tabulated function.†

In the central part of the line where v is small the function

$$\frac{1}{a^2+(v-y)^2}$$

passes through a maximum within a small range of values of the variable within which e^{-y^2} undergoes very little change. Now when a is small the greatest contribution to the integral in equation (110) for small v comes from values of the variable near $y = v$. Setting $y = v+x$ we obtain

$$\int_{-\infty}^\infty \frac{e^{-y^2}\, dy}{a^2+(v-y)^2} \doteq e^{-v^2}\int_{-\infty}^\infty \frac{dx}{a^2+x^2} = \frac{\pi}{a}e^{-v^2}.$$

With this approximation to the integral we obtain from (110)

$$\alpha(\nu)_D = \alpha(\nu_0)_D\, e^{-\{(\nu-\nu_0)/b\}^2}. \tag{111}$$

In the wings of the line where $v \gg 1$ the main contribution to the

† F. Hjerting, *Ap. J.* **88**, 508 (1938); D. L. Harris, ibid. **108**, 112 (1948).

integral comes from values of $y \ll v$. Neglecting a^2, expanding $(y-v)^2$ as a series in y/v, and retaining only the first two terms, we find

$$\int_{-\infty}^{\infty} \frac{e^{-v^2}\, dy}{(v-y)^2} \doteq \frac{1}{v^2} \int_{-\infty}^{\infty} e^{-v^2}\left(1 + 2\frac{y}{v}\right) dy = \frac{1}{v^2}\sqrt{\pi}.$$

Hence
$$\frac{\alpha(\nu)_D}{\alpha(\nu_0)_D} = \frac{ab^2}{\sqrt{\pi}} \frac{1}{(\nu-\nu_0)^2} = \frac{b}{\sqrt{\pi}} \frac{\delta}{(\nu-\nu_0)^2}. \tag{112}$$

Equations (108) and (112) give

$$\alpha(\nu)_D = \frac{\pi e^2}{mc} f \frac{\delta}{\pi} \frac{1}{(\nu-\nu_0)^2}, \tag{113}$$

which is the original form for the absorption coefficients for $\nu-\nu_0 \gg \delta$. From equations (111) and (112) we conclude that the Doppler effect modifies the absorption coefficient to give an error curve in the core of the line without any change in the wings. Combining equations (108), (111), and (112) into a single formula we have

$$\alpha(\nu)_D = \frac{\pi e^2}{mc} f \frac{1}{b\sqrt{\pi}} \left(e^{-v^2} + \frac{1}{b\sqrt{\pi}} \frac{\delta}{v^2}\right), \tag{114}$$

in which it is to be understood that the first term applies for small values of v, only the second term being used for large values of v appropriate to the wings of the line. Now $v = (\nu-\nu_0)/b$, so that b is the value of $\nu-\nu_0$ for which the Doppler core absorption falls to e^{-1} of its maximum value. It is convenient to refer to b as the *Doppler half width*. Thus v measures the deviation from the line centre in units of the Doppler half width; a being the ratio of the half width δ and the Doppler half width, where δ includes both natural damping and collision damping.

THE COHERENT FORMATION OF ABSORPTION LINES

1. Introduction

MOST stellar spectra consist of a continuum interrupted by a number of absorption lines. These absorption lines appear as minima in the spectral distribution of the light from the star. In most cases the line is narrow, its total recognizable effect being contained within a few angstrom units: in very many cases the line is contained within less than one angstrom, but in exceptional cases the influence of a line can be traced over tens of angstrom units.

The absorption lines in the solar spectrum were not noticed by Newton on account of the impurity of his spectrum. They were first seen by Wollaston (1802) but are named after Fraunhofer, who published an atlas of the solar spectrum in the year 1814. At first it was thought that the lines were natural divisions between the colours in the spectrum, but their significance was later realized by Kirchhoff and Bunsen (1859), who noticed that two conspicuous dark lines in the yellow part of the solar spectrum coincided with two bright lines in the spectrum of sodium. When the solar spectrum was examined after passing the light through a sodium flame it was noted: '*If the sunlight were sufficiently reduced in intensity there appeared in place of the two dark D lines two bright lines: but if the intensity surpassed a certain limit the two dark D lines showed themselves in much greater distinctness than without the salt flame.*'

In a classical paper under the title 'Radiation through a Foggy Atmosphere' Schuster† considered the problem of the flow of radiation through a selectively absorbing layer lying above a surface radiating with a given intensity—a simplified stellar model with a sharp boundary between the radiating *photosphere* and the selectively absorbing region of line formation. This *reversing layer* was considered to be transparent to all radiation except for frequencies within the absorption line. The case of an atmosphere with a reversing layer on the top of the photosphere is usually referred to as the *Schuster–Schwarzschild Model*.

It is an oversimplification to treat the region of line absorption as quite distinct from that in which the continuous absorption occurs, a more suitable method being to treat the process of line formation as

† A. Schuster, *Ap. J.* **21**, 1 (1905).

taking place in the presence of the stellar material which gives rise to continuous absorption. The model in which there is both line absorption and continuous absorption at all levels in the atmosphere is referred to as the *Milne–Eddington Model*. On the basis of this model we now investigate how the line processes considered in Chapter VI lead to the formation of absorption lines in a stellar spectrum. The problem is to find the contour, that is the shape of the depression in the intensity of the continuous spectrum caused by the line absorption. In order to do this we have to establish and obtain solutions of the fundamental equation of line formation which gives the variation of intensity with depth in the atmosphere in terms of the absorption and emission coefficients for the stellar material. In this chapter we confine our attention to an elementary theory in which the simplifying assumption is made that the radiation absorbed by the atom is re-emitted in the same frequency as the absorption. This is the process of *coherent scattering*.

2. The equation of line formation by coherent scattering

Consider a stellar atmosphere consisting of plane parallel layers bounded at the plane $x = 0$ and extending to infinity in the negative direction of the x-axis which is normal to the layers. The fundamental equation for the flow of radiation in a direction making an angle θ with the x-axis for a frequency v within an absorption line may be taken from Chapter IV, equation (1), namely

$$\cos\theta \frac{dI_v(\theta)}{\rho\,dx} = -k_v I_v(\theta) + j_v, \tag{1}$$

where both k_v and j_v are now rapidly varying functions of the frequency.

The absorption coefficient k_v may be divided into a part whose variation with frequency within the absorption line may be neglected—the continuous absorption; and a rapidly changing part—the line absorption. Accordingly we set
$$k_v = k + l_v. \tag{2}$$

The line absorption coefficient l_v is the absorption coefficient for the atoms present per unit mass of the atmosphere. Let N be the concentration of the line absorbing atoms and ρ the density of the atmosphere. The absorption coefficient per unit volume is ρl_v, and this will be equal to $N\alpha(v)_D$, where $\alpha(v)_D$ is the Doppler modification of the atomic line absorption coefficient. Hence

$$l_v = \frac{N\alpha(v)_D}{\rho}. \tag{3}$$

When the velocity distribution of the atoms is Maxwellian $\alpha(v)_D$ is given by equation (110), Chapter VI. The general equation of line formation can now be written as

$$\cos\theta \frac{dI_\nu(\theta)}{\rho\,dx} = -(k+l_\nu)I_\nu(\theta)+j_\nu. \tag{4}$$

In this chapter we investigate the special circumstance in which the radiation absorbed by atoms taking part in the formation of the line is re-emitted without change of frequency. This kind of scattering can occur when the atom absorbs from an infinitely sharp energy state, undergoes a transition to an excited state in which the atom persists for a short interval of time, and then returns to the lower state with the spontaneous emission of a quantum. If we neglect the small change in frequency due to the velocity of recoil of the atom during the emission process, the frequency of the quantum emitted is the same as that of the quantum absorbed. We exclude the possibility of spontaneous transitions taking place in a line entirely different from that in which the absorption occurs.

The emission in the frequency ν per unit mass of the atmosphere is comprised of two parts (a) re-emission from the selectively absorbing atoms, and (b) re-emission from the atmospheric constituents which give rise to the continuous absorption. The emission (a) is the coherent scattering in the frequency ν due to spontaneous emission of quanta by atoms excited by radiation. If we assume that the direction of emission from an excited atom is independent of the direction of the absorbed quantum, the re-emission by an assembly of atoms may be taken as isotropic. Thus, if *all* the energy absorbed by the atoms is emitted as isotropic radiation, the emission (a) will be the absorption averaged over all directions of incidence of the radiation. This will be given by

$$\frac{1}{4\pi}\int l_\nu I_\nu(\theta)\,d\omega = l_\nu J_\nu. \tag{5}$$

We suppose that the emission (b) takes place as in local thermodynamic equilibrium, and is given by $kB(\nu, T)$. Hence

$$j_\nu = l_\nu J_\nu + kB(\nu, T). \tag{6}$$

With the emission coefficient given by (6), equation (4) describes the coherent formation of an absorption line when the atoms are subject only to radiative transitions between two energy levels.

Consider now the effect of collisions on the emission of radiation by excited atoms. If an atom experiences a collision during the natural lifetime in the excited state, the energy of excitation may be transformed into kinetic energy, and the atom and colliding particle rebound from their *super-elastic* collision with increased velocity, sharing the energy of excitation between them. If the fraction ϵ of atoms excited by radiation of frequency ν is prevented from contributing to the coherent re-emission by super-elastic collisions, the line emission given by (5) will be reduced to $(1-\epsilon)l_\nu J_\nu$. Now in thermodynamic equilibrium the conversion of radiation into kinetic energy by super-elastic collisions is exactly balanced by the reverse process of conversion of kinetic energy into radiation by way of inelastic collisions. Thus the emission in the frequency ν by atoms excited by inelastic collisions may be found from the fact that it balances the amount $\epsilon l_\nu J_\nu$ lost to the radiation field by super-elastic collisions when J_ν has its equilibrium value $B(\nu, T)$. The total emission is therefore

$$j_\nu = (1-\epsilon)l_\nu J_\nu + \epsilon l_\nu B(\nu, T) + k B(\nu, T), \tag{7}$$

and equation (1) may then be written in the form

$$\cos\theta \frac{dI_\nu(\theta)}{\rho\, dx} = -(k+l_\nu)I_\nu(\theta) + (1-\epsilon)l_\nu J_\nu + (k+\epsilon l_\nu)B(\nu, T), \tag{8}$$

a result due to Eddington.†

To find an approximate solution of equation (8) we proceed as in Chapter IV, making use of the abbreviations

$$J_\nu = \frac{1}{4\pi}\int I_\nu(\theta)\, d\omega, \qquad H_\nu = \frac{1}{4\pi}\int I_\nu(\theta)\cos\theta\, d\omega,$$

$$K_\nu = \frac{1}{4\pi}\int I_\nu(\theta)\cos^2\theta\, d\omega$$

in which the integration is made over all directions. We obtain

$$\frac{dH_\nu}{\rho\, dx} = -(k+\epsilon l_\nu)(J_\nu - B_\nu), \tag{9}$$

$$\frac{dK_\nu}{\rho\, dx} = -(k+l_\nu)H_\nu. \tag{10}$$

In equation (9) we have written B_ν instead of $B(\nu, T)$ in order to avoid a complex array of brackets. If we measure the optical depth in the continuous spectrum just outside the line so that $d\tau = -k\rho\, dx$, and set $\eta_\nu = l_\nu/k$, equations (9) and (10) become

$$\frac{dH_\nu}{d\tau} = (1+\epsilon\eta_\nu)(J_\nu - B_\nu), \tag{11}$$

$$\frac{dK_\nu}{d\tau} = (1+\eta_\nu)H_\nu. \tag{12}$$

† A. S. Eddington, *M.N.* **89**, 623 (1929).

3. Eddington's solution for η constant

If we assume that η_ν is independent of τ the equations can be readily integrated. Introducing the geometrical approximation $K_\nu = \frac{1}{3}J_\nu$, equations (11) and (12) combine to give

$$\frac{d^2 J_\nu}{d\tau^2} = q_\nu^2 (J_\nu - B_\nu), \tag{13}$$

where

$$q_\nu^2 = 3(1+\epsilon\eta_\nu)(1+\eta_\nu).$$

Now let

$$B_\nu = a_\nu + b_\nu \tau, \tag{14}$$

so that $d^2 B_\nu / d\tau^2 = 0$. Equation (13) may then be written in the form

$$\frac{d^2}{d\tau^2}(J_\nu - B_\nu) = q_\nu^2 (J_\nu - B_\nu). \tag{15}$$

This reduces to equation (11) of Chapter IV when $q_\nu^2 = 3$, corresponding to a frequency outside the line where $\eta_\nu = 0$.

The solution of equation (15) is subject to the approximate boundary condition that $J_\nu = 2H_\nu$ at $\tau = 0$, and the requirement that $J_\nu - B_\nu$ shall not increase exponentially as $\tau \to \infty$. Hence

$$J_\nu = B_\nu + A_\nu e^{-q_\nu \tau}. \tag{16}$$

From equation (12), and with $K_\nu = \frac{1}{3}J_\nu$, we find

$$H_\nu = \frac{1}{3(1+\eta_\nu)} \frac{dJ_\nu}{d\tau}, \tag{17}$$

where

$$\frac{dJ_\nu}{d\tau} = b_\nu - q_\nu A_\nu e^{-q_\nu \tau}.$$

The boundary condition $J_\nu = 2H_\nu$ therefore gives

$$a_\nu + A_\nu = \frac{2}{3(1+\eta_\nu)}(b_\nu - q_\nu A_\nu),$$

so that

$$A_\nu = \frac{-a_\nu(1+\eta_\nu) + \frac{2}{3}b_\nu}{1+\eta_\nu+\frac{2}{3}q_\nu}. \tag{18}$$

Hence

$$J_\nu = a_\nu + b_\nu \tau - \frac{a_\nu(1+\eta_\nu) - \frac{2}{3}b_\nu}{1+\eta_\nu+\frac{2}{3}q_\nu} e^{-q_\nu \tau}. \tag{19}$$

The solution (19) for the mean intensity J_ν enables us to find the intensity within the absorption line at any depth, and in any direction, by solving the fundamental equation of line formation

$$\cos\theta \frac{dI_\nu(\theta)}{d\tau} = (1+\eta_\nu)I_\nu(\theta) - (1-\epsilon)\eta_\nu J_\nu - (1+\epsilon\eta_\nu)B_\nu, \tag{20}$$

J_ν and B_ν being known functions of τ. The solution for $I_\nu(\theta)$ can be written down immediately since equation (20) is simply a linear differential equation with constant coefficients.

4. Residual intensity in an absorption line

Let r_ν be the ratio of the intensity of radiation of frequency ν within an absorption line to the intensity in the continuous spectrum just outside the line. There are two cases to be considered, the line contour for radiation received from the star as a whole, and the contour at any point on the disk.

4.1. *The mean contour. Central intensity*

Since each unit of area on the surface of the star projects into an area $\cos \theta$ on the disk, radiation received from the star as a whole is the emergent radiation $I_\nu(0, \theta) \, d\omega$ weighted by the factor $\cos \theta$ and integrated over the visible hemisphere of directions. This is, of course, the net flux of radiation at the boundary of the star. We refer to the contour of an absorption line in the total light from a star as the *mean contour* since the amount of radiation received is given by the weighted mean of the intensities across the disk. The residual intensity in the mean contour is given by

$$r_\nu = \left(\frac{H_\nu}{H}\right)_{\tau=0}, \tag{21}$$

where the omission of the suffix ν means *outside the line*. By virtue of the boundary condition $J_\nu = 2H_\nu$ we also have

$$r_\nu = \left(\frac{J_\nu}{J}\right)_{\tau=0}.$$

Now equation (19) with $\tau = 0$ gives

$$J_\nu = \frac{2}{3} \frac{b_\nu + a_\nu q_\nu}{1 + \eta_\nu + \frac{2}{3}q_\nu}. \tag{22}$$

Outside the line $\eta_\nu = 0$ and $q_\nu = \sqrt{3}$ so that the contour of the absorption line will be given by

$$r_\nu = \frac{1 + \frac{2}{3}\sqrt{3}}{b_\nu + a_\nu \sqrt{3}} \frac{b_\nu + a_\nu q_\nu}{1 + \eta_\nu + \frac{2}{3}q_\nu}. \tag{23}$$

Equation (23) takes a somewhat simpler form in a region of the spectrum where $b_\nu = \frac{3}{2}a_\nu$. In this case

$$r_\nu = \frac{1 + \frac{2}{3}q_\nu}{1 + \eta_\nu + \frac{2}{3}q_\nu}, \tag{24}$$

an equation due to Eddington.

To evaluate a_ν and b_ν in the Taylor series (14) for $B(\nu, T)$ expanded about $\tau = 0$, we take the temperature distribution in the atmosphere to be

$$T^4 = T_0^4(1 + \tfrac{3}{2}\bar{\tau}),$$

where $\bar{\tau}$ is the optical depth in the continuous spectrum defined in terms of the mean coefficient of absorption $\bar{k}$. If $k/\bar{k}$ is independent of depth

$$\tau = (k/\bar{k})\bar{\tau}, \tag{25}$$

and equation (14) may be written

$$B(\nu, T) = a_\nu + b_\nu n_\nu \bar{\tau}, \tag{26}$$

where

$$n_\nu = k/\bar{k}.$$

Now

$$a_\nu = B(\nu, T_0),$$

$$b_\nu = \frac{1}{n_\nu}\left(\frac{dB}{d\bar{\tau}}\right)_{\bar{\tau}=0} = \frac{1}{n_\nu}\left(\frac{dB}{dT}\frac{dT}{d\bar{\tau}}\right)_{\bar{\tau}=0}.$$

Hence

$$\frac{b_\nu}{a_\nu} = \frac{3}{8}\frac{x_0}{n_\nu}, \tag{27}$$

where

$$x_0 = \frac{h\nu/RT_0}{1 - e^{-h\nu/RT_0}}.$$

The condition $b_\nu = \tfrac{3}{2}a_\nu$, which leads to equation (24), is now seen to apply to a region of the spectrum where $x_0 = 4n_\nu$. In the case of a grey atmosphere we have $n_\nu = 1$ so that the restriction is then simply $x_0 = 4$. Equations (23) and (27) give the contour of a line formed in a non-grey atmosphere, and in any part of the spectrum

$$r_\nu = \frac{1 + \tfrac{2}{3}\sqrt{3}}{\tfrac{1}{4}(x_0/n_\nu) + \tfrac{2}{3}\sqrt{3}}\frac{\tfrac{1}{4}(x_0/n_\nu) + \tfrac{2}{3}q_\nu}{1 + \eta_\nu + \tfrac{2}{3}q_\nu}. \tag{28}$$

Let r_c be the residual intensity at the centre of the absorption line; r_c is referred to as the *central intensity*. We now consider the physical processes which determine the central intensity. When $\epsilon = 0$ all the radiation absorbed by the atoms taking part in the formation of the line is returned to the radiation field as isotropic emission. This corresponds to monochromatic radiative equilibrium so far as the line process is concerned. Now the value of η_ν at the centre of the line is large, so that with $\epsilon = 0$ we have $q_\nu \doteq \sqrt{(3\eta_\nu)}$. Hence

$$r_c = \frac{\tfrac{2}{3}\sqrt{(3\eta_\nu)}}{\eta_\nu + \tfrac{2}{3}\sqrt{(3\eta_\nu)}} \doteq \frac{2}{\sqrt{(3\eta_\nu)}}. \tag{29}$$

Thus the central intensity of the absorption line when $\epsilon = 0$ is determined only by the central value of η_ν. But when ϵ is not zero and $\eta_\nu \gg 1$ we may write $q_\nu \doteq \eta_\nu \sqrt{(3\epsilon)}$. In this case we have

$$r_c \doteq \frac{\frac{2}{3}\sqrt{(3\epsilon)}}{1+\frac{2}{3}\sqrt{(3\epsilon)}}, \tag{30}$$

and the central intensity is seen to depend only on ϵ.

Consider now the extreme case in which $\epsilon = 1$. This corresponds to a state of local thermodynamic equilibrium. Equation (30) then gives

$$r_c \doteq \frac{2}{2+\sqrt{3}} = 0\cdot 54. \tag{31}$$

This is the central intensity of the darkest line which can be seen in a stellar spectrum if the atmosphere is in local thermodynamic equilibrium for frequencies within the absorption line.

We conclude that in monochromatic radiative equilibrium the absorption lines are almost *black* at the centre, whilst in thermodynamic equilibrium the contrast is very limited, the lines being quite shallow.

4.2. *Variation from centre to limb*

We now find an expression for the contour of an absorption line in the radiation which emerges at any angle θ to the normal to the surface of the star, that is, the contour $r_\nu(\theta)$ at any point on the disk.

Consider a line formed in a region of the spectrum where $b_\nu = \frac{3}{2}a_\nu$. From equation (18) we now have

$$A_\nu = \frac{-a_\nu \eta_\nu}{1+\eta_\nu+\frac{2}{3}q_\nu}. \tag{32}$$

Outside the line A_ν is zero, and from equation (16) we then find $J_\nu = B_\nu$. This gives $dH_\nu/d\tau = 0$ in equation (11) so that, with $\eta_\nu = 0$ and $K_\nu = \frac{1}{3}J_\nu$, equations (11) and (12) give

$$J = B = H(2+3\tau), \tag{33}$$

where $H = \frac{1}{2}a_\nu$. We have omitted the suffix ν on the symbols in equation (33) as it applies to the continuum in the chosen spectral region; B_ν is taken to be the same both outside and inside the line. The value of J_ν within the line is given by equation (16), and will now be

$$J_\nu = H(2+3\tau) - \frac{2H\eta_\nu}{1+\eta_\nu+\frac{2}{3}q_\nu} e^{-q_\nu \tau}. \tag{34}$$

To obtain the emergent intensity at the surface of the star we have to solve equation (4), namely

$$\cos\theta \frac{dI_\nu(\theta)}{d\tau} = (1+\eta_\nu)I_\nu(\theta) - j_\nu/k, \tag{35}$$

with $$j_\nu/k = (1-\epsilon)\eta_\nu J_\nu + H(1+\epsilon\eta_\nu)(2+3\tau),$$

J_ν being given by equation (34). The solution for the intensity $I_\nu(\tau,\theta)$ proceeds as in Chapter I, Section 4. For η_ν constant the integrating factor will be

$$e^{-(1+\eta_\nu)\tau\sec\theta}.$$

The solution for the emergent intensity is

$$I_\nu(0,\theta) = \int_0^\infty e^{-(1+\eta_\nu)\tau\sec\theta}(j_\nu/k)\sec\theta\,d\tau \tag{36}$$

$$= H\left\{2+3\,\frac{\cos\theta}{1+\eta_\nu} - (1-\epsilon)\frac{2\eta_\nu^2}{1+\eta_\nu+\tfrac{2}{3}q_\nu}\,\frac{1}{1+\eta_\nu+q_\nu\cos\theta}\right\}. \tag{37}$$

Setting $\eta_\nu = 0$ the intensity in the continuous spectrum just outside the line will be

$$I(0,\theta) = H(2+3\cos\theta),$$

a result which we obtained in Chapter I for the integrated radiation for which $dH/d\tau$ is also zero. The contour of the line for radiation emerging in the direction θ is given by the ratio of the intensity $I_\nu(0,\theta)$ inside the line to the intensity $I(0,\theta)$ in the continuous spectrum. Hence

$$r_\nu(\theta) = \frac{1}{1+\tfrac{3}{2}\cos\theta}\left\{1+\frac{3}{2}\frac{\cos\theta}{1+\eta_\nu} - (1-\epsilon)\frac{\eta_\nu^2}{1+\eta_\nu+\tfrac{2}{3}q_\nu}\,\frac{1}{1+\eta_\nu+q_\nu\cos\theta}\right\},$$

$$\tag{38}$$

an equation given in another notation by Plaskett.[†]

We now find the residual intensity for an absorption line formed in any part of the spectrum. In equation (36) we set

$$j_\nu/k = (1-\epsilon)\eta_\nu J_\nu + (1+\epsilon\eta_\nu)(a_\nu+b_\nu\tau),$$

where $$J_\nu = a_\nu + b_\nu\tau - \frac{a_\nu(1+\eta_\nu)-\tfrac{2}{3}b_\nu}{1+\eta_\nu+\tfrac{2}{3}q_\nu}e^{-q_\nu\tau}.$$

We then find

$$I_\nu(0,\theta) = a_\nu + b_\nu\frac{\cos\theta}{1+\eta_\nu} - (1-\epsilon)\frac{a_\nu(1+\eta_\nu)-\tfrac{2}{3}b_\nu}{1+\eta_\nu+\tfrac{2}{3}q_\nu}\,\frac{\eta_\nu}{1+\eta_\nu+q_\nu\cos\theta}. \tag{39}$$

Hence

$$r_\nu(\theta) = \frac{1}{a_\nu+b_\nu\cos\theta}\left\{a_\nu+b_\nu\frac{\cos\theta}{1+\eta_\nu} - (1-\epsilon)\frac{a_\nu(1+\eta_\nu)-\tfrac{2}{3}b_\nu}{1+\eta_\nu+\tfrac{2}{3}q_\nu}\,\frac{\eta_\nu}{1+\eta_\nu+q_\nu\cos\theta}\right\}.$$

$$\tag{40}$$

From equations (27) and (40) we get

$$r_\nu(\theta) = \frac{1}{1+\tfrac{1}{4}(x_0/n_\nu)\tfrac{3}{2}\cos\theta}\left\{1+\frac{1}{4}\frac{x_0}{n_\nu}\frac{3}{2}\frac{\cos\theta}{1+\eta_\nu} - \right.$$

$$\left. -(1-\epsilon)\frac{1+\eta_\nu-\tfrac{1}{4}(x_0/n_\nu)}{1+\eta_\nu+\tfrac{2}{3}q_\nu}\,\frac{\eta_\nu}{1+\eta_\nu+q_\nu\cos\theta}\right\}. \tag{41}$$

[†] H. H. Plaskett, *M.N.* **91**, 913 (1931).

Equation (41) brings into prominence the dependence of the residual intensity on the non-greyness of the atmosphere.

Consider the behaviour of the central intensities from centre to limb. When $\epsilon = 0$ we have $q_\nu^2 = 3(1+\eta_\nu)$, and for large q_ν equation (38) leads to the following expansion:

$$r_\nu(\theta) = \frac{2}{q_\nu} + \frac{1}{q_\nu^2} \frac{4-3\cos\theta - 18\cos^2\theta}{2+3\cos\theta} + \dots. \tag{42}$$

At the centre of the line, where η_ν is large, $q_\nu \doteq \sqrt{(3\eta_\nu)}$, and we have approximately

$$r_\nu(\theta) \doteq \frac{2}{\sqrt{(3\eta_\nu)}},$$

whatever the value of θ. Thus, for $\epsilon = 0$, the central parts of absorption lines are very deep and do not change appreciably from the centre of the disk to the limb. Now when $\epsilon = 1$ equation (38) takes the simple form

$$r_\nu(\theta) = \frac{1}{1+\frac{3}{2}\cos\theta}\left(1+\frac{3}{2}\frac{\cos\theta}{1+\eta_\nu}\right). \tag{43}$$

With $\cos\theta = 1$ the central intensity has the value $\frac{2}{5}$, whilst for $\cos\theta = 0$ we have $r_\nu = 1$. Thus in thermodynamic equilibrium the darkest line has a central intensity 0·4 at the centre of the disk, and the lines disappear completely at the limb.

The variation of the residual intensity from centre to limb will be intermediate between the two extremes of local thermodynamic equilibrium and monochromatic radiative equilibrium considered above.

4.3. *Second approximation to the mean contour*

Starting from the approximate boundary condition $J_\nu = 2H_\nu$ and the geometrical approximation $K_\nu = \frac{1}{3}J_\nu$ we have found the emergent intensity within an absorption line to be given by equation (39):

$$I_\nu(0,\theta) = a_\nu + b_\nu\frac{\cos\theta}{1+\eta_\nu} - (1-\epsilon)\frac{a_\nu(1+\eta_\nu)-\frac{2}{3}b_\nu}{1+\eta_\nu+\frac{2}{3}q_\nu}\frac{\eta_\nu}{1+\eta_\nu+q_\nu\cos\theta}.$$

We may now derive a second approximation to the mean contour of the line by calculating a revised value of H_ν at the boundary. Since

$$H_\nu(0) = \frac{1}{4\pi}\int I_\nu(0,\theta)\cos\theta\,d\omega,$$

the contour of the line will be given by

$$r_\nu = \frac{H_\nu(0)}{H(0)} = \frac{\int I_\nu(0,\theta)\cos\theta\,d\omega}{\int I(0,\theta)\cos\theta\,d\omega}. \tag{44}$$

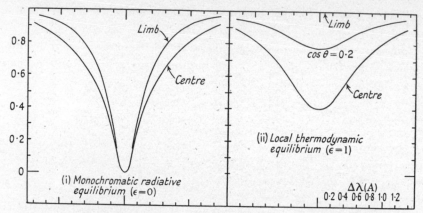

FIG. 24. Variation of residual intensity from centre to limb exhibited by an absorption line formed in an atmosphere in which η is constant with depth. When $\epsilon = 0$, the line absorption and emission take place as in monochromatic radiative equilibrium. The left-hand part of the diagram shows the line contour for coherent formation under these conditions. When $\epsilon = 1$, all the radiation absorbed by the atoms is converted into kinetic energy by means of collisions, and the state of local thermodynamic equilibrium persists. In this case, the lines are shallow and disappear completely at the limb, as shown in the right-hand part of the figure.

It readily follows that

$$r_\nu = \frac{1}{a_\nu + \frac{2}{3}b_\nu}\left[a_\nu + \frac{2}{3}\frac{b_\nu}{1+\eta_\nu} - (1-\epsilon)\frac{a_\nu(1+\eta_\nu)-\frac{2}{3}b_\nu}{1+\eta_\nu+\frac{2}{3}q_\nu}\frac{2\eta_\nu}{q_\nu^2}\times\right.$$
$$\left.\times\left\{q_\nu - (1+\eta_\nu)\ln\frac{1+\eta_\nu+q_\nu}{1+\eta_\nu}\right\}\right].$$

If we set $b_\nu = \frac{3}{2}a_\nu$ this simplifies to

$$r_\nu = \frac{1}{2}\left(1+\frac{1}{1+\eta_\nu}\right) - (1-\epsilon)\frac{\eta_\nu^2/q_\nu^2}{1+\eta_\nu+\frac{2}{3}q_\nu}\left\{q_\nu - (1+\eta_\nu)\ln\frac{1+\eta_\nu+q_\nu}{1+\eta_\nu}\right\}. \quad (45)$$

When $\epsilon = 0$ we have $q_\nu^2 = 3(1+\eta_\nu)$, and equation (45) may be written

$$r_\nu = \frac{1}{2}\left(1+\frac{3}{q_\nu^2}\right) - \frac{1}{3}\frac{(q_\nu^2-3)^2}{q_\nu^2(2+q_\nu)}\left\{1-\tfrac{1}{3}q_\nu\ln\left(1+\frac{3}{q_\nu}\right)\right\}. \quad (46)$$

5. A comparison of solutions. Errors of the approximate solutions

The exact solution to the equation of coherent line formation in an η-constant atmosphere in which $B_\nu = a_\nu + b_\nu\tau_\nu$ has been carried out by Chandrasekhar.† When $\epsilon = 0$ and $b_\nu = \frac{3}{2}a_\nu$, the solution for the emergent intensity takes the form

$$I_\nu(0,\mu) = \tfrac{3}{2}a_\nu\lambda^{\frac{1}{2}}H(\mu)\{\tfrac{2}{3}+\mu\lambda+\tfrac{1}{2}\lambda^{\frac{1}{2}}(1-\lambda)\alpha_1\}, \quad (47)$$

† S. Chandrasekhar, *Ap. J.* **106**, 145 (1947); see also *Radiative Transfer* (Oxford), chap. xii, section 84.

where
$$\mu = \cos\theta, \qquad \lambda = \frac{1}{1+\eta},$$

$H(\mu)$ is the solution of the integral equation

$$H(\mu) = 1 + \tfrac{1}{2}(1-\lambda)\mu H(\mu) \int_0^1 \frac{H(\mu')\,d\mu'}{\mu+\mu'},$$

and α_1 is the first moment of $H(\mu)$ given by

$$\alpha_1 = \int_0^1 \mu H(\mu)\,d\mu.$$

In the continuous spectrum outside the line $\lambda = 1$, $H(\mu) \equiv 1$ and equation (47) gives
$$I(0,\mu) = \tfrac{3}{2}a_\nu(\mu+\tfrac{2}{3}).$$

Hence
$$r(\mu) = \frac{I_\nu(0,\mu)}{I(0,\mu)} = H(\mu)\frac{\lambda^{\frac{1}{2}}}{\mu+\tfrac{2}{3}}\{\tfrac{2}{3}+\mu\lambda+\tfrac{1}{2}\lambda^{\frac{1}{2}}(1-\lambda)\alpha_1\}. \qquad (48)$$

The mean contour of the line, given by the flux of radiation at the surface, will be

$$r = \frac{\displaystyle\int_0^1 \mu I_\nu(0,\mu)\,d\mu}{\displaystyle\int_0^1 \mu I(0,\mu)\,d\mu} = 3\lambda^{\frac{1}{2}}\{\tfrac{1}{2}\lambda\alpha_2 + \tfrac{1}{3}\alpha_1 + \tfrac{1}{4}\lambda^{\frac{1}{2}}(1-\lambda)\alpha_1^2\}. \qquad (49)$$

We now compare the exact solutions (48) and (49) with the approximate formulae (24), (38), and (45) in which, for $\epsilon = 0$, we set

$$q^2 = 3(1+\eta) = \frac{3}{\lambda}, \qquad \eta = \frac{1-\lambda}{\lambda}.$$

Corresponding to the exact equation (48) we have the approximation (38),

$$r(\mu) = \frac{1}{\mu+\tfrac{2}{3}}\left\{\tfrac{2}{3}+\mu\lambda - \tfrac{2}{3}\frac{(1-\lambda)^2}{\{1+2\sqrt{(\tfrac{1}{3}\lambda)}\}\{1+3\mu\sqrt{(\tfrac{1}{3}\lambda)}\}}\right\}. \qquad (50)$$

Eddington's approximation to the mean contour (24) is

$$r = \frac{3+2\sqrt{(3/\lambda)}}{3/\lambda+2\sqrt{(3/\lambda)}}, \qquad (51)$$

and the second approximation (46) may be written

$$r = \tfrac{1}{2}(1+\lambda) - \frac{(1-\lambda)^2}{\lambda\{2+\sqrt{(3/\lambda)}\}}[1-\tfrac{1}{3}\sqrt{(3/\lambda)}\ln\{1+3\sqrt{(\tfrac{1}{3}\lambda)}\}]. \qquad (52)$$

Equations (51) and (52) are to be compared with the exact solution (49).

The upper panel of Fig. 25 shows the corrections to be applied to the approximate solutions (51) and (52) for the mean contour. Eddington's equation (51) requires a maximum correction to the residual intensity of amount $\Delta r = -0 \cdot 014$ at $\lambda \sim 0 \cdot 4$. Since this corresponds to $\eta \sim 1 \cdot 5$ the correction will apply mainly to weak lines or the wings of strong lines. The second approximation (52) reduces the maximum correction to $\Delta r = +0 \cdot 004$. The maximum now occurs at $\lambda \sim 0 \cdot 1$ corresponding to

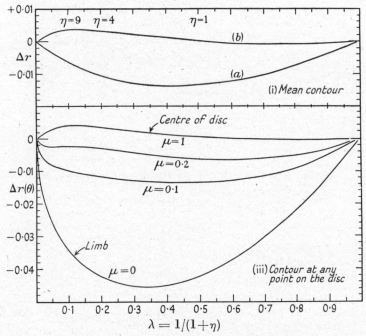

FIG. 25. Comparison between exact and approximate solutions for the residual intensity when η is constant with depth. The ordinate gives the correction Δr (that is the exact solution minus the approximation) to be applied to (i) the residual intensity in the mean contour as given by (a) Eddington's equation (51), and (b) the second approximation (52); (ii) the residual intensity at any point on the disk according to equation (50).

$\eta \sim 9 \cdot 0$, and the correction farther out in the wings of the line is reduced to a negligible amount. This approximation may be conveniently used when one is obliged to work with broken values of λ which necessitates interpolation in tables of $H(\mu)$ and the first and second moments α_1 and α_2. The lower panel of the figure gives the centre to limb corrections to formula (51). The large correction required at the extreme limb ($\cos \theta = 0$) is due to the use of the approximate boundary condition $J_\nu = 2H_\nu$. But the error rapidly diminishes as one approaches the centre of the disk, and at $\cos \theta = 0 \cdot 2$ the residual intensity in the wings of the line needs to be corrected by an amount $\Delta r = -0 \cdot 006$.

6. Line formation when η varies with the depth

In the preceding sections of this chapter the simplifying assumption was made that the ratio $\eta_\nu = l_\nu/k$ of the coefficients of line absorption to continuous absorption was constant throughout the region of line formation. This assumption enabled us to study the formation of an absorption line under somewhat idealized conditions for which we gave no physical justification.

6.1. *The dependence of η on physical conditions*

We now make an examination of the various factors on which η_ν depends. From equation (3) we have

$$\eta_\nu = \frac{N\alpha(\nu)_D}{k\rho}, \tag{53}$$

where N is the concentration of atoms forming the absorption line, k is the coefficient of continuous absorption per unit mass of an atmosphere with density ρ, whilst $\alpha(\nu)_D$ is the atomic line absorption coefficient modified by Doppler effect due to thermal motion of the atoms.

Consider the line absorption due to a metal atom with an abundance a relative to all kinds of metal atoms present, and let A be the abundance of hydrogen relative to the total metal content of the atmosphere. If N_a, N_M, and N_H denote the concentrations of the line-forming metal atoms, the metal mixture, and the hydrogen atoms, the relative abundances are defined by the ratios

$$a = \frac{N_a}{N_M}, \qquad A = \frac{N_H}{N_M}.$$

We shall assume that the atmosphere is well mixed so that both a and A may be treated as constant throughout the relevant part of the atmosphere. Equation (53) may be written in the form

$$\eta_\nu = \frac{N}{N_a}\frac{a}{A}\frac{\alpha(\nu)_D}{km_H}. \tag{54}$$

If the line absorption is due to a neutral metal atom, for example sodium absorbing from its ground state, the ratio N/N_a gives the proportion of metal atoms which are not ionized. Thus

$$\frac{N}{N_a} = 1 - x_a,$$

where x_a is the degree of ionization of the metal. The ratio N/N_a varies with depth since the degree of ionization increases with temperature and decreases with electron pressure. Now the continuous absorption coefficient increases with depth so that both the metal ionization and the continuous absorption contrive to bring about a change of η_ν with depth.

The behaviour of $\alpha(\nu)_D$ with depth depends on the part of the line considered. According to equation (108) of Chapter VI, at the centre of the line we have

$$\alpha(\nu_0)_D = \frac{\pi e^2}{mc} f \frac{1}{b\sqrt{\pi}},$$

where

$$b = \frac{\nu_0}{c} \sqrt{\left(\frac{2RT}{M}\right)}.$$

Since T does not increase greatly in the region of line formation $\alpha(\nu_0)_D$, which varies with $T^{-\frac{1}{2}}$, only decreases slowly with depth. In the wings of the line, equation (113) of Chapter VI gives

$$\alpha(\nu)_D \doteqdot \alpha(\nu) \doteqdot \frac{\pi e^2}{mc} f \frac{\delta}{\pi} \frac{1}{(\nu - \nu_0)^2},$$

where

$$\delta = \delta_n + \delta_c.$$

The radiation damping constant δ_n is independent of the physical conditions but, according to equation (61) of Chapter VI, we have

$$\delta_c \propto p/T^{7/10}.$$

These considerations indicate that it is by no means true in general that η_ν is constant, although the approximate constancy of η_ν with depth may apply in some fortunate circumstances. It is therefore necessary to examine the case where η_ν varies with the depth.

6.2. *Soluble cases for empirical forms*

In Eddington's classical paper† on absorption lines the case in which $1/(1+\eta_\nu)$ is a linear function of optical depth was shown to lead to a Bessel equation of order zero for imaginary argument. Other soluble cases are known for a variety of functional forms for η_ν. These are as follows:

M. Krook, *M.N.* **98**, 477 (1938); $\eta_\nu = \alpha_\nu + \beta_\nu e^{-\lambda\tau}$,

H. R. Hulme, *M.N.* **99**, 730 (1939); $1/(1+\eta_\nu) = \alpha_\nu + \beta_\nu \tau + \gamma_\nu \tau^2$,

L. Spitzer, *Ap. J.* **87**, 1 (1938); $1 + \eta_\nu = \alpha_\nu(1 + \beta_\nu \tau)^s$.

The usefulness of all of these formulae except Krook's is restricted by the necessity for recalculating the values of the parameters for different parts of the line; a greater objection is the difficulty of ascertaining

† A. S. Eddington, *M.N.* **89**, 620 (1929).

whether the formulae represent actual distributions sufficiently faithfully.

6.3. *The treatment of arbitrary variations*

We now consider the formation of an absorption line when η is subject to·small but otherwise arbitrary variations with optical depth. From equations (11) and (12) with $\epsilon = 0$ and $K_\nu = \frac{1}{3}J_\nu$, we obtain

$$\frac{dH_\nu}{d\tau} = J_\nu - B_\nu, \tag{55}$$

$$\frac{dJ_\nu}{d\tau} = 3(1+\eta_\nu)H_\nu. \tag{56}$$

Hence
$$\frac{d^2H_\nu}{d\tau^2} = 3(1+\eta_\nu)H_\nu - \frac{dB_\nu}{d\tau}. \tag{57}$$

Let η_0 be some suitably chosen value of η_ν, and set
$$q_\nu^2 = 3(1+\eta_0), \qquad \delta_\nu = 3(\eta_\nu - \eta_0),$$
so that equation (57) becomes

$$\frac{d^2H_\nu}{d\tau^2} = q_\nu^2 H_\nu - \frac{dB_\nu}{d\tau} + \delta_\nu H_\nu. \tag{58}$$

Except for the appearance of the perturbing term $\delta_\nu H_\nu$, equation (58) would apply to an atmosphere with η_ν constant and equal to η_0. Now if δ_ν were small, equation (58) could be readily solved by the standard perturbation methods in differential equations. In many cases the magnitude of the η-variations leads to perturbations in equation (58) which are too large to be dealt with by these methods. But the perturbation method can still be applied if we make a different choice of independent variable. Instead of measuring the optical depth in the continuous spectrum as in equations (11) and (12), we introduce a new independent variable defined by

$$dt_\nu = (1+\eta_\nu)\,d\tau, \tag{59}$$

so that t_ν is the optical depth measured in the line-plus-continuum. With this substitution equations (11) and (12) become

$$\frac{dH}{dt} = \frac{1+\epsilon\eta}{1+\eta}(J-B), \tag{60}$$

$$\frac{dK}{dt} = H, \tag{61}$$

where the suffix ν has been omitted for convenience in writing the equations in the following discussion. Introducing the geometrical approximation $K = \frac{1}{3}J$, equations (60) and (61) may be combined without any demands on η such as one had to make in order to obtain (13) from (11) and (12). This is due to the substitution (59). We now have

$$\frac{d^2J}{dt^2} = 3\lambda(J-B),\tag{62}$$

where

$$\lambda = \frac{1+\epsilon\eta}{1+\eta}.$$

Subtracting d^2B/dt^2 from both sides of equation (62)

$$\frac{d^2}{dt^2}(J-B) = 3\lambda(J-B)-\frac{d^2B}{dt^2}.\tag{63}$$

Let λ_0 be some suitably chosen mean value of λ, and set

$$\lambda = \lambda_0+\delta.\tag{64}$$

Equation (63) may be written

$$\frac{d^2}{dt^2}(J-B) = 3\lambda_0(J-B)-\frac{d^2B}{dt^2}+3\delta(J-B).\tag{65}$$

This equation is superior to equation (58) if perturbation methods are to be used. This may be seen as follows: for $\epsilon = 0$ we have $\lambda = 1/(1+\eta)$, and if η ranges from 0 to ∞ then $1/(1+\eta)$ only ranges from 1 to 0. Hence the perturbing term in equation (65) will only be small even though the range of variation of η be large. The same cannot be said of the perturbing term in equation (58).

6.31. *Strömgren's solution† for the emergent flux in an absorption line*

Let the general solution of equation (65) be

$$J-B = C(t)e^{p_0t}+D(t)e^{-p_0t},\tag{66}$$

where

$$p_0 = \surd(3\lambda_0).$$

We then have

$$\frac{d}{dt}(J-B) = p_0\,Ce^{p_0t}-p_0\,De^{-p_0t},$$

provided the functions C and D are such that

$$\frac{dC}{dt}e^{p_0t}+\frac{dD}{dt}e^{-p_0t} = 0.$$

When this condition is satisfied we have

$$\frac{d^2}{dt^2}(J-B) \equiv p_0^2(J-B)+p_0\frac{dC}{dt}e^{p_0t}-p_0\frac{dD}{dt}e^{-p_0t}.\tag{67}$$

Equation (65) now gives

$$p_0\frac{dC}{dt}e^{p_0t}-p_0\frac{dD}{dt}e^{-p_0t} = 3\delta(J-B)-\frac{d^2B}{dt^2}.\tag{68}$$

† B. Strömgren, *Ap. J.* **86**, 1 (1937).

Solving equations (67) and (68) for the derivatives of C and D we find

$$\frac{dC}{dt} = \frac{1}{2p_0}\left\{3\delta(J-B)-\frac{d^2B}{dt^2}\right\}e^{-p_0 t}; \tag{69}$$

$$\frac{dD}{dt} = \frac{-1}{2p_0}\left\{3\delta(J-B)-\frac{d^2B}{dt^2}\right\}e^{+p_0 t}. \tag{70}$$

We write the solutions for C and D in the form

$$C(t) = \frac{-1}{2p_0}\int_t^{c_1} e^{-p_0 t}\left\{3\delta(J-B)-\frac{d^2B}{dt^2}\right\}dt, \tag{71}$$

$$D(t) = \frac{1}{2p_0}\int_t^{c_2} e^{+p_0 t}\left\{3\delta(J-B)-\frac{d^2B}{dt^2}\right\}dt. \tag{72}$$

The two integration constants c_1 and c_2 are determined by the usual boundary conditions $J = 2H$ at $t = 0$, and the requirement that $J-B$ shall not increase exponentially as $t \to \infty$. This latter condition gives $c_1 = \infty$ since for c_1 finite the term $Ce^{p_0 t}$ in the solution (66) would diverge exponentially. The constant c_2 may be determined from the condition $J_0 = 2H_0$, where the zero suffix denotes the value at the boundary. We proceed in the following way: from equation (66) we have

$$J_0 = B_0+C_0+D_0, \tag{73}$$

where

$$C_0 = \frac{-1}{2p_0}\int_0^{\infty} e^{-p_0 t}\left\{3\delta(J-B)-\frac{d^2B}{dt^2}\right\}dt, \tag{74}$$

$$D_0 = \frac{1}{2p_0}\int_0^{c_2} e^{+p_0 t}\left\{3\delta(J-B)-\frac{d^2B}{dt^2}\right\}dt. \tag{75}$$

Now the condition $J_0 = 2H_0 = \frac{2}{3}(dJ/dt)_0$ gives

$$J_0 = \frac{2}{3}\left\{\left(\frac{dB}{dt}\right)_0+p_0(C_0-D_0)\right\}. \tag{76}$$

To simplify the notation we set $a = B_0$, $g = (dB/dt)_0$, then from equations (73) and (76)

$$-D_0 = \frac{1}{1+\frac{2}{3}p_0}\{a-\tfrac{2}{3}g+(1-\tfrac{2}{3}p_0)C_0\}, \tag{77}$$

an equation which gives the constant c_2 implicitly.

This completes the general solution (66) of equation (65). To apply the solution to the line-contour problem we only need to calculate the quantity H_0 which gives the intensity of the radiation within the absorption line when the star is viewed as a whole. Since $J_0 = 2H_0$ equation (76) gives

$$H_0 = \tfrac{1}{3}\{g+p_0(C_0-D_0)\}. \qquad (78)$$

Substituting in (78) for C_0 and D_0 from (74) and (76) we find

$$H_0 = \frac{1}{3}\frac{g+ap_0}{1+\tfrac{2}{3}p_0} - \frac{\tfrac{1}{3}}{1+\tfrac{2}{3}p_0} \int_0^{\infty} e^{-p_0 t}\left\{3\delta(J-B)-\frac{d^2B}{dt^2}\right\}dt. \qquad (79)$$

Since

$$\int_0^{\infty} e^{-p_0 t}\frac{d^2B}{dt^2}\,dt = -(g+ap_0)+p_0^2\int_0^{\infty} e^{-p_0 t}B\,dt, \qquad (80)$$

equation (79) may be written

$$H_0 = \frac{\tfrac{1}{3}p_0^2}{1+\tfrac{2}{3}p_0}\int_0^{\infty} e^{-p_0 t}B\,dt - \frac{1}{1+\tfrac{2}{3}p_0}\int_0^{\infty} e^{-p_0 t}\delta(J-B)\,dt. \qquad (81)$$

The treatment thus far has been quite general. In the special case when η is constant, that is $\delta = 0$ for all t, equation (81) gives

$$H_0 = \frac{\tfrac{1}{3}p_0^2}{1+\tfrac{2}{3}p_0}\int_0^{\infty} e^{-p_0 t}B\,dt, \qquad (82)$$

a general form for an η-constant atmosphere, similar to an expression derived by Milne,† without any assumption about the behaviour of B with depth. The integral in equation (82) is proportional to the mean value throughout the atmosphere of the function B weighted by the factor $e^{-p_0 t}$. Now equation (59) with η constant gives $t = (1+\eta)\tau$ so that

$$p_0 t = (1+\eta)p_0\tau = q\tau,$$

where

$$q = \sqrt{\{3(1+\epsilon\eta)(1+\eta)\}}.$$

Equation (82) may now be written

$$H_0 = \frac{\tfrac{1}{3}q^2}{1+\eta+\tfrac{2}{3}q}\int_0^{\infty} e^{-q\tau}B\,d\tau. \qquad (83)$$

The greater the value of η, and hence q, the nearer to the surface are the layers which carry most weight in determining the integral in equation (83). This means that *the stronger lines are formed nearer the surface than the weaker lines.*

† E. A. Milne, *Phil. Trans.* A **223**, 201 (1923), equation (60).

When $B = a+b\tau$, equation (83) gives

$$H_0 = \frac{\frac{1}{3}q^2}{1+\eta+\frac{2}{3}q}\left(\frac{a}{q}+\frac{b}{q^2}\right) = \frac{1}{3}\frac{b+aq}{1+\eta+\frac{2}{3}q},$$

which is Eddington's equation (22).

When δ is not zero equation (79) and the alternative form (81) give H_0, and hence the residual intensity in the absorption line, if a solution for $J-B$ is known. The second terms in these two equations give the corrections to be applied to the η-constant value of H_0 on account of the η variations. If the approximate form for $J-B$ adopted is only in error by a quantity of the first order, and if δ and d^2B/dt^2 are small quantities of the first order, the corrections will then be found from the integrals with an error of the second order.

If we adopt as our approximate formula for $J-B$ the solution of equation (65) for $\delta = 0$ and $d^2B/dt^2 = 0$, we have

$$J-B = -\frac{a-\frac{2}{3}g}{1+\frac{2}{3}p_0}e^{-p_0t}. \tag{84}$$

Substitute (84) in equations (79) and (81) and we get

$$H_0 = \frac{1}{3}\frac{y+ap_0}{1+\frac{2}{3}p_0} + \frac{a-\frac{2}{3}g}{(1+\frac{2}{3}p_0)^2}\int_0^\infty e^{-2p_0t}\delta\,dt + \frac{\frac{1}{3}}{1+\frac{2}{3}p_0}\int_0^\infty e^{-p_0t}\frac{d^2B}{dt^2}dt, \tag{85}$$

and

$$H_0 = \frac{\frac{1}{3}p_0^2}{1+\frac{2}{3}p_0}\int_0^\infty e^{-p_0t}B\,dt + \frac{a-\frac{2}{3}g}{(1+\frac{2}{3}p_0)^2}\int_0^\infty e^{-2p_0t}\delta\,dt. \tag{86}$$

Equations (85) and (86) complete the solution for the value of H at the boundary.

6.32. *Formulae for numerical calculation of the mean contour*

For convenience in numerical work equation (85) may be put into a compact form by means of the following transformations. Rewrite equation (85) as follows:

$$H_0 = a\left\{\frac{\frac{1}{3}p_0}{1+\frac{2}{3}p_0} + \frac{1}{(1+\frac{2}{3}p_0)^2}\int_0^\infty e^{-2p_0t}\delta\,dt\right\} + \frac{\frac{1}{3}}{1+\frac{2}{3}p_0}\int_0^\infty e^{-p_0t}\frac{d^2B}{dt^2}dt +$$

$$+\frac{1}{3}g\left\{\frac{1}{1+\frac{2}{3}p_0} - \frac{2}{(1+\frac{2}{3}p_0)^2}\int_0^\infty e^{-2p_0t}\delta\,dt\right\}. \tag{87}$$

Since $\lambda = \lambda_0+\delta$, $p_0 = \sqrt{(3\lambda_0)}$ we have $p = \sqrt{(3\lambda)} = p_0+\Delta p$, where

$$\Delta p \doteqdot \frac{1}{2}\frac{\delta}{\lambda_0}p_0.$$

Hence
$$\delta \doteqdot 2\lambda_0 \frac{\Delta p}{p_0} = \tfrac{2}{3} p_0 \Delta p.$$

The term in equation (87) which involves a may now be written

$$\tfrac{1}{3}a \left\{ \frac{p_0}{1+\tfrac{2}{3}p_0} + \frac{1}{(1+\tfrac{2}{3}p_0)^2} \int\limits_0^\infty e^{-2p_0 t} \Delta p \, d(2p_0 t) \right\}.$$

Set
$$\overline{\Delta p} = \int\limits_0^\infty e^{-2p_0 t} \Delta p \, d(2p_0 t).$$

Then since
$$\frac{1}{(1+\tfrac{2}{3}p_0)^2} = \frac{d}{dp_0}\left(\frac{p_0}{1+\tfrac{2}{3}p_0} \right),$$

we have
$$\frac{p_0}{1+\tfrac{2}{3}p_0} + \frac{d}{dp_0}\left(\frac{p_0}{1+\tfrac{2}{3}p_0} \right)\overline{\Delta p} \doteqdot \frac{p_0 + \overline{\Delta p}}{1+\tfrac{2}{3}(p_0 + \overline{\Delta p})}.$$

Let
$$\bar{p} = p_0 + \overline{\Delta p} = \int\limits_0^\infty e^{-2p_0 t} p \, d(2p_0 t),$$

then
$$a\left\{ \frac{\tfrac{1}{3}p_0}{1+\tfrac{2}{3}p_0} + \frac{1}{(1+\tfrac{2}{3}p_0)^2} \int\limits_0^\infty e^{-2p_0 t} \delta \, dt \right\} = \frac{1}{3} \cdot \frac{a\bar{p}}{1+\tfrac{2}{3}\bar{p}}.$$

Similarly the term in equation (87) which involves g may be written

$$\tfrac{1}{3}g \left\{ \frac{1}{1+\tfrac{2}{3}p_0} - \frac{\tfrac{2}{3}}{(1+\tfrac{2}{3}p_0)^2} \int\limits_0^\infty e^{-2p_0 t} \Delta p \, d(2p_0 t) \right\}$$

$$= \tfrac{1}{3}g \left\{ \frac{1}{1+\tfrac{2}{3}p_0} + \frac{d}{dp_0}\left(\frac{1}{1+\tfrac{2}{3}p_0} \right)\overline{\Delta p} \right\} = \frac{1}{3} \cdot \frac{g}{1+\tfrac{2}{3}\bar{p}}.$$

Equation (87) may now be written in the form

$$H_0 = \frac{1}{3} \frac{g+a\bar{p}}{1+\tfrac{2}{3}\bar{p}} + \frac{1}{3} \frac{1}{1+\tfrac{2}{3}p_0} \int\limits_0^\infty e^{-p_0 t} \frac{d^2 B}{dt^2} \, dt. \qquad (88)$$

Comparing equation (85), with $\delta = 0$, and equation (88) we see that the main difference between the results for η constant and η variable is the replacement of p_0 by the mean value

$$\bar{p} = \int\limits_0^\infty e^{-2p_0 t} p \, d(2p_0 t). \qquad (89)$$

If $d^2 B/dt^2$ is small, and of the first order, we can substitute $\bar{p}$ for p_0

in the second term of equation (88) and only introduce an error of the second order. Now, from equation (80), we have

$$\frac{1}{1+\frac{2}{3}\bar{p}} \int_0^\infty e^{-\bar{p}t}\frac{d^2B}{dt^2}\,dt = -\frac{g+a\bar{p}}{1+\frac{2}{3}\bar{p}}+\frac{\bar{p}}{1+\frac{2}{3}\bar{p}}\int_0^\infty e^{-\bar{p}t}\,B\,d(\bar{p}t).$$

Equation (88) may now be written

$$H_0 = \frac{\frac{1}{3}\bar{p}}{1+\frac{2}{3}\bar{p}}\,\bar{B},$$

where

$$\bar{B} = \int_0^\infty e^{-\bar{p}t}B\,d(\bar{p}t). \tag{90}$$

This result is formally the same as Milne's equation (82) for η constant.

As an approximation to the Planck function in the region of line formation we cannot use a linear expansion in the line-plus-continuum optical depth t. Such a variation is only true in special circumstances, so we use $B = a+b\tau$, where the optical depth is measured in the continuous spectrum just outside the line. We shall introduce the necessary refinement of the mean optical depth at a later stage.

Since $dt = (1+\eta)\,d\tau$ we have

$$\frac{dB}{dt} = b\,\frac{1}{1+\eta}.$$

Hence

$$B = a+b\int_0^t \frac{dt}{1+\eta}.$$

Evaluating the integral in equation (90) we have

$$\bar{B} = a+b\int_0^\infty e^{-\bar{p}t}\frac{1}{1+\eta}\,dt. \tag{91}$$

Let

$$\mu = \frac{1}{1+\eta},$$

and define the mean values

$$\bar{\lambda} = \int_0^\infty e^{-\bar{p}t}\lambda\,d(\bar{p}t), \qquad \bar{\mu} = \int_0^\infty e^{-\bar{p}t}\mu\,d(\bar{p}t). \tag{92}$$

Equation (91) is then

$$\bar{B} = a+b\bar{\mu}/\bar{p},$$

and from (90) we have

$$H_0 = \frac{1}{3}\frac{b\bar{\mu}+a\bar{p}}{1+\frac{2}{3}\bar{p}}. \tag{93.1}$$

But when $\epsilon = 0$ we have $\lambda = \mu \; (= 1/(1+\eta))$. In this case

$$\Pi_0 = \frac{1}{3}\frac{b\bar{\lambda}+a\bar{p}}{1+\frac{2}{3}\bar{p}}. \tag{93.2}$$

Equations (93.1) and (93.2) are of the same form as the results for η constant. When η varies with depth the mean values $\bar{\lambda}, \bar{\mu}$, and $\bar{p}$ appear in place of the constants λ_0, μ_0, and p_0.

Convenient formulae for computing the mean values may be readily obtained. When η is constant and $\epsilon = 0$ we have

$$p_0 t = (1+\eta)p_0\tau = 3\tau/p_0. \tag{94}$$

We suppose that an error of the second order only is introduced if we make the substitution (94) in equation (89),

$$\bar{p} = \int_0^\infty e^{-2p_0 t}p \; d(2p_0 t).$$

This may be written

$$\overline{\sqrt{\lambda}} = \int_0^\infty e^{-2\sqrt{(3/\lambda_0)}\tau}\sqrt{\lambda} \; d\{2\sqrt{(3/\lambda_0)}\tau\}. \tag{95}$$

In order to compute $\bar{\lambda}$ (or $\bar{\mu}$) we set $\bar{p}t = 3\tau/p_0$ in equations (92). This gives

$$\bar{\lambda} = \int_0^\infty e^{-3\tau/p_0}\lambda \; d(3\tau/p_0) = \int_0^\infty e^{-\sqrt{(3/\lambda_0)}\tau}\lambda \; d\{\sqrt{(3/\lambda_0)}\tau\}, \tag{96}$$

$$\bar{\mu} = \int_0^\infty e^{-3\tau/p_0}\mu \; d(3\tau/p_0) = \int_0^\infty e^{-\sqrt{(3/\lambda_0)}\tau}\mu \; d\{\sqrt{(3/\lambda_0)}\tau\}. \tag{97}$$

The mean contour. In the continuous spectrum just outside the line we have $\lambda = \bar{\lambda} = 1$, $\mu = \bar{\mu} = 1$, $p = \bar{p} = \sqrt{3}$. The residual intensity within the absorption line for the general case $\epsilon \neq 0$ is therefore

$$r = \frac{1+\frac{2}{3}\sqrt{3}}{b+a\sqrt{3}}\frac{b\bar{\mu}+a\bar{p}}{1+\frac{2}{3}\bar{p}}, \tag{98}$$

where

$$\bar{p} = \sqrt{3}\overline{\sqrt{\lambda}}.$$

From equation (27) we have $\dfrac{b}{a} = \dfrac{3}{8}\dfrac{x_0}{n}$, where $n = k/\bar{k}$. Hence

$$r = \frac{1+\frac{2}{3}\sqrt{3}}{\frac{1}{4}(x_0/n)+\frac{2}{3}\sqrt{3}}\frac{\frac{1}{4}(x_0/n)\bar{\mu}+\frac{2}{3}\sqrt{3}\overline{\sqrt{\lambda}}}{1+\frac{2}{3}\sqrt{3}\overline{\sqrt{\lambda}}}. \tag{99}$$

For a region of the spectrum where $b = \frac{3}{2}a$, corresponding to $x_0 = 4n$, and with $\epsilon = 0$, equation (99) takes the simpler form

$$r = \frac{\bar{\lambda} + \frac{2}{3}\sqrt{3}\overline{\sqrt{\lambda}}}{1 + \frac{2}{3}\sqrt{3}\overline{\sqrt{\lambda}}}. \tag{100}$$

In numerical work, values of $\lambda \ (= 1/(1+\eta))$ are calculated by means of equation (54). But the atomic line absorption coefficient as modified by damping and the Doppler effect (see Chapter VI) can only be found as a function of optical depth if the physical conditions (that is the temperature and pressure) in the atmosphere are known. The required values of T, p, and p_e are given as a function of the mean optical depth by tables of model atmospheres (Chapter IX).

To compute the mean values (95) and (96) required in equations (99) and (100) we make the substitution (25):

$$\tau = (k/\bar{k})\bar{\tau} = n\bar{\tau}.$$

If we set

$$x = e^{-\sqrt{(3/\lambda_0)}n\bar{\tau}}$$

in equation (96), we obtain

$$\bar{\lambda} = \int_0^1 \lambda(x) \, dx.$$

If we approximate to the integral by means of a quadrature formula

$$\sum_j a_j \lambda(x_j),$$

where the a_j are the weights and x_j the division points, the value of $\bar{\tau}_j$ corresponding to x_j is given by

$$\bar{\tau}_j = \frac{1}{n} \sqrt{\frac{\lambda_0}{3}} \ln\left(\frac{1}{x_j}\right).$$

In choosing the quadrature formula it should be kept in mind that the $\bar{\tau}_j$ values should lie within the range of values of mean optical depth for which the model stellar atmosphere is computed. A convenient choice which meets this desideratum is a five-point Gaussian summation for which the weights and division points are given in Table XXIII.

TABLE XXIII

Weight Factors and Points of Division for the Evaluation of $\bar{\lambda}$ and $\bar{\mu}$ by Numerical Quadrature

j	1	2	3	4	5
a_j	0·119	0·239	0·284	0·239	0·119
$\bar{\tau}_j$†	0·028	0·151	0·400	0·846	1·767

† Values of $\bar{\tau}_j$ in the table are to be multiplied by $(1/n)\sqrt{\lambda_0}$. For the evaluation of $\overline{\sqrt{\lambda}}$ the weight factors are the same as for $\bar{\lambda}$ and $\bar{\mu}$, but the values of $\bar{\tau}_j$ are one-half those given in the table, i.e. multiply the values shown by $(1/2n)\sqrt{\lambda_0}$.

The treatment in this section is based on the approximate boundary condition $J = 2H$, and the geometrical approximation $K = \frac{1}{3}J$. This gave Strömgren's formula

$$r = \frac{1+\frac{2}{3}\sqrt{3}}{b+a\sqrt{3}} \frac{b\bar{\mu}+a\sqrt{3}\overline{\sqrt{\lambda}}}{1+\frac{2}{3}\sqrt{3}\overline{\sqrt{\lambda}}}, \tag{101}$$

which reduces to Eddington's formula for r when λ and μ are constant with depth in the atmosphere. A formula similar to (101) has been derived by Tuberg† in an investigation based on Chandrasekhar's Gaussian sum method of approximation. In the first approximation we have

$$r = \frac{2}{b+a\sqrt{3}} \frac{b\bar{\mu}+a\sqrt{3}\overline{\sqrt{\lambda}}}{1+\overline{\sqrt{\lambda}}}. \tag{102}$$

This reduces to Chandrasekhar's solution‡ in the first approximation when η is constant. Equation (102) is the same as Strömgren's formula (101) with the factor $\frac{2}{3}\sqrt{3}$ replaced by unity both in the numerator and denominator. Since the geometrical approximation $K = \frac{1}{3}J$ is implicit in Chandrasekhar's first approximation (see Chapter II, Section 2.5), the difference between the two formulae may be attributed to the different boundary conditions used.

In practical application of the formulae, a quantity of importance is the equivalent width, defined by $W = \int_0^\infty (1-r)\, dv$. Equivalent widths computed from (101) are about 2 per cent. greater than those given by (102). The ratio of the equivalent widths of two lines computed from either formula will therefore be practically the same.

† M. Tuberg, *Ap. J.* **103**, 145 (1946).

‡ S. Chandrasekhar, ibid. **100**, 76 (1944); *Radiative Transfer* (Oxford), chap. xii, section 84.2.

VIII

THE FORMATION OF ABSORPTION LINES
BY NON-COHERENT PROCESSES

1. The nature of non-coherent scattering

In Eddington's classical paper 'The Formation of Absorption Lines'†
occurs the passage:

The crucial question is whether light absorbed in one part of the line is re-
emitted in precisely the same part of the line. If so, the blackening in this frequency
is independent of what is happening in neighbouring frequencies. . . . For example,
if the process is regarded as one of transition between two energy levels, which
are not sharp but are composed of narrow bands of energy, the atom is not likely
to return to the precise spot in the lower level from which it started, and the
re-emission will not be the exact reverse of the absorption. In that case the line
can only be studied as a whole. Modern attempts to interpret the contours of
absorption lines assume (rightly or wrongly) that there is no such redistribution
of frequencies.

When there is no redistribution, the line is said to be formed by
coherent scattering, and the differential equations are those of Chapter
VII. In the present chapter we examine the more general case where
redistribution can occur. Besides redistribution of the kind mentioned
in the passage just quoted, Eddington noticed another departure from
the simple case, which he called *interlocking* of lines. If two or more
lines in a spectrum have a common upper state, the atom can be excited
to that state by absorption in either line: but the re-emission will take
place according to the transition probability regardless of the path by
which the excitation was made. The equations of formation of the
lines are not independent but contain cross terms.

The equation for the intensity in a particular frequency of a spectral
line might then, in general, contain an infinite set of terms involving the
intensities of the other frequencies in the same line, as well as terms
involving the intensities in a finite number of other lines in the same
spectrum. Fortunately, these difficulties do not arise in some important
cases, namely principal lines in spectra, in which the ground state is sharp.
The reason for this is that the distribution of energy levels within a
state depends on the life of the state. If γ_j is the probability of transition
from the energy state j, that is, the reciprocal of the mean life of the
state, the probability $W_j(E)\,dE$ that the energy of an atom in a state

† A. S. Eddington, *M.N.* **89**, 620 (1929).

whose mean energy is E_j lies between E and $E+dE$ is given by equation (76) of Chapter VI, namely

$$W_j(E)\,dE = \frac{(\gamma_j/h)\,dE}{(2\pi/h)^2(E-E_j)^2+(\tfrac{1}{2}\gamma_j)^2}.$$

As the ground state has a very long life compared with that of other states, γ_j is very small and $W_j(E)$ takes small values unless $E-E_j$ is of order γ_j. The spread of energy in the ground state can therefore be ignored. The same is true of metastable states, which may be considered as sharp.

The fundamental equation for the formation of a line, under any circumstances, is given by equation (4) of Chapter VII:

$$\cos\theta\frac{dI_\nu(\theta)}{\rho\,dx} = -(k_\nu+l_\nu)I_\nu(\theta)+j_\nu.$$

In the case of coherent scattering we had

$$j_\nu = (k_\nu+\epsilon l_\nu)B(\nu,T)+(1-\epsilon)l_\nu J_\nu, \tag{1}$$

which we now replace by the more general expression

$$j_\nu = (k_\nu+\epsilon l_\nu)B(\nu,T)+(1-\epsilon)\int_0^\infty p(\nu,\nu')l(\nu')J(\nu')\,d\nu'. \tag{2}$$

When $p(\nu,\nu')=1$ for $\nu'=\nu$ and is zero for all other ν', we recover the case of coherent formation. Otherwise $p(\nu,\nu')$ must have non-zero values for all frequencies ν' which are connected with the frequency ν either by interlocking or by redistribution.

2. Interlocking without redistribution

2.1. *Lines with a common upper state*

After coherent scattering, the next simplest case is that of interlocking of principal lines, for then $p(\nu,\nu')$ takes a small number only of non-zero values. Examples of this are the principal lines of Al, $^2S_{\frac{1}{2}}-^2P_{\frac{3}{2}}$ at $\lambda3,962$ A, and $^2S_{\frac{1}{2}}-^2P_{\frac{1}{2}}$ at $\lambda3,944$ A, in which $^2P_{\frac{1}{2}}$ is the ground state and $^2P_{\frac{3}{2}}$ metastable: and the principal triplet of Mg, $^3S_1-^3P_2$ at $\lambda5,184$ A, $^3S_1-^3P_1$ at $\lambda5,173$ A, and $^3S_1-^3P_0$ at $\lambda5,167$ A. In this case $^3P_2$ and $^3P_0$ are metastable, and $^3P_1$ is linked by an intercombination line to the ground state $^1S_0$.

We consider the case where there are three lines, the formulae for two lines being very simply obtained from those of the more complicated case. Let ν_1, ν_2, and ν_3 be the central frequencies of the lines, and suppose that when a quantum of frequency $\nu_1+\Delta\nu$ is absorbed the energy of the upper state is $E_0+h\,\Delta\nu$ and the subsequent re-emission is either $\nu_1+\Delta\nu$ $\nu_2+\Delta\nu$, or $\nu_3+\Delta\nu$. These three frequencies are interlocked with each other but with no other frequencies. For each value of $\Delta\nu$ there are three simultaneous equations:

$$\cos\theta\frac{dI_1(\theta)}{\rho\,dx} = -(k_1+l_1)I_1(\theta)+(k_1+\epsilon_1 l_1)B(\nu_1,T)+$$
$$+(1-\epsilon_1)\{p(11)l_1 J_1+p(12)l_2 J_2+p(13)l_3 J_3\}, \quad (3.1)$$

$$\cos\theta\frac{dI_2(\theta)}{\rho\,dx} = -(k_2+l_2)I_2(\theta)+(k_2+\epsilon_2 l_2)B(\nu_2,T)+$$
$$+(1-\epsilon_2)\{p(21)l_1 J_1+p(22)l_2 J_2+p(23)l_3 J_3\}, \quad (3.2)$$

$$\cos\theta\frac{dI_3(\theta)}{\rho\,dx} = -(k_3+l_3)I_3(0)+(k_3+\epsilon_3 l_3)B(\nu_3,T)+$$
$$+(1-\epsilon_3)\{p(31)l_1 J_1+p(32)l_2 J_2+p(33)l_3 J_3\}. \quad (3.3)$$

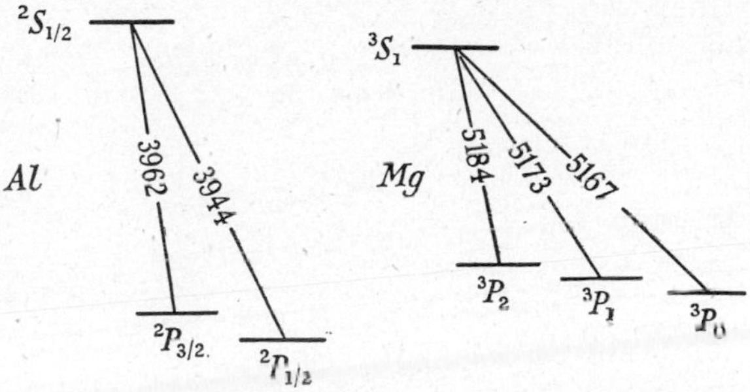

FIG. 26. Interlocked principal lines of Al and Mg.

We now have to evaluate the quantities $p(n,r)$. To do this we note that the number of transitions per c.c. per sec. from the three lower states to a band of sub-states of the upper state lying within $E_0+h\,\Delta\nu$ to $E_0+h(\Delta\nu+\delta\nu)$ is

$$\rho\,dx\delta\nu\left\{\frac{l(\nu_1+\Delta\nu)J(\nu_1+\Delta\nu)}{h(\nu_1+\Delta\nu)}+\frac{l(\nu_2+\Delta\nu)J(\nu_2+\Delta\nu)}{h(\nu_2+\Delta\nu)}+\frac{l(\nu_3+\Delta\nu)J(\nu_3+\Delta\nu)}{h(\nu_3+\Delta\nu)}\right\}.$$

This must be equal to the number of transitions leaving the upper sub-state into the three lines per c.c. per sec. Let the population of the upper state with energies between

$$E_0+h\,\Delta\nu \quad\text{and}\quad E_0+h(\Delta\nu+\delta\nu)$$

be $N_u(\Delta\nu)\,\delta\nu$: then the number of transitions is

$$N_u(\Delta\nu)\,\delta\nu\{A_{u1}+A_{u2}+A_{u3}\}.$$

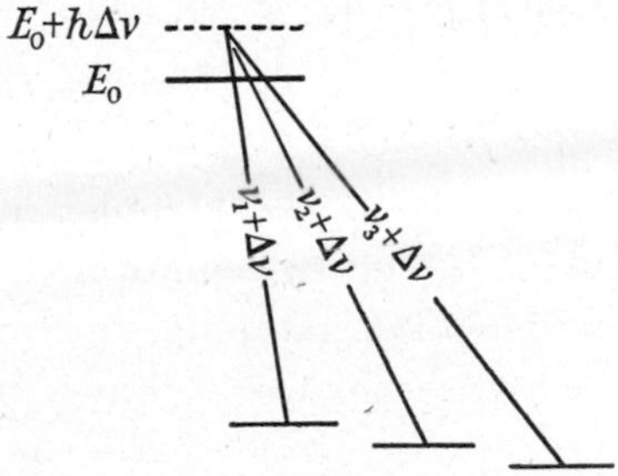

The secular equilibrium of the sub-state gives

$$N_u(\Delta\nu)\{A_{u1}+A_{u2}+A_{u3}\} = \rho\,dx\left\{\frac{l(\nu_1+\Delta\nu)J(\nu_1+\Delta\nu)}{h(\nu_1+\Delta\nu)}+\dots+\dots\right\}.$$

FIG. 27. The formation of three interlocked lines with a common upper state.

The energy emitted in the first line is $N_u(\Delta\nu)A_{u1}h(\nu_1+\Delta\nu)$, and similarly for the other lines. Accordingly

$$p(n,r) = \frac{\nu_n+\Delta\nu}{\nu_r+\Delta\nu}\frac{A_{un}}{A_{u1}+A_{u2}+A_{u3}}. \tag{4}$$

The equations can be written more simply if we suppose that the three lines are so close together that we may ignore differences in the frequencies, and set $k_1 = k_2 = k_3 = k$, and $B(\nu_1, T) = B(\nu_2, T) = B(\nu_3, T) = B$. Equation (4) may then be written as

$$p(n,r) = \frac{A_{un}}{A_{u1}+A_{u2}+A_{u3}}. \tag{5}$$

Since p does not involve r we set $p(n,r) = \alpha_n$, noting that $\alpha_1+\alpha_2+\alpha_3 = 1$. Then with $\epsilon_1 = \epsilon_2 = \epsilon_3 = \epsilon$ equations (3.1), (3.2), and (3.3) become

$$\cos\theta\frac{dI_1(\theta)}{d\tau} = (1+\eta_1)I_1(\theta)-(1+\epsilon\eta_1)B-(1-\epsilon)\alpha_1\{\eta_1 J_1+\eta_2 J_2+\eta_3 J_3\},$$
$$\tag{6.1}$$

$$\cos\theta\frac{dI_2(\theta)}{d\tau} = (1+\eta_2)I_2(\theta)-(1+\epsilon\eta_2)B-(1-\epsilon)\alpha_2\{\eta_1 J_1+\eta_2 J_2+\eta_3 J_3\},$$
$$\tag{6.2}$$

$$\cos\theta\frac{dI_3(\theta)}{d\tau} = (1+\eta_3)I_3(\theta)-(1+\epsilon\eta_3)B-(1-\epsilon)\alpha_3\{\eta_1 J_1+\eta_2 J_2+\eta_3 J_3\}.$$
$$\tag{6.3}$$

In these equations references to the particular $\Delta\nu$ have been omitted for the sake of clarity.

Further simplifications may be introduced by the following consideration of the nature of η for the three lines. From equation (53) of Chapter VII, we have

$$\eta = \frac{N\alpha(\nu)_D}{k\rho}, \tag{7}$$

where $\alpha(\nu)_D$ is the Doppler modification of the atomic absorption coefficient given by equation (110) of Chapter VI. Since the lower states are sharp the damping constant a ($= \delta/b$) of each line depends only on the lifetime in the common upper state. Now the three lower states have been supposed nearly equal in excitation. Hence from Boltzmann's equation we have

$$\frac{N_1}{q_1} = \frac{N_2}{q_2} = \frac{N_3}{q_3}, \tag{8}$$

where the q's are the statistical weights. From equations (7) and (8) we obtain $\eta_n = \text{const.}\times q_n f$, the oscillator strength f being related to the downward transition probability by equation (73) of Chapter VI, namely

$$f = \frac{1}{3}\frac{q_u}{q_n}\frac{A_{un}}{\gamma_n},$$

where γ_n is the classical damping constant $8\pi^2 e^2 v_0^2/3mc^3$. Since γ is the same for the three lines, $\eta_1/A_{u1} = \eta_2/A_{u2} = \eta_3/A_{u3}$ for all Δv, and from equation (5), which defines α_n, we obtain

$$\frac{\eta_1}{\alpha_1} = \frac{\eta_2}{\alpha_2} = \frac{\eta_3}{\alpha_3}. \tag{9}$$

Hence $\qquad \alpha_1(\eta_1+\eta_2+\eta_3) = (\alpha_1+\alpha_2+\alpha_3)\eta_1 = \eta_1.$

In equation (6.1) we can therefore put

$$\alpha_1(\eta_1 J_1 + \eta_2 J_2 + \eta_3 J_3) = \alpha_1\{\eta_1(J_1-B)+\eta_2(J_2-B)+\eta_3(J_3-B)\}+\eta_1 B$$
$$= \eta_1\{\alpha_1(J_1-B)+\alpha_2(J_2-B)+\alpha_3(J_3-B)\}+\eta_1 B.$$

Equations (6.1), (6.2), and (6.3) now take the form

$$\cos\theta\frac{dI_1(\theta)}{d\tau} = (1+\eta_1)\{I_1(\theta)-B\}-$$
$$-(1-\epsilon)\eta_1\{\alpha_1(J_1-B)+\alpha_2(J_2-B)+\alpha_3(J_3-B)\}, \tag{10.1}$$

$$\cos\theta\frac{dI_2(\theta)}{d\tau} = (1+\eta_2)\{I_2(\theta)-B\}-$$
$$-(1-\epsilon)\eta_2\{\alpha_1(J_1-B)+\alpha_2(J_2-B)+\alpha_3(J_3-B)\}, \tag{10.2}$$

$$\cos\theta\frac{dI_3(\theta)}{d\tau} = (1+\eta_3)\{I_3(\theta)-B\}-$$
$$-(1-\epsilon)\eta_3\{\alpha_1(J_1-B)+\alpha_2(J_2-B)+\alpha_3(J_3-B)\}. \tag{10.3}$$

To solve these equations we proceed as in Chapter VII, setting

$$J_n = \frac{1}{4\pi}\int I_n(\theta)\,d\omega, \quad H_n = \frac{1}{4\pi}\int I_n(\theta)\cos\theta\,d\omega, \quad K_n = \frac{1}{4\pi}\int I_n(\theta)\cos^2\theta\,d\omega,$$

making use of Eddington's approximation $K_n = \frac{1}{3}J_n$, and the approximate boundary condition $J_n = 2H_n$. When η_n is constant, and B a linear function of τ, we have

$$\frac{d^2}{d\tau^2}(J_n-B) = q_{n1}^2(J_1-B)+q_{n2}^2(J_2-B)+q_{n3}^2(J_3-B) \quad (n=1,2,3), \tag{11}$$

where $\qquad q_{nn}^2 = 3(1+\eta_n)\{1+\eta_n[1-(1-\epsilon)\alpha_n]\},$
$$q_{nm}^2 = -3(1-\epsilon)\eta_n(1+\eta_n)\alpha_m.$$

The solution of these equations is

$$J_n-B = \sum_{m=1}^{3} A_{nm}\,e^{-p_m\tau}. \tag{12}$$

Since $B = a + b\tau$, we have

$$J_n(0) = a + \sum_m A_{nm},$$

$$H_n(0) = \frac{1}{3(1+\eta_n)}\left(\frac{dJ_n}{d\tau}\right)_0 = \frac{1}{3(1+\eta_n)}\left(b - \sum_m p_m A_{nm}\right).$$

Hence the boundary condition gives the three equations:

$$a(1+\eta_n) - \tfrac{2}{3}b + \sum_m (1+\eta_n+\tfrac{2}{3}p_m)A_{nm} = 0. \tag{13}$$

Substituting the solution (12) in equation (11), and equating coefficients of $e^{-p_m\tau}$ with $m = 1$, 2, and 3, we get the nine equations:

$$(q_{11}^2 - p_m^2)A_{1m} + q_{12}^2 A_{2m} + q_{13}^2 A_{3m} = 0, \tag{14.1}$$

$$q_{21}^2 A_{1m} + (q_{22}^2 - p_m^2)A_{2m} + q_{23}^2 A_{3m} = 0, \tag{14.2}$$

$$q_{31}^2 A_{1m} + q_{32}^2 A_{2m} + (q_{33}^2 - p_m^2)A_{3m} = 0. \tag{14.3}$$

We have altogether twelve equations for the three p's and the nine A's. The p's satisfy the equation

$$\begin{vmatrix} q_{11}^2 - p^2 & q_{12}^2 & q_{13}^2 \\ q_{21}^2 & q_{22}^2 - p^2 & q_{23}^2 \\ q_{31}^2 & q_{32}^2 & q_{33}^2 - p^2 \end{vmatrix} = 0, \tag{15}$$

only the three positive roots being taken, since negative values of p are excluded by the boundary condition that $J_n - B$ shall not diverge exponentially as $\tau \to \infty$. Each of three sets of the A_{nm} satisfies a pair of equations. For example, with $m = 1$ equations (14.2) and (14.3) become

$$q_{21}^2 A_{11} + (q_{22}^2 - p_1^2)A_{21} + q_{23}^2 A_{31} = 0,$$

$$q_{31}^2 A_{11} + q_{32}^2 A_{21} + (q_{33}^2 - p_1^2)A_{31} = 0,$$

from which the ratios A_{21}/A_{11} and A_{31}/A_{11} can be calculated. The solution of similar pairs from the set (14) together with the boundary condition, equation (13), gives the nine coefficients A_{nm}. This completes the solution (12).

The residual intensity within the three lines is given by

$$r_n = (H_n/H)_0 = (J_n/J)_0,$$

where J and H apply to the continuous spectrum outside the lines. From equation (22) of Chapter VII, we have

$$J = \frac{2}{3}\frac{b+a\sqrt{3}}{1+\tfrac{2}{3}\sqrt{3}}.$$

Hence $$r_n = \frac{3}{2}\frac{1+\tfrac{2}{3}\sqrt{3}}{b+a\sqrt{3}}\left(a + \sum_{m=1}^{3} A_{nm}\right). \tag{16}$$

To illustrate the effect of interlocking, we calculate the quantity

$$\tfrac{1}{2}w = \int_{\eta=\infty}^{0} (1-r)\, d\eta^{-\frac{1}{2}}$$

for doublet and triplet lines in a region of the spectrum where $b = \tfrac{3}{2}a$, and with $\epsilon = 0$. For doublet lines with $\alpha_1 = \tfrac{1}{3}$ (weaker line) and $\alpha_2 = \tfrac{2}{3}$ (stronger line), we obtain $\tfrac{1}{2}w_1 = 0\cdot966$ and $\tfrac{1}{2}w_2 = 0\cdot940$. These are little altered from the coherent value $\tfrac{1}{2}w^* = 0\cdot951$ for the standard model. Calculations for a triplet in which $\alpha_1 = \tfrac{1}{9}$, $\alpha_2 = \tfrac{3}{9}$, and $\alpha_3 = \tfrac{5}{9}$ (for example, the magnesium triplet) give the following results:

$$\tfrac{1}{2}w_1 = 0\cdot988, \qquad \tfrac{1}{2}w_2 = 0\cdot951, \qquad \tfrac{1}{2}w_3 = 0\cdot933.$$

Since the ratios w/w^* are all close to unity, neglect of interlocking is a good approximation. But the number of oscillators deduced from the intensity of a strong line is proportional to w^2, and in the case of the triplet lines $(w/w^*)^2$ takes values $1\cdot08$, $1\cdot00$, and $0\cdot96$ for the weaker, central, and stronger lines respectively. Neglect of interlocking in this case causes one to attribute 8 per cent. too many oscillators to the weaker line, and 4 per cent. too few to the stronger one. Thus, interlocking has an effect on the curve of growth (the relation between the equivalent width and the number of oscillators) which should be appreciable but not markedly so.

The quantity w^* is of some importance. It is given by

$$\tfrac{1}{2}w^* = \int_{\eta=\infty}^{0} (1-r^*)\, d\eta^{-\frac{1}{2}},$$

where
$$r^* = \frac{1+\tfrac{2}{3}q}{1+\eta+\tfrac{2}{3}q}, \qquad q^2 = 3(1+\eta),$$

and it is, accordingly, proportional to the equivalent width of a line formed by coherent scattering with η independent of depth and $\epsilon = 0$, provided that the line is so strong that $\alpha(\nu)_D \propto (\nu-\nu_0)^{-2}$ is a good approximation. The actual equivalent width W^* of a standard-model line† is related to w^* by

$$W^* = w^*\lambda_0^2 N^{\frac{1}{2}}\left(\frac{e^2 f\delta}{k\rho mc^2}\right)^{\frac{1}{2}}.$$

The value of w^* is $2\sqrt{3}\ln\sqrt{3}$, or $1\cdot903$.

2.2 Rosseland's theorem of cycles

Suppose that there is an atom with three states connected with each other by possible radiation transitions, but connected with no other

† See Chapter IX, Section 5.3.

states: and suppose that this atom is exposed to dilute temperature radiation. Then Rosseland's theorem asserts that cyclical changes will proceed more often in the sense which absorbs the quantum of highest energy and emits the other two quanta, than in the reverse direction.

If the states are denoted by 1, 2, and 3, and are such that state 1 has the lowest energy and 3 the highest, as in Fig. 28, Rosseland's theorem states that the absorption of the quantum $h\nu_{13}$, followed by the emission of $h\nu_{32}$ and $h\nu_{21}$, takes place more often than the absorption of $h\nu_{12}$ and $h\nu_{23}$ followed by the emission of $h\nu_{31}$.

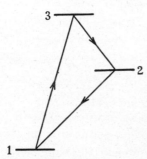

FIG. 28. Cyclical transitions between three energy states of an atom in the presence of dilute radiation.

For the proof of this theorem we consider a more general atom. Let $\mathfrak{A}_{rs}$ be the probability of a transition from state r to state s (depending, in general, on the radiation present), and let there be N_r atoms per c.c. in the state r. The number of transitions from r to s per c.c. per sec. is $N_r\,\mathfrak{A}_{rs}$, and in secular equilibrium the number of atoms arriving at each state is equal to the number leaving it. Hence

$$N_r \sum_s{}' \mathfrak{A}_{rs} = \sum_s{}' N_s\,\mathfrak{A}_{sr},$$

where the primes on the summations denote the exclusion of the terms with $s = r$. If we define $\mathfrak{A}_{rr}$ by

$$\mathfrak{A}_{rr} = -\sum_s{}' \mathfrak{A}_{rs}, \qquad (17)$$

then the condition of secular equilibrium is

$$\sum_s N_s\,\mathfrak{A}_{sr} = 0.$$

If there are p possible states of the atom, there are p of these equations between $p-1$ unknowns, namely the ratios N_2/N_1, N_3/N_1, etc., so that the coefficient determinant vanishes, that is

$$\begin{vmatrix} \mathfrak{A}_{11} & \mathfrak{A}_{21} & \cdot & \cdot & \mathfrak{A}_{p1} \\ \mathfrak{A}_{12} & \mathfrak{A}_{22} & \cdot & \cdot & \mathfrak{A}_{p2} \\ \cdot & \cdot & \cdot & \cdot & \cdot \\ \mathfrak{A}_{1p} & \mathfrak{A}_{2p} & \cdot & \cdot & \mathfrak{A}_{pp} \end{vmatrix} = 0.$$

The populations N_1, N_2, etc., are proportional to the minors of any row in the determinant.

Thus far the argument is perfectly general. In the special conditions laid down for Rosseland's Theorem there are only three states and the radiation intensity is $WB(\nu, T)$, where W is a fraction less than unity. Now

$$\mathfrak{A}_{12} = B_{12}\,WB(\nu_{12}, T), \qquad\qquad \mathfrak{A}_{21} = A_{21} + B_{21}\,WB(\nu_{12}, T),$$

$$\mathfrak{A}_{23} = B_{23}\,WB(\nu_{23}, T), \qquad\qquad \mathfrak{A}_{32} = A_{32} + B_{32}\,WB(\nu_{23}, T),$$

$$\mathfrak{A}_{31} = A_{31} + B_{31}\,WB(\nu_{13}, T), \qquad \mathfrak{A}_{13} = B_{13}\,WB(\nu_{13}, T),$$

where the A's and B's are the Einstein transition coefficients. Following Pannekoek we write 13 for $\mathfrak{A}_{13}$, etc., and we have

$$|\mathfrak{A}_{sr}| = \begin{vmatrix} 11 & 21 & 31 \\ 12 & 22 & 32 \\ 13 & 23 & 33 \end{vmatrix}. \tag{18}$$

By evaluating the minors in the determinant and using the relation (17), we find

$$\frac{N_3}{N_1} = \frac{12.23 - 13.22}{22.33 - 23.32} = \frac{12.23 + 13(21 + 23)}{21.32 + 31(21 + 23)}. \tag{19}$$

The ratio of the number of transitions from state $3 \to 1$ to the number from state $1 \to 3$ will then be

$$\frac{N_3\,\mathfrak{A}_{31}}{N_1\,\mathfrak{A}_{13}} = \frac{12.23.31 + 13.31(21 + 23)}{13.21.32 + 13.31(21 + 23)}.$$

Hence $N_3\,\mathfrak{A}_{31} < N_1\,\mathfrak{A}_{13}$ if $12.23.31 < 13.21.32$. By direct substitution we find

$$\frac{12.23.31}{13.21.32} = \frac{W(e^{h\nu_{13}/RT} - 1 + W)}{(e^{h\nu_{12}/RT} - 1 + W)(e^{h\nu_{23}/RT} - 1 + W)}.$$

Let $e^{h\nu_{12}/RT} = 1 + \alpha$, and $e^{h\nu_{23}/RT} = 1 + \beta$, then $e^{h\nu_{13}/RT} = 1 + \alpha + \beta + \alpha\beta$, and we have

$$\frac{12.23.31}{13.21.32} = \frac{W^2 + (\alpha + \beta + \alpha\beta)W}{(W + \alpha)(W + \beta)} = 1 - \frac{\alpha\beta(1 - W)}{W^2 + (\alpha + \beta)W + \alpha\beta}.$$

Since α and β are both positive, and W is less than unity, the required ratio is also less than unity. Accordingly

$$N_3\,\mathfrak{A}_{31} < N_1\,\mathfrak{A}_{13},$$

and the number of cycles $13 \to 32 \to 31$ is greater than the number $12 \to 23 \to 31$. This completes the proof.

The theorem cannot be applied to three line transitions in any significant case, as at least one of the transitions must be forbidden by the selection rules. However, it can be applied if state 3 is a continuum (the ionized state), and the theorem asserts that in a field of dilute tempera- ture radiation the Lyman continuum is converted by fluorescence into the Balmer continuum and the Lyman α line. This gives a microscopic analysis (of a qualitative kind) which illustrates the way in which the outer layers of a star receive radiation from rather hotter layers beneath themselves, and radiate at the relatively cool surface tempera- ture.

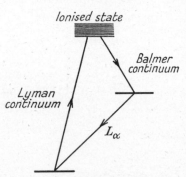

FIG. 29. Fluorescence of the hydro- gen atom whereby radiation in the Lyman continuum is converted into the Balmer continuum and Lyman alpha radiation.

A corollary to Rosseland's theorem may be given. If there are only three possible states of an atom in equilibrium with dilute radiation, the populations of the intermediate state and the upper state are less than the equilibrium value at the temperature of the radiation. In other words, the excitation temperature and the ionization temperature are less than the radiation temperature. The proof is as follows:

Since the ratio of the number of atoms in states 1 and 2 is given by the ratio of the minors of the second and first elements of the first row in the determinant (18), we have

$$\frac{N_2}{N_1} = \frac{13.32+12(31+32)}{21.32+31(21+23)} = \frac{13.32+12(31+32)}{31.23+21(31+32)}. \tag{20}$$

Neglecting the induced emission terms, the transition probabilities are

$$12 = B_{12}\,WB(\nu_{12},\,T), \qquad 21 = A_{21},$$
$$23 = B_{23}\,WB(\nu_{23},\,T), \qquad 32 = A_{32},$$
$$31 = A_{31}, \qquad\qquad 13 = B_{13}\,WB(\nu_{13},\,T).$$

Now by equations (65) and (66) of Chapter VI, we have

$$B_{12} = (q_2/q_1)B_{21}, \qquad A_{21} = (2h\nu_{12}^3/c^2)B_{21}.$$

Hence

$$\frac{12}{21} = \frac{W(q_2/q_1)}{e^{h\nu_{12}/RT}-1} \doteqdot W(q_2/q_1)e^{-h\nu_{12}/RT},$$

with similar results for the ratios 13/31 and 23/32. The ratio of the populations in the states 2 and 1, due to excitation by equilibrium radiation at temperature T, is given by Boltzmann's equation

$$(N_2/N_1)_T = (q_2/q_1)e^{-h\nu_{12}/RT}.$$

We now have

$$\frac{12}{21} = W\left(\frac{N_2}{N_1}\right)_T,$$

and equation (20) may be written

$$\frac{N_2}{N_1} = \left(\frac{N_2}{N_1}\right)_T \frac{31.23 + 21(31 + 32)W}{31.23 + 21(31 + 32)}. \tag{21}$$

From equation (19) the corresponding result for N_3/N_1 is

$$\frac{N_3}{N_1} = W\left(\frac{N_3}{N_1}\right)_T \frac{21.32W + 31(21 + 23)}{21.32 + 31(21 + 23)}. \tag{22}$$

Thus for all $W < 1$ the population of the upper states is less than the population in thermodynamic equilibrium. Since the strongest transitions are $2 \to 1$ and $3 \to 1$, equations (21) and (22) may be written $N_2/N_1 = W(N_2/N_1)_T$ and $N_3/N_1 = W(N_3/N_1)_T$ approximately.

This corollary to Rosseland's theorem throws some light upon the fact that so-called excitation temperatures are usually unduly low. Excitation temperatures are found by observing the intensities of subordinate lines, and determining the populations of excited states relative to the ground state. If the ratio of the populations is compared with Boltzmann's equation, the value of T so found is much lower than the temperature of the atmosphere found in other ways, in particular from ionization. But the excitation temperatures T_2 and T_3 of the states 2 and 3 in the ideal Rosseland atmosphere are related to the actual temperature T by the equations

$$\frac{h\nu_{12}}{RT} = \frac{h\nu_{12}}{RT_2} + \ln W, \qquad \frac{h\nu_{13}}{RT} = \frac{h\nu_{13}}{RT_3} + \ln W.$$

The difference between T_2 and T is much greater than the difference between T_3 and T, if $h\nu_{13}$ is considerably greater than $h\nu_{12}$. For example, consider an ideal atmosphere in which $W = \frac{1}{2}$ and $RT = \frac{1}{2}$ volt, and containing atoms for which $h\nu_{12} = 1$ volt, and $h\nu_{13} = 7.5$ volts. Then $RT_2 = 0.372$ volts, and $RT_3 = 0.478$ volts. The corresponding temperatures are $4,290°$ (excitation) and $5,380°$ (ionization), the actual temperature of the atmosphere being $5,770°$.

2.3. *The effect of electron capture*

In this section we consider the absorption and emission of radiation by an atom with only three energy states: the ground state, a bound state k, and the ionized state, the k-state being linked with the continuum of energy states by photo-ionization from that state, and by recombination to it. The effect of this process on the central intensity of principal lines has been examined by Strömgren.† In his original paper the bound state was considered as a group of sub-states, but this complication has no influence on the result, and will be omitted here for the sake of brevity.

Let N_1, N_k, and N^+ be the number of atoms per c.c. in the ground state, the excited state, and the ionized state respectively, and N_e the number of electrons per c.c. The number of transitions per c.c. per sec. into the k-state is the sum of $N_1 B_{1k} J(\nu)$ radiative transitions from the ground state, $N_1 N_e \sigma_{1k}$ transitions due to inelastic collisions in the ground state, and $\alpha_k N_e N^+$ transitions due to electron captures by ions resulting in an atom in the k-state. The number of transitions away from the k-state is the sum of $N_k A_{k1}$ spontaneous radiative transitions to the ground state, $\sigma_{k1} N_k N_e$ transitions on account of super-elastic collisions, and $N_k C_{kf}$ transitions due to photo-electric ionization from the k-state. In secular equilibrium the sum of transitions to and from the k-state balance, so that

$$N_k\{A_{k1}+\sigma_{k1}N_e+C_{kf}\} = N_1 B_{1k} J(\nu)+\sigma_{1k}N_1 N_e+\alpha_k N_e N^+.$$

In thermodynamic equilibrium the processes balance independently, so that if N_k^0 is the equilibrium value of N_k at the temperature concerned,

$$N_k^0\{A_{k1}+\sigma_{k1}N_e+C_{kf}^0\} = N_1 B_{1k} B(\nu,T)+\sigma_{1k}N_1 N_e+\alpha_k N_e N^+.$$

Let $N_k = \xi N_k^0$, and suppose for the moment that we may put $C_{kf} = C_{kf}^0$. We then have

$$\xi = \frac{N_1 B_{1k} J(\nu)+\sigma_{1k}N_1 N_e+\alpha_k N_e N^+}{N_1 B_{1k} B(\nu,T)+\sigma_{1k}N_1 N_e+\alpha_k N_e N^+},$$

or, converting all the quantities by their equilibrium relations

$$N_1 B_{1k} B(\nu,T) = N_k^0 A_{k1}, \text{ etc.,}$$

$$\xi = \frac{A_{k1} J(\nu)/B(\nu,T)+\sigma_{k1}N_e+C_{kf}}{A_{k1}+\sigma_{k1}N_e+C_{kf}}. \tag{23}$$

Let $$\epsilon' = \frac{\sigma_{k1}N_e+C_{kf}}{A_{k1}+\sigma_{k1}N_e+C_{kf}}, \tag{24}$$

then $$\xi = (1-\epsilon')J(\nu)/B(\nu,T)+\epsilon'. \tag{25}$$

But the emission from the k-state is ξ times the equilibrium value, that is $\xi l(\nu)\times 4\pi B(\nu,T)$ per gm. of atmosphere per sec. The total emission in the frequency ν is made up of line emission and continuous emission. Thus

$$j_\nu = \xi l(\nu)B(\nu,T)+kB(\nu,T),$$

† B. Strömgren, *Zs. f. Ap.* **10**, 237 (1935).

and with ξ from equation (25) we get

$$j_\nu = (1-\epsilon')l(\nu)J(\nu)+\{k+\epsilon'l(\nu)\}B(\nu, T). \qquad (26)$$

Equations (1) and (26) are formally the same; the quantity ϵ' may therefore be taken as an *effective collision constant*.

In deducing equation (25) we have assumed that $N_e N^+/N_1$ had the equilibrium value $(N_e N^+/N_1)_T$, also that C_{kf} was equal to C^0_{kf}. In general this is not so. Let $N_e N^+/N_1 = W(N_e N^+/N_1)_T$, and set $C_{kf} = (W/Q)C^0_{kf}$. Then since $\alpha_k(N_e N^+/N_1)_T = (N^0_k/N_1)C^0_{kf}$, we must have

$$\alpha_k N_e N^+ = N^0_k W C^0_{kf} = N^0_k Q C_{kf}.$$

We then find in place of equation (23)

$$\xi = \frac{A_{k1} J(\nu)/B(\nu, T)+\sigma_{k1} N_e+QC_{kf}}{A_{k1}+\sigma_{k1} N_e+C_{kf}}.$$

Using the same definition (24) for the quantity ϵ', and neglecting $N_e\sigma_{k1}$ compared with C_{kf}, we get Strömgren's equation

$$j_\nu = (1-\epsilon')l(\nu)J(\nu)+\{k+\epsilon'l(\nu)Q\}B(\nu, T).$$

To calculate the super-elastic collision constant σ_{k1} we note that in thermodynamic equilibrium the number of super-elastic and inelastic collisions balance. Hence

$$\sigma_{k1} = (N_1/N_k)S(T),$$

where $S(T)$ is given by equation (100) of Chapter VI:

$$S(T) = \frac{f}{RT} \frac{12\pi e^4}{(2\pi m RT)^{\frac{1}{2}}} \frac{e^{-x}}{x}\{1-xe^x E_1(x)\}, \qquad x = h\nu/RT.$$

Now in thermodynamic equilibrium we have $N_1/N_k = (q_1/q_k)e^{h\nu/RT}$. Hence

$$\sigma_{k1} = \frac{f}{RT} \frac{q_1}{q_2} \frac{12\pi e^4}{(2\pi m RT)^{\frac{1}{2}}} \frac{1}{x}\{1-xe^x E_1(x)\}$$

$$= A_{k1}\frac{3me^2}{2\pi h^2 c} \frac{RT\lambda^4}{(2\pi m RT)^{\frac{1}{2}}} x\{1-xe^x E_1(x)\},$$

the transition probability A_{k1} having been introduced by equation (73) of Chapter VI.

Now from equation (24) we get

$$\frac{\epsilon'}{1-\epsilon'} = \frac{1}{A_{k1}}\{\sigma_{k1} N_e+C_{kf}\}.$$

Let ϵ be the value of ϵ' when $C_{kf} = 0$, then

$$\frac{\epsilon}{1-\epsilon} = N_e\frac{3me^2}{2\pi h^2 c} \frac{\lambda^4 RT}{(2\pi m RT)^{\frac{1}{2}}} x\{1-xe^x E_1(x)\}.$$

This is essentially equation (102.1) of Chapter VI. In the present discussion, however, we have neglected stimulated emission and the factor $1-e^{-x}$ does not appear. In the absence of photo-ionization from the upper state of the line, Strömgren's ϵ' reduces to Eddington's ϵ. We have in fact

$$\frac{\epsilon'}{1-\epsilon'} = \frac{\epsilon}{1-\epsilon} + \frac{C_{kf}}{A_{k1}}. \tag{27}$$

But C_{kf}, the probability of photo-ionization from the k-state, is given by

$$C_{kf} = 4\pi \int_{\nu_0}^{\infty} \kappa(\nu) J(\nu) \, d\nu/h\nu.$$

For practical purposes we may substitute $B(\nu, T)$ for $J(\nu)$. Now the atomic continuous absorption coefficient $\kappa(\nu)$ for hydrogen-like atoms is related to f_c, the oscillator strength to the continuum, by

$$\kappa(\nu) = f_c \frac{2\pi e^2 \nu_0^2}{mc} \frac{1}{\nu^3}.$$

Hence
$$C_{kf} = f_c \frac{16\pi^2 e^2 \nu_0^2}{mc^3} \int_{\nu_0}^{\infty} \frac{d\nu}{\nu(e^{h\nu/RT}-1)} \simeq f_c \frac{16\pi^2 e^2 \nu_0^2}{mc^3} E_1\left(\frac{h\nu_0}{RT}\right).$$

On the other hand A_{k1} is related to the oscillator strength f for the upward transition from the ground state to the k-state by

$$A_{k1} = 3f(q_1/q_2)\gamma = 3f\frac{q_1}{q_2}\frac{8\pi^2 e^2 \nu_0^2}{3mc^3}.$$

Accordingly
$$\frac{C_{kf}}{A_{k1}} = \frac{f_c}{f}\frac{2q_2}{q_1} E_1\left(\frac{\chi_k}{RT}\right),$$

where χ_k ($= h\nu_0$) is the binding energy of the k-state.

The oscillator strengths for hydrogen are given in Table XX. From this table we find for the H_α line, $f_c/f = 0\cdot161/0\cdot637 = 0\cdot252$. For this line $q_2/q_1 = (3/2)^2$ and $\chi_k = 3\cdot40$ volts. With $T = 6{,}000^\circ$ K. we have $RT = 0\cdot518$ volts, and $\chi_k/RT = 6\cdot5$ nearly. Hence

$$C_{kf}/A_{k1} = 2\cdot3\times10^{-4}.$$

This contribution to $\epsilon'/(1-\epsilon')$ in equation (27) is smaller than that made by the collision term $\epsilon/(1-\epsilon)$, calculated in Chapter VI, Section 5. This is chiefly due to the value of χ_k/RT in the example chosen.

3. Redistribution in frequency

3.1. *Effect in a single atom*

The function $p(\nu, \nu')$ introduced in Section 1 is such that if an atom is exposed to a radiation field from which it absorbs the amount

$4\pi\alpha(\nu')J(\nu')\,d\nu'$ within the frequency range ν' to $\nu'+d\nu'$, the quantity of radiation emitted in all directions and switched to the frequency range ν to $\nu+d\nu$ is

$$p(\nu,\nu')\times4\pi\alpha(\nu')J(\nu')\,d\nu d\nu'.$$

The number of quanta emitted in the frequency range ν to $\nu+d\nu$ by an atom exposed to isotropic radiation of unit intensity and absorbing radiation in the frequency range ν' to $\nu'+d\nu'$ will therefore be

$$p(\nu,\nu')\,d\nu d\nu'\times4\pi\alpha(\nu')/h\nu. \tag{28}$$

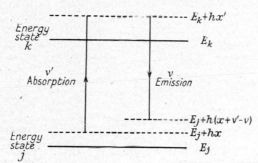

FIG. 30. Non-coherent scattering due to the breadth of the energy states of an atom.

We now inquire into the form of the probability function $p(\nu,\nu')$ in the case in which redistribution is due to the breadth of the two energy states involved, following closely the notation of Section 4.3 of Chapter VI.

The probability that a quantum within the frequency range ν' to $\nu'+d\nu'$ is absorbed by an atom in the sub-state E_j+hx to $E_j+h(x+dx)$ of the state j is

$$b_{jk}(x,x+\nu'-\nu_0)\,dxd\nu,$$

where the function b_{jk} is given by equation (81) of Chapter VI. The compound probability that this event occurs, and is followed by a spontaneous downward transition giving rise to the emission of a quantum in the frequency range ν to $\nu+d\nu$ is

$$b_{jk}(x,x+\nu'-\nu_0)W_j(x+\nu'-\nu)\,dxd\nu d\nu', \tag{29}$$

where $W_j(x+\nu'-\nu)$, given by equation (77) of Chapter VI, is the *a priori* probability of finding the atom in a j sub-state with energy $E_j+h(x+\nu'-\nu)$. The total probability of the emission of a quantum of frequency within ν to $\nu+d\nu$ subsequent to the absorption of a quantum within ν' to $\nu'+d\nu'$ is obtained by integrating the function (29) over all x, that is over the entire range of initial j sub-states. Thus the expression

$$d\nu d\nu'\int_{-\infty}^{\infty} b_{jk}(x,x+\nu'-\nu_0)W_j(x+\nu'-\nu)\,dx \tag{30}$$

gives the number of quanta of frequency ν to $\nu+d\nu$ emitted by an atom absorbing in the frequencies ν' to $\nu'+d\nu'$. Equating (28) and (30) we obtain

$$p(\nu,\nu')\alpha(\nu')$$

$$= \frac{1}{4\pi} B_{jk} h\nu \frac{\delta_j^2 \delta_k}{\pi^3} \int_{-\infty}^{\infty} \frac{dx}{(x^2+\delta_j^2)[(x+\nu'-\nu_0)^2+\delta_k^2][(x+\nu'-\nu)^2+\delta_j^2]}. \quad (31)$$

Further

$$\int_0^\infty p(\nu,\nu')\alpha(\nu')\,d\nu'$$

$$= \frac{1}{4\pi} B_{jk} h\nu \frac{\delta_j^2 \delta_k}{\pi^3} \int_{-\infty}^{\infty}\int_0^{\infty} \frac{dx\,d\nu'}{(x^2+\delta_j^2)[(x+\nu'-\nu_0)^2+\delta_k^2][(x+\nu'-\nu)^2+\delta_j^2]}$$

$$= \frac{1}{4\pi} B_{jk} h\nu \frac{\delta_j}{\pi^2} \frac{\delta_j+\delta_k}{(\nu-\nu_0)^2+(\delta_j+\delta_k)^2} \int_{-\infty}^{\infty} \frac{dx}{x^2+\delta_j^2}$$

$$= \frac{1}{4\pi} B_{jk} \frac{h\nu}{\pi} \frac{\delta_j+\delta_k}{(\nu-\nu_0)^2+(\delta_j+\delta_k)^2}.$$

According to equation (89) of Chapter VI this is the value of $\alpha(\nu)$, so that we have

$$\alpha(\nu) = \int_0^\infty p(\nu,\nu')\alpha(\nu')\,d\nu', \quad (32)$$

a result which also follows from first principles, since in detailed balancing the number of quanta of frequency ν returned to the radiation field must be equal to the number of quanta of the same frequency removed from it by absorption.

To evaluate the integral in the expression (31) for $p(\nu,\nu')$ we may proceed exactly as in Section 4.3 of Chapter VI. In this way it may be shown[†] that

$$\frac{\delta_1\delta_2\delta_3}{\pi^3} \int_{-\infty}^{\infty} \frac{dx}{[(x-x_1)^2+\delta_1^2][(x-x_2)^2+\delta_2^2][(x-x_3)^2+\delta_3^2]}$$

$$= \frac{\delta_1\delta_2\delta_3\,4(\delta_1+\delta_2+\delta_3)}{\pi^2[(x_1-x_2)^2+(\delta_1+\delta_2)^2][(x_2-x_3)^2+(\delta_2+\delta_3)^2][(x_3-x_1)^2+(\delta_3+\delta_1)^2]} +$$

$$+ \frac{\delta_1\delta_2}{\pi^2} \frac{1}{[(x_2-x_3)^2+(\delta_2+\delta_3)^2][(x_3-x_1)^2+(\delta_3+\delta_1)^2]} +$$

$$+ \frac{\delta_2\delta_3}{\pi^2} \frac{1}{[(x_3-x_1)^2+(\delta_3+\delta_1)^2][(x_1-x_2)^2+(\delta_1+\delta_2)^2]} +$$

$$+ \frac{\delta_3\delta_1}{\pi^2} \frac{1}{[(x_1-x_2)^2+(\delta_1+\delta_2)^2][(x_2-x_3)^2+(\delta_2+\delta_3)^2]}.$$

† L. G. Henyey, *Ap. J.* **103**, 347 (1946).

This gives the value of $(4\pi/h\nu B_{jk})p(\nu,\nu')\alpha(\nu')$ with $x_1 = 0$, $x_2 = \nu_0-\nu'$, $x_3 = \nu-\nu'$, and $\delta_1 = \delta_3 = \delta_j$, $\delta_2 = \delta_k$. Thus we have

$$(4\pi/h\nu B_{jk})p(\nu,\nu')\alpha(\nu')$$

$$= \frac{\delta_j^2\delta_k}{\pi^2}\frac{4(2\delta_j+\delta_k)}{[(\nu'-\nu_0)^2+(\delta_j+\delta_k)^2][(\nu-\nu_0)^2+(\delta_j+\delta_k)^2][(\nu-\nu')^2+4\delta_j^2]}+$$

$$+\frac{\delta_j\delta_k}{\pi^2}\frac{1}{[(\nu-\nu_0)^2+(\delta_j+\delta_k)^2][(\nu-\nu')^2+4\delta_j^2]}+$$

$$+\frac{\delta_j\delta_k}{\pi^2}\frac{1}{[(\nu-\nu')^2+4\delta_j^2][(\nu'-\nu_0)^2+(\delta_j+\delta_k)^2]}+$$

$$+\frac{\delta_j^2}{\pi^2}\frac{1}{[(\nu'-\nu_0)^2+(\delta_j+\delta_k)^2][(\nu-\nu_0)^2+(\delta_j+\delta_k)^2]}. \quad (33)$$

Interchanging the arguments ν and ν' we find

$$p(\nu,\nu')\alpha(\nu')/h\nu = p(\nu',\nu)\alpha(\nu)/h\nu', \quad (34)$$

a result which also follows from detailed balancing.

When $\nu-\nu_0$ is large compared with δ_j or δ_k, the denominators of the first, second, and fourth terms on the right-hand side of equation (33) are always large but pass through minimum values at $\nu' = \nu$ and $\nu' = \nu_0$, as also does the denominator of the third term. The function $p(\nu,\nu')\alpha(\nu')$ therefore has two maxima corresponding to these two values of ν'. When $\nu' = \nu+\xi$, with ξ small, the first and fourth terms are of order $\delta^2/(\nu-\nu_0)^4$ and equation (33) may be written

$$p(\nu,\nu+\xi)\alpha(\nu+\xi) = \frac{1}{4\pi}B_{jk}h\nu\left(\frac{2}{\pi^2}\frac{\delta_j\delta_k}{(\nu-\nu_0)^2(\xi^2+4\delta_j^2)}+O\left\{\frac{\delta^2}{(\nu-\nu_0)^4}\right\}\right). \quad (35)$$

When $\nu' = \nu_0+\xi$ the first and second terms are of order $\delta^2/(\nu-\nu_0)^4$, and we have

$$p(\nu,\nu_0+\xi)\alpha(\nu_0+\xi) = \frac{1}{4\pi}B_{jk}h\nu\left(\frac{1}{\pi^2}\frac{\delta_j}{(\nu-\nu_0)^2}\frac{\delta_j+\delta_k}{\xi^2+(\delta_j+\delta_k)^2}+O\left\{\frac{\delta^2}{(\nu-\nu_0)^4}\right\}\right). \quad (36)$$

Integrating (35) and (36) over a range of values of ξ so large compared with δ_j or δ_k that the limits may be taken as infinite yet small compared with $\nu-\nu_0$, we obtain the approximate results

$$\int p(\nu,\nu+\xi)\alpha(\nu+\xi)\,d\xi = \frac{1}{4\pi}B_{jk}\frac{h\nu}{\pi}\frac{1}{(\nu-\nu_0)^2} = \frac{\delta_k}{\delta_j+\delta_k}\alpha(\nu), \quad (37)$$

$$\int p(\nu,\nu_0+\xi)\alpha(\nu_0+\xi)\,d\xi = \frac{1}{4\pi}B_{jk}\frac{h\nu}{\pi}\frac{\delta_j}{(\nu-\nu_0)^2} = \frac{\delta_j}{\delta_j+\delta_k}\alpha(\nu). \quad (38)$$

Equations (37) and (38) give the total probability for the emission of a quantum of frequency ν such that $\nu - \nu_0 \gg \delta_j$ or δ_k, when the frequency ν' of the incident quantum is nearly equal to ν or ν_0. The total probability in the two zones adds up to $\alpha(\nu)$, as it should, in accordance with equation (32).

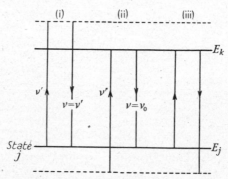

FIG. 31. Most probable transitions involving the absorption of a quantum of frequency ν'. In the transitions (i) the emission takes place in the same frequency as the absorption, and in (ii) the emission is grouped around the central frequency. The transitions (iii) are the reverse of (ii), but according to detailed balancing they occur with equal probability.

The physical explanation for the appearance of two maxima in the function $p(\nu, \nu')\alpha(\nu')$ is that the most probable ways in which the absorption of a quantum $h\nu'$ can occur lie in transitions from the middle of the j-state, or in transitions to the middle of the k-state. The former are most probably followed by emission of the same frequency ν', and the latter are followed by the emission of a quantum having the central frequency ν_0: in both cases we mean a small band of energies whose half-width is of order δ_j or δ_k. From the preceding paragraph the emission in the frequency ν is greatest when $\nu' = \nu$ or $\nu' = \nu_0$. The former corresponds to the transitions (i) in Fig. 31, the latter to the transitions (iii). According to equation (34) the transitions (ii) and (iii) occur with equal probability. The relative probabilities of these occurrences are therefore $\delta_k/(\delta_j + \delta_k)$ for the emission of the same frequency, and $\delta_j/(\delta_j + \delta_k)$ for the emission of the central frequency.

In the case of the principal lines $\delta_j \ll \delta_k$ and $p(\nu, \nu) \sim 1$, while $p(\nu, \nu_0)$ is small. We recover, in fact, the coherent formula (1) for the emission.

3.2. Effects due to other atoms

Some time ago Orthmann and Pringsheim† demonstrated that when the resonance line $\lambda 2{,}537$ A of mercury is excited in a vessel containing

† W. Orthmann and P. Pringsheim, *Zs. f. Phys.* **43**, 9 (1927).

enough foreign gas to widen the line appreciably, the spectral distribution in the line so excited is independent of the spectral distribution of the exciting radiation. They found, in fact, that the foreign gas brought about non-coherent scattering. A rough physical picture of the process may be drawn by supposing that when an atom absorbs a quantum while it is in the neighbourhood of a disturbing particle, the precise sub-state of the upper level of the absorbing atom depends not only on the frequency of the quantum absorbed but also on the field due to the perturbing atom. If this field changes, on account of the relative motions of the atoms, before a quantum is emitted, the energy available will have changed to a value different from that of the quantum absorbed, and the energy of the quantum emitted will have this altered value.

It was later shown by Zanstra† that on the classical theory the behaviour of an atom when simultaneously perturbed by radiation and collisions is different in emission from what it is in absorption. Let γ_n be the natural damping constant of an undisturbed oscillator, and γ_c the collision damping constant. The absorption of radiation then takes place as for an undisturbed oscillator with damping constant $\gamma_n + \gamma_c$, but according to Zanstra the radiated wave consists of two parts, a coherent part and a non-coherent part. The fraction $\gamma_n/(\gamma_n+\gamma_c)$ of the emission is coherent, and the remainder $\gamma_c/(\gamma_n+\gamma_c)$ is grouped around the central frequency of the line with a frequency distribution of the same form as the emission from an undisturbed oscillator with damping constant $\gamma_n+\gamma_c$. In other words the non-coherent part of the emission has the same variation with frequency as the profile of the disturbed oscillator in absorption.

Let j''_ν be the coefficient of line emission in the frequency ν, then

$$j''_\nu = \frac{\gamma_n}{\gamma_n+\gamma_c} l_\nu J_\nu + \frac{\gamma_c}{\gamma_n+\gamma_c} \mu l_\nu, \qquad (39)$$

where μ is independent of the frequency. The value of μ may be found from the equilibrium of the line as a whole. Integrating over the line frequencies, and equating absorption and emission, we have

$$\int l_\nu J_\nu \, d\nu = \frac{\gamma_n}{\gamma_n+\gamma_c} \int l_\nu J_\nu \, d\nu + \frac{\gamma_c}{\gamma_n+\gamma_c} \mu \int l_\nu \, d\nu.$$

Hence
$$\mu = \int l_\nu J_\nu \, d\nu \Big/ \int l_\nu \, d\nu = \bar{J}(\tau), \qquad (40)$$

so that $\bar{J}(\tau)$ is the average value of J_ν weighted by the line absorption coefficient. Accordingly, when energy J_ν is absorbed in the frequency ν

† H. Zanstra, *M.N.* **101**, 273 (1941); **106**, 225 (1946).

only the fraction $\bar{J}/J_\nu$ of this absorption reappears in the same frequency, the remaining fraction undergoes *complete redistribution* and may be described as *completely non-coherent*. The total emission in the frequency ν is the sum of the continuous emission and the line emission. Hence

$$j_\nu = (k_\nu + \epsilon l_\nu) B(\nu, T) + (1-\epsilon) \left\{ \frac{\gamma_n}{\gamma_n + \gamma_c} l_\nu J_\nu + \frac{\gamma_c}{\gamma_n + \gamma_c} l_\nu \bar{J} \right\}. \tag{41}$$

3.3. *Influence of the Doppler effect*

We now consider the absorption and emission of radiation by an assembly of atoms in random motion undergoing transitions between two broadened states. Let $I_{\nu'}(\theta)$ be the intensity of ν'-radiation in a direction making an angle θ with a given direction, ν' being the frequency with respect to a stationary frame of reference. The frequency of this radiation relative to an atom moving with velocity V in a direction making an angle φ with the given direction will be

$$\xi' = \nu' \left[1 - \frac{V}{c} \cos(\theta - \varphi) \right]. \tag{42}$$

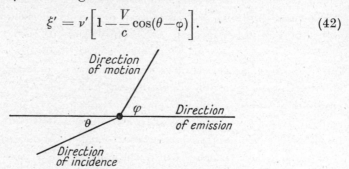

Fig. 32. The absorption and emission of radiation
by a moving atom.

Let the radiation emitted by the atom have a frequency ξ relative to its own frame of reference, and a frequency ν in the fixed frame. The frequency relation for emission in the given direction is taken to be

$$\xi = \nu \left(1 - \frac{V}{c} \cos \varphi \right), \tag{43}$$

the magnitude and direction of the velocity of the atom being assumed to be unchanged in the process of absorption and emission.

If the atom absorbs radiation incident within the solid angle $d\omega$ in the θ-direction and scatters it isotropically, the amount of radiation with frequency ξ relative to the atom scattered into unit solid angle in any direction is given by

$$\frac{d\omega}{4\pi} \int p(\xi, \xi') \alpha(\xi') I_{\xi'} \, d\xi'. \tag{44}$$

Now $p(\xi, \xi')$ is very small except when ξ' takes values near ξ and $\xi_0 (= \nu_0)$. The integral in (44) may therefore be written as the sum of two integrals with the intensities outside the signs of integration. From equations (37) and (38) we then obtain the following approximation:

$$\int p(\xi, \xi')\alpha(\xi')I_{\xi'}\,d\xi' \doteqdot \frac{\delta_k}{\delta_k + \delta_j}\,\alpha(\xi)I_\xi + \frac{\delta_j}{\delta_k + \delta_j}\,\alpha(\xi)I_{\xi_0}.$$

From (42) and (43) the condition $\xi' = \xi$ gives

$$\nu' = \nu\left[1 + \frac{V}{c}\cos(\theta - \varphi) - \frac{V}{c}\cos\varphi\right],$$

and from (42) with $\xi' = \nu_0$ we have

$$\nu' = \nu_0\left[1 + \frac{V}{c}\cos(\theta - \varphi)\right].$$

Hence (44) becomes

$$\frac{\delta_k}{\delta_k + \delta_j}\,\alpha\left\{\nu\left(1 - \frac{V}{c}\cos\varphi\right)\right\}I\left\{\nu\left[1 + \frac{V}{c}\cos(\theta - \varphi)\right]\right\}\frac{d\omega}{4\pi} +$$

$$+ \frac{\delta_j}{\delta_k + \delta_j}\,\alpha\left\{\nu\left(1 - \frac{V}{c}\cos\varphi\right)\right\}I\left\{\nu_0\left[1 + \frac{V}{c}\cos(\theta - \varphi)\right]\right\}\frac{d\omega}{4\pi}.$$

Integrating over all directions of incidence θ we get the emission in the frequency ν per unit solid angle in the given direction per atom with velocity V in the φ-direction. This integration converts I into J, and the emission per atom will be given by

$$\frac{\delta_k}{\delta_k + \delta_j}\,\alpha\left\{\nu\left(1 - \frac{V}{c}\cos\varphi\right)\right\}J\left\{\nu\left(1 - \frac{V}{c}\cos\varphi\right)\right\} +$$

$$+ \frac{\delta_j}{\delta_k + \delta_j}\,\alpha\left\{\nu\left(1 - \frac{V}{c}\cos\varphi\right)\right\}J(\nu_0). \qquad (45)$$

In an assembly of N atoms there are $Nf(V)\,dV$ atoms with space velocities within V to $V + dV$, where

$$f(V) = \frac{4}{\sqrt{\pi}}\frac{1}{V_0^3}e^{-(V/V_0)^2}V^2\,dV,$$

and the fraction $\frac{1}{2}\sin\varphi\,d\varphi$ have directions of motion within φ to $\varphi + d\varphi$. Hence the emission in the frequency ν by the assembly is obtained by multiplying the expression (45) by $Nf(V)\,dV \cdot \frac{1}{2}\sin\varphi\,d\varphi$ and integrating.

Now

$$\int_0^\infty \int_0^\pi \alpha\left\{\nu\left(1 - \frac{V}{c}\cos\varphi\right)\right\}f(V)\tfrac{1}{2}\sin\varphi\,dV\,d\varphi$$

is merely $\alpha(\nu)_D$ in Section 6, Chapter VI. Hence the second term in (45) gives

$$\frac{\delta_j}{\delta_k+\delta_j}\,\alpha(\nu)_D\,J(\nu_0).$$

The first term may be written as

$$\frac{\delta_k}{\delta_k+\delta_j}\,\alpha(\nu)_D\,J(\nu)$$

provided that the variation of $J(\nu)$ with ν is small in the effective range of integration. It is sufficient for $J(\nu)$ to vary linearly with ν when $\nu-\nu_0 > \nu_0\,V/c$. If we set

$$J\left\{\nu\left(1-\frac{V}{c}\cos\varphi\right)\right\} \doteq J(\nu)-\frac{\nu V}{c}\frac{dJ}{d\nu}\cos\varphi,$$

we find

$$\iint \alpha\left\{\nu\left(1-\frac{V}{c}\cos\varphi\right)\right\}J\left\{\nu\left(1-\frac{V}{c}\cos\varphi\right)\right\}f(V)\tfrac{1}{2}\sin\varphi\,dV d\varphi$$

$$= J(\nu)\iint \alpha\left\{\nu\left(1-\frac{V}{c}\cos\varphi\right)\right\}f(V)\tfrac{1}{2}\sin\varphi\,dV d\varphi-$$

$$-\frac{dJ}{d\nu}\iint \alpha\left\{\nu\left(1-\frac{V}{c}\cos\varphi\right)\right\}\frac{\nu V}{c}f(V)\tfrac{1}{2}\sin\varphi\cos\varphi\,dV d\varphi$$

$$= \alpha(\nu)_D\,J(\nu)-\alpha(\nu_0)_D\frac{2a}{\pi}\frac{\nu V_0}{c}\frac{dJ}{d\nu}\iint\frac{e^{-v^2}y^3\sin\varphi\cos\varphi\,dy d\varphi}{a^2+(v-y\cos\varphi)^2},$$

in the notation of equation (105) of Chapter VI. Now the integral

$$\int_0^\pi\frac{\sin\varphi\cos\varphi\,d\varphi}{a^2+(v-y\cos\varphi)^2}$$

vanishes if $v=0$, and is small if $v\gg y$. But $v=(\nu-\nu_0)/b$ and $y=V/V_0$, so that $v/y=(\nu-\nu_0)c/V$. In the wings of the line this is large and the φ integral is therefore small in the effective range in the integration with respect to y. Thus, ignoring the second derivative $d^2J/d\nu^2$, the emission in the frequency ν by an assembly of N atoms is

$$N\alpha(\nu)_D\left\{\frac{\delta_k}{\delta_k+\delta_j}\,J(\nu)+\frac{\delta_j}{\delta_k+\delta_j}\,J(\nu_0)\right\}.$$

The line emission per gramme of the atmosphere by non-coherent scattering due to the natural breadth of the energy states involved is therefore

$$l_\nu\left\{\frac{\delta_k}{\delta_k+\delta_j}\,J(\nu)+\frac{\delta_j}{\delta_k+\delta_j}\,J(\nu_0)\right\}. \tag{46}$$

We may now further generalize equation (39) for the emission co-efficient j'_ν by replacing the coherent emission term $l_\nu J_\nu$ by (46). With $\delta_n = \delta_k + \delta_j$ we have

$$j'_\nu = l_\nu \left\{ \frac{\delta_k}{\delta_n + \delta_c} J(\nu) + \frac{\delta_j}{\delta_n + \delta_c} J(\nu_0) + \frac{\delta_c}{\delta_n + \delta_c} \bar{J} \right\}.$$

Set $a = \delta_k/(\delta_n + \delta_c)$, $b = \delta_j/(\delta_n + \delta_c)$, and $c = \delta_c/(\delta_n + \delta_c)$ so that $a + b + c = 1$, then the emission coefficient for continuous emission and line emission may be written in the form

$$j_\nu = (k_\nu + \epsilon l_\nu) B(\nu, T) + (1 - \epsilon) l_\nu \{ a J(\nu) + b J(\nu_0) + c\bar{J} \}. \tag{47}$$

This equation is subject to the restriction that $\nu - \nu_0$ is large compared with δ_j or δ_k.

4. Approximate solution of the equations

The natural width of a typical line is of order 10^{-3} A at most, so that the restriction that $\nu - \nu_0$ must be large compared with δ_j and δ_k is one which leaves us free to deal with most of the line—if we can somehow manage the centre, or at all events its effect on the rest of the line. The equation for the non-coherent formation of an absorption line is

$$\cos \theta \frac{dI_\nu(\theta)}{d\tau} = (1 + \eta) I_\nu(\theta) - (1 + \epsilon \eta) B - (1 - \epsilon) \eta \{ a J(\nu) + b J(\nu_0) + c\bar{J} \}, \tag{48}$$

where

$$a = \delta_k/(\delta_j + \delta_k + \delta_c), \qquad b = \delta_j/(\delta_j + \delta_k + \delta_c), \qquad c = \delta_c/(\delta_j + \delta_k + \delta_c),$$

and from equation (40)

$$\bar{J} = \int \eta(\nu) J(\nu) \, d\nu \Big/ \int \eta(\nu) \, d\nu.$$

Since $\eta(\nu)$ attains large values near the centre of the line, nearly all of the weight in the averaging of $J(\nu)$ is very near the centre of the line $\nu = \nu_0$. We might take as an approximation $\bar{J} = J(\nu_0)$, but instead we will suppose that $\bar{J} = J(\bar{\nu})$, where $\bar{\nu}$ is not very different from ν_0. We next suppose that both $J(\nu_0)$ and $J(\bar{\nu})$ have their coherent values. By equation (34) of Chapter VII

$$J(\nu_0) = B - \frac{2H\eta_0}{1 + \eta_0 + \frac{2}{3}q_0} e^{-q_0 \tau}, \qquad J(\bar{\nu}) = B - \frac{2H\bar{\eta}}{1 + \bar{\eta} + \frac{2}{3}\bar{q}} e^{-\bar{q}\tau},$$

where $B = H(2 + 3\tau)$. With these assumptions equation (47) may be solved by Eddington's approximation. Equation (48) reduces to

$$\frac{d^2}{d\tau^2} \{ J(\nu) - B \} = p_\nu^2 \{ J(\nu) - B \} + \frac{6(1 - \epsilon) b\eta(1 + \eta)\eta_0}{1 + \eta_0 + \frac{2}{3}q_0} H e^{-q_0 \tau} +$$

$$+ \frac{6(1 - \epsilon) c\eta(1 + \eta)\bar{\eta}}{1 + \bar{\eta} + \frac{2}{3}\bar{q}} H e^{-\bar{q}\tau}, \tag{49}$$

where $$p_\nu^2 = 3\eta(1+\eta)\{1+b+c+\epsilon a\}.$$

The solution of equation (49) is

$$J(\nu)-B = C(\nu)e^{-p_\nu\tau}+6(1-\epsilon)\eta(1+\eta)H \times$$

$$\times\left\{\frac{b\eta_0 e^{-q_0\tau}}{(q_0^2-q_\nu^2)(1+\eta_0+\tfrac{2}{3}q_0)}+\frac{c\bar{\eta}e^{-\bar{q}\tau}}{(\bar{q}^2-q_\nu^2)(1+\bar{\eta}+\tfrac{2}{3}\bar{q})}\right\}.$$

The boundary condition $J = 2H$ at $\tau = 0$ gives

$$\frac{C(\nu)}{H} = -\frac{2\eta}{1+\eta+\tfrac{2}{3}p}-\frac{6(1-\epsilon)\eta(1+\eta)}{1+\eta+\tfrac{2}{3}p}\times$$

$$\times\left\{\frac{1+\eta+\tfrac{2}{3}q_0}{1+\eta_0+\tfrac{2}{3}q_0}\frac{b\eta_0}{q_0^2-q_\nu^2}+\frac{1+\eta+\tfrac{2}{3}\bar{q}}{1+\bar{\eta}+\tfrac{2}{3}\bar{q}}\frac{c\bar{\eta}}{\bar{q}^2-q_\nu^2}\right\}.$$

The residual intensity within the line $r(\nu) = \{H(\nu)/H\}_{\tau=0} = \{J(\nu)/J\}_{\tau=0}$ is given by

$$r(\nu) = \frac{1+\tfrac{2}{3}p}{1+\eta+\tfrac{2}{3}p}-\frac{2b(1-\epsilon)\eta(1+\eta)\eta_0}{(p+q_0)(1+\eta+\tfrac{2}{3}p)(1+\eta_0+\tfrac{2}{3}q_0)}-$$

$$-\frac{2c(1-\epsilon)\eta(1+\eta)\bar{\eta}}{(p+\bar{q})(1+\eta+\tfrac{2}{3}p)(1+\bar{\eta}+\tfrac{2}{3}\bar{q})}. \quad (50)$$

If both η_0 and $\bar{\eta}$ are large compared with η (and compared with unity), the second and third terms in equation (50) are small, and we are left with

$$r(\nu) = \frac{1+\tfrac{2}{3}p}{1+\eta+\tfrac{2}{3}p}, \quad (51)$$

which only differs from the coherent formula (24) of Chapter VII by the appearance of p for q, that is by the appearance of a quasi-collision term $b+c+\epsilon a$ in place of the true collision term ϵ. *This is exactly the result which we should have obtained if we had adopted as our approximation* $J(\nu_0) = \bar{J} = B$. The physical reason for this is the rapid recovery of the line intensity J to the equilibrium value B at very small optical depths in the centre of the line: since $J-B$ is of the form const.$\times e^{-q\tau}$ (for coherent scattering) this recovery takes place at small values of τ wherever q is large. Accordingly the approximations used for $\bar{J}$ and $J(\nu_0)$ will give quite good results for the greater part of the line, as the central frequencies only affect the wing frequencies in so far as the intensities in the former do not quite hold up to the black-body values very near the surface.

Some numerical results will show the orders of magnitude involved. Let us consider a line at $\lambda 5,000$ A, due to an element of mass 40, at a temperature of $6,000°$ K. The radiation damping constant δ is $8\cdot9\times10^7$ sec.$^{-1}$, $\delta/\nu_0 = 1\cdot5\times10^{-7}$, and the Doppler half-width b_D is

$3\cdot2\times10^9$ sec.$^{-1}$ If we now consider the integral $\int_{\nu_0}^{\infty} l(\nu)\,d\nu$, one-half of its value is contributed in the range $\nu = \nu_0$ to $\nu = \nu_0+0\cdot477b_D$; and at this point $l(\nu) \doteq 0\cdot8l(\nu_0)$. It might then be a good approximation to put $\bar{J} = J(\nu_0+0\cdot477b_D)$, or $\bar{\eta} = 0\cdot8\eta_0$. Now if we substitute in equation (50) using, for example, $\eta = 1$, $\eta_0 = 10^4$, $\bar{\eta} = 8\times10^3$, and with $\epsilon = 0$, $a = \frac{1}{2}$, $b = c = \frac{1}{6}$, we get

$$r = 0\cdot75000-0\cdot00097-0\cdot00104 = 0\cdot74799,$$

the coherent value for $\eta = 1$ being $r = 0\cdot62021$.

This example shows that the correction to equation (51) is small, and that the result of making a distinction between $\bar{J}$ and $J(\nu_0)$ is very small, being in this case less than one unit in the fourth place of decimals.

While some confidence may be felt that equation (51) represents quite well the behaviour of all but the centre of a line formed by non-coherent scattering, so long as the intensity at the centre recovers to the black-body intensity very rapidly with increasing optical depth, the equation does not, of course, represent the behaviour of the centre itself. For this no satisfactory treatment can at present be offered.

THE PHOTOSPHERE

1. Introduction

THE distinction between the photosphere and reversing layer was originally suggested by the appearance of the solar spectrum. The Fraunhofer lines were taken to be the absorption spectrum of a cooler atmosphere on top of the photosphere, which radiated the continuous spectrum. These views were embodied in Schuster's treatment of the problem of stellar absorption lines, but later writers, beginning with Eddington and Milne, have pointed out that there is no real distinction between photosphere and reversing layer. We have seen in Chapter VII that on the Milne–Eddington model the part of a stellar atmosphere in which a given line is formed depends upon the region of the line considered. In the central frequencies of strong lines the absorption coefficient is so large compared with the continuous absorption coefficient outside the line that it is reasonable to think of the centres of these lines as being formed above the bulk of the photosphere. But there is a steady progression of 'the level at which the line is mainly formed' as we proceed from the centre of the line, where the level is relatively high, to the extreme wings, where it is coextensive with the photosphere. The photosphere and reversing layer are therefore one and the same region, or at most two aspects of the same region.

The photospheric layers may be divided into two zones—the radiative zone and the convective zone. In the radiative zone the flow of heat is maintained by radiation and the distribution of temperature follows the law $T^4 = T_0^4(1 + \frac{3}{2}\tau)$, whilst in the convective zone a fraction of the radiation is carried by convection and the actual temperature gradient is less than the radiative gradient but greater than the adiabatic gradient. In this chapter we confine our attention to the structure of the photosphere in the radiative zone, convection being discussed in the following chapter.

2. Mechanical equilibrium of the photosphere

The forces which control the mechanical equilibrium of the photospheric layers are due to radiation pressure, gas pressure, and gravity. The *radiation pressure* here refers to general radiation pressure which arises from continuous absorption. The *gas pressure* is the sum of the partial pressures of the various elements in the photospheric mixture, hydrogen being by far the most abundant element. The *acceleration due to gravity* is given by $g = GM/R^2$, where G is the constant of gravitation and M the stellar mass within a sphere of radius R. In the photosphere there is no appreciable variation of gravity with depth and g may be taken as constant and equal to the surface gravity of the star.

2.1. *Radiation pressure*

Consider the absorption of radiation by matter between parallel planes at depths x and $x+dx$ beneath the surface of the photosphere. Let $I_\nu(\theta)\,d\nu d\omega$ be the flow of radiation for frequencies between ν and $\nu+d\nu$ into the solid angle $d\omega$ in a direction making an angle θ with the outward normal. The amount of energy absorbed per second by matter within an oblique cylinder of height dx and length $ds = dx \sec\theta$, and having unit base in the plane at depth x, will then be $I_\nu(\theta)\,d\nu d\omega \times k_\nu \rho\,dx$, where k_ν is the coefficient of continuous absorption.

Since radiant energy E_ν carries momentum E_ν/c in the direction of flow, continuous absorption by matter in the oblique cylinder removes momentum $(1/c)I_\nu(\theta)\,d\nu d\omega \times k_\nu \rho\,dx$ from the flow of radiation in the θ-direction. Thus the x-component of momentum communicated to the matter will be $(1/c)I_\nu(\theta)\cos\theta\,d\nu d\omega \times k_\nu \rho\,dx$. Integrating over the outward directions $0 < \theta < \tfrac{1}{2}\pi$, the rate of transfer of momentum from the outgoing radiation to the matter between the parallel planes is $(1/c)k_\nu F_\nu^+\,d\nu \times \rho\,dx$, where F_ν^+ is the flux outwards. Similarly, absorption of the incoming radiation results in the transfer of momentum

$$\frac{1}{c}k_\nu F_\nu^-\,d\nu \times \rho\,dx,$$

where F_ν^- is the flux inwards. But the net flux outwards is $F_\nu = F_\nu^+ - F_\nu^-$, so that the resultant outward momentum communicated to the absorbing matter is

$$\frac{1}{c}k_\nu F_\nu\,d\nu \times \rho\,dx. \tag{1}$$

Now the mean coefficient of absorption is defined by

$$\overline{k} = \frac{1}{F}\int k_\nu F_\nu\,d\nu.$$

Hence integrating (1) we obtain $(1/c)F\overline{k}\rho\,dx$ for the rate at which outward momentum is communicated to matter within the parallel planes by continuous absorption of the integrated net flux F. This is the resultant force outwards, per unit area of the planes, due to radiation pressure. Let p_r and p_r+dp_r be the radiation pressures at x and $x+dx$,

N

then the equation for p_r will be $p_r-(p_r+dp_r) = (1/c)F\bar{k}\rho\,dx$. Setting $d\tau = -\bar{k}\rho\,dx$ and $F = \sigma T_e^4$ we have

$$\frac{dp_r}{d\tau} = \frac{1}{c}F = \frac{\sigma}{c}T_e^4. \tag{2}$$

But $T^4 = \frac{1}{2}T_e^4(1+\frac{3}{2}\tau)$, so that by differentiation $dT^4/d\tau = \frac{3}{4}T_e^4$. Equation (2) now becomes

$$\frac{dp_r}{d\tau} = \frac{4}{3}\frac{\sigma}{c}\frac{dT^4}{d\tau}.$$

Hence

$$p_r = \frac{4}{3}\frac{\sigma}{c}T^4. \tag{3}$$

This is the exact result in radiation theory for the pressure due to equilibrium radiation at temperature T. It applies to the vertical component of the radiation pressure in the photosphere by virtue of the approximate solution adopted for the temperature distribution.

2.2. *Hydrostatic equilibrium*

Consider the vertical equilibrium of matter contained in an element of volume at a depth x beneath the surface of the photosphere. The

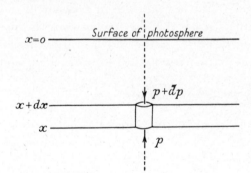

FIG. 33. Mechanical equilibrium of the photosphere.

equation of mechanical equilibrium in the vertical direction for matter contained in an elementary cylindrical volume of unit section and length dx will be

$$p-\left(p+\frac{dp}{dx}dx\right) = g\rho\,dx.$$

Hence

$$\frac{dp}{dx} = -g\rho, \tag{4}$$

which is the equation of hydrostatic equilibrium. Now the pressure p

is made up of the gas pressure p_g and the radiation pressure p_r. With $p = p_g + p_r$ equation (4) becomes

$$\frac{dp_g}{dx} = -g\rho - \frac{dp_r}{dx}.$$

Introducing the optical depth we have

$$\frac{dp_g}{d\tau} = (g - g_r)/\bar{k}, \tag{5}$$

where

$$g_r = \bar{k}\frac{dp_r}{d\tau} = \bar{k}\frac{\sigma}{c}T_e^4. \tag{6}$$

Thus the effect of radiation pressure is to reduce gravity by an amount g_r proportional to the fourth power of the effective temperature. The reduction is not constant with depth owing to the appearance of $\bar{k}$ in equation (6).

TABLE XXIV

The Effect of Radiation Pressure

T_e degrees K.	$\dfrac{dp_r}{d\tau} = \dfrac{\sigma}{c}T_e^4$	$dp_g/d\tau$		
		$g/\bar{k} = 10^3$	$g/\bar{k} = 10^4$	$g/\bar{k} = 10^5$
		multiply by 10^3	multiply by 10^4	multiply by 10^5
5,000	1·18	1·00	1·00	1·00
10,000	18·9	0·98	1·00	1·00
15,000	95·7	0·90	0·99	1·00
20,000	302	0·70	0·97	1·00
25,000	738	0·26	0·93	0·99
30,000	1,530	−0·53	0·85	0·98

The effect of radiation pressure on the gradient of the gas pressure in an atmosphere in hydrostatic equilibrium is shown in Table XXIV for typical values of $g/\bar{k}$. For the higher effective temperatures $dp_g/d\tau$ is reduced by radiation pressure to small, and even negative, values. In this case $dp/d\tau$, the gradient of the total pressure, exceeds the equilibrium value $g/\bar{k}$ and mechanical equilibrium is impossible, the atmosphere being expelled by radiation pressure.

In the case of the Sun we have

$$g = 2·74 \times 10^4 \text{ cm. sec.}^{-2}, \qquad T_e = 5,740° \text{ K.},$$

and $\bar{k}$ is of order unity. The effect of radiation pressure in the solar photosphere is therefore quite negligible.

3. The structure of the outer layers

The structure of a stellar atmosphere is determined by the effective temperature T_e, surface gravity g, and the chemical composition of the atmosphere. Given these parameters the continuous spectrum and the line spectrum of the star can be computed from the physical theory of the continuous absorption coefficient of Chapter IV, and the line absorption coefficient of Chapter VI. Following the deductive method of analysis it may be concluded that the model atmosphere is identical with the actual stellar atmosphere if there is agreement between the theoretical and observed spectra. In this section we consider the determination of the temperature T, total gas pressure p and density ρ, electron pressure p_e, and the mean coefficient of absorption $\bar{k}$ as a function of optical depth and geometrical depth in the atmosphere. In Section 5 we apply the derived structure to the calculation of absorption lines.

3.1. The method of model atmospheres

To derive the structure of the photosphere we have to integrate the equation of mechanical equilibrium

$$\frac{dp}{d\tau} = g/\bar{k}. \tag{7}$$

If the main source of opacity is neutral hydrogen and the negative hydrogen ion, we have from equation (41) of Chapter IV

$$\bar{k} = \frac{1}{m_{\mathrm{H}}}(1-x_{\mathrm{H}})[a(\mathrm{H})+p_e\,a(\mathrm{H}^-)], \tag{8}$$

where x_{H} is the degree of ionization of hydrogen, and $a(\mathrm{H})$, $a(\mathrm{H}^-)$ are known functions of τ. Before we can proceed with the numerical integration of equation (7) we have to find the connexion between p_e and p.

The electron pressure p_e is determined by the degree of ionization of the photospheric mixture of elements, and by the abundance of hydrogen to metals, that is the ratio of the number of hydrogen atoms and ions to the number of metal atoms and ions present. Let A be the hydrogen to metal ratio, and α_i the abundance of metal atoms of a particular kind relative to the total number of metal atoms present ($\sum \alpha_i = 1$). Table XXV gives the relative abundances α_i of the metals actually used by Strömgren in compiling his tables,[†] together with the ionization potentials of the metal atom and the ion. These abundances are in good agreement with other analyses of the solar atmosphere. Since there is not much difference between the ionization potentials of the metal atoms in the mixture, the supply of electrons from ionization of the metals does not depend much on the relative abundances adopted.

† B. Strömgren, *Publ. Copenhagen Observatory*, No. 138 (1944).

We may therefore use the same metal mixture in all calculations of electron pressure, keeping as the variable parameter A, the hydrogen abundance relative to the total metal content.

TABLE XXV

Relative Abundances and Ionization Potentials of Metal Atoms

Element	Relative abundance	Ionization potential (volts)	
		Atom	Ion
Mg	0·30	7·64	15·03
Si	0·33	8·14	16·34
Fe	0·30	7·89	16·23
Ca	0·02	6·11	11·87
Al	0·03	5·98	18·83
Na	0·02	5·14	47·29

Comparing the ionization potentials of the metal ions with that of hydrogen (13·59 volts) we conclude that in view of the great abundance of hydrogen, the higher stages of ionization of the metals contribute an even smaller number of electrons than hydrogen itself. The contribution of the metals to the electron pressure may therefore be computed only from the first stage of ionization. Define a mean degree of ionization x_M of the metals by the relation

$$x_M = \sum \alpha_i x_i,$$

where x_i is the degree of ionization of a particular metal in the mixture. The number of free electrons per unit volume will then be

$$N_e = N_H x_H + N_M x_M, \tag{9}$$

where N_H is the number of H atoms (and ions), and N_M the total number of metal atoms (and ions) per unit volume. The total number of particles per unit volume will be

$$N = N_H(1+x_H) + N_M(1+x_M). \tag{10}$$

Since $A \ (= N_H/N_M)$ may be taken to be of order 10^3, we may neglect the second term in equation (10) so that

$$N \doteq N_H(1+x_H). \tag{11}$$

Now the equation of state is

$$p = NRT, \tag{12}$$

where R is Boltzmann's constant. Hence from equations (9), (11), and (12) the relation between p_e and p will be

$$\frac{p_e}{p} = \frac{x_H}{1+x_H} + \frac{1}{A}\frac{x_M}{1+x_H}. \tag{13}$$

The second term in equation (13) is small compared with the first term except when x_H is very small, as in the outer layers of the Sun where hydrogen is mainly neutral. Neglecting x_H in the second term, we have

$$\frac{p_e}{p} = \frac{x_H}{1+x_H} + \frac{1}{A}x_M. \tag{14}$$

The determination of the structure of the photosphere, that is p, p_e, and $\bar{k}$ as functions of τ, now follows from equations (7), (8), and (14). Eliminating p_e between equations (8) and (14) we obtain $\bar{k}$ as a function of p and τ. The numerical integration of equation (7) then gives p as a function of τ, hence p_e from equation (13), and $\bar{k}$ from equation (8).

The relation between geometrical depth and optical depth in the model atmosphere may be obtained by integrating the equation

$$d\tau = -\bar{k}\rho\,dx. \tag{15}$$

Now equations (11) and (12) give

$$p = \frac{1}{m_H}(1+x_H)\rho RT, \tag{16}$$

where ρ is the density of the atmosphere. Hence

$$x_0 - x = (R/m_H)\int_{\tau_0}^{\tau}(1+x_H)(T/\bar{k}p)\,d\tau,$$

where x_0 is the geometrical depth corresponding to the optical depth τ_0. For the purpose of carrying out the numerical quadrature it is convenient to change the variable to $\log p$. We then have, writing θ for $5{,}040/T$,

$$x - x_0 = \frac{5040R}{gm_H\log e}\int_{p=p_0}^{p}\frac{1+x_H}{\theta}d\log p. \tag{17}$$

3.2. *A model for the solar atmosphere*

In the outermost layers of the solar atmosphere hydrogen is mainly neutral so that equations (8) and (14) may be written approximately as

$$\bar{k} = p_e a(H^-)/m_H, \tag{18}$$

$$p_e = (x_M/A)p. \tag{19}$$

In equation (18) we have

$$a(H^-) = \int \kappa'_\lambda(F_\lambda/F)\,d\lambda, \tag{20}$$

κ'_λ being the absorption coefficient per neutral H atom present at unit electron pressure, as given in Table VIII, and F_λ/F the monochromatic flux in units of the integrated net flux. This can only be determined without a detailed knowledge of the structure of the atmosphere in the special case of a 'grey' atmosphere (k_λ independent of λ). In practice it is necessary to use the flux ratio for a grey atmosphere (see Table VI) in order to compute $a(\mathrm{H}^-)$ by equation (20) and proceed to determine p, p_e, and $\bar{k}$ as functions of the optical depth. The solution so found leads to revised values of F_λ/F, but fortunately the change is reasonably small and it is not necessary to iterate. The mean coefficient of absorption $\bar{k}$ is therefore an explicit function of p_e and τ.

In the computation of $a(\mathrm{H}^-)$ as a function of optical depth it should be noted that with sufficient accuracy we may set

$$a(\mathrm{H}^-) = a(\mathrm{H}^-)_{\theta_e}\, \phi(\theta)/\phi(\theta_e), \tag{21}$$

where θ_e is the value of θ when $T = T_e$, and $\phi(\theta)$ is the number of negative ions per neutral H atom present at unit electron pressure:

$$\phi(\theta) = 4{\cdot}158 \times 10^{-10}\theta^{5/2}e^{1{\cdot}726\theta}.$$

Now from equations (18) and (19)

$$\bar{k} = (x_M/A)p\,a(\mathrm{H}^-)/m_\mathrm{H}, \tag{22}$$

and the equation of hydrostatic equilibrium may be written

$$p\frac{dp}{d\tau} = \phi(\theta_e)\frac{gm_\mathrm{H}A}{a(\mathrm{H}^-)_{\theta_e}}\frac{1}{x_M\,\phi(\theta)}. \tag{23}$$

Since p is zero at $\tau = 0$, equation (23) gives

$$\tfrac{1}{2}p^2 = \phi(\theta_e)\frac{gm_\mathrm{H}A}{a(\mathrm{H}^-)_{\theta_e}} \int\limits_0^\tau \frac{d\tau}{x_M\,\phi(\theta)}. \tag{24}$$

For an assumed variation of x_M with τ we compute p from (24), then p_e from (19). This enables us to find a revised variation of x_M with depth from tables of x_M as a function of θ and p_e. We then proceed with successive iterations until the variation of p_e (and hence x_M) with depth is such that equations (19) and (24) are consistent.

The contribution of neutral H to the mean coefficient of absorption is an added complication. To allow for it, we consider the equation

$$(x_M/A)a(\mathrm{H}^-)p\frac{dp}{d\tau} + a(\mathrm{H})\frac{dp}{d\tau} = gm_\mathrm{H}. \tag{25}$$

This equation replaces (23). Since the appearance of the term $a(\mathrm{H})dp/d\tau$ $(= a(\mathrm{H})g/\bar{k})$ only introduces a small perturbation in the equation, we may write the solution of (25) in the form

$$\tfrac{1}{2}p^2 = gm_\mathrm{H}\,A \int\limits_0^\tau \frac{1 - a(\mathrm{H})/\bar{k}^0}{x_M^0\,a(\mathrm{H}^-)}d\tau,$$

where the quantities x_M^0 and $\bar{k}^0$ are given by the solution which neglects neutral hydrogen. The correction Δp^2 $(= p^2 - p^{02})$ will therefore be given by

$$\Delta p^2 = 2gm_{\mathrm{H}} A \int\limits_0^{\tau} \frac{a(\mathrm{H})\,d\tau}{\bar{k}^0 x_M^0\, a(\mathrm{H}^-)}.$$

Table XXVI gives the structure of the solar atmosphere derived in the manner described, using $g = 2 \cdot 74 \times 10^4$ cm. sec.$^{-2}$, $\log A = 3 \cdot 8$, and $T_e = 5,740^\circ$ K. It is based on the work of Münch† who used a temperature distribution $T^4 = \frac{3}{4} T_e^4[\tau + q(\tau)]$, with $q(\tau)$ given by Chandrasekhar's fourth approximation. The boundary temperature T_0 then has the Hopf–Bronstein value $(\sqrt{3}/4)^{\frac{1}{4}} T_e$.

An alternative system of approximations involving the use of the Rosseland mean has been used by Strömgren.‡ This is described in Section 3.22 of Chapter XIII.

Table XXVI
Structure of the Solar Atmosphere
$T_e = 5,740^\circ$ K., $g = 2 \cdot 74 \times 10^4$ cm. sec.$^{-2}$, $\log A = 3 \cdot 8$.

τ	T	θ	$\log p$	$\log p_e$	$\log \bar{k}$	$\log \rho$	$\Delta h\ km.$
0	4,654	1·083	..	..	..	..	..
0·01	4,688	1·075	3·74	$\bar{1}$·85	$\bar{2}$·69	$\bar{8}$·15	0
0·02	4,715	1·069	4·01	0·09	$\bar{2}$·92	$\bar{8}$·42	87
0·04	4,768	1·057	4·19	0·27	$\bar{1}$·06	$\bar{8}$·59	147
0·06	4,818	1·046	4·30	0·36	$\bar{1}$·15	$\bar{8}$·70	184
0·08	4,865	1·036	4·38	0·44	$\bar{1}$·21	$\bar{8}$·78	207
0·10	4,912	1·026	4·43	0·50	$\bar{1}$·25	$\bar{8}$·82	225
0·12	4,956	1·017	4·46	0·56	$\bar{1}$·29	$\bar{8}$·86	240
0·14	4,995	1·009	4·51	0·61	$\bar{1}$·32	$\bar{8}$·89	253
0·16	5,035	1·001	4·54	0·64	$\bar{1}$·35	$\bar{8}$·92	265
0·18	5,076	0·993	4·57	0·68	$\bar{1}$·38	$\bar{8}$·95	276
0·20	5,112	0·986	4·60	0·71	$\bar{1}$·40	$\bar{8}$·97	284
0·24	5,185	0·972	4·64	0·77	$\bar{1}$·43	$\bar{7}$·01	303
0·28	5,250	0·960	4·68	0·82	$\bar{1}$·46	$\bar{7}$·04	317
0·32	5,311	0·949	4·71	0·87	$\bar{1}$·49	$\bar{7}$·07	329
0·36	5,373	0·938	4·74	0·92	$\bar{1}$·51	$\bar{7}$·09	340
0·40	5,425	0·929	4·77	0·96	$\bar{1}$·54	$\bar{7}$·12	350
0·50	5,563	0·906	4·82	1·06	$\bar{1}$·60	$\bar{7}$·16	368
0·60	5,682	0·887	4·86	1·15	$\bar{1}$·65	$\bar{7}$·19	383
0·70	5,793	0·870	4·89	1·24	$\bar{1}$·70	$\bar{7}$·21	395
0·80	5,902	0·854	4·91	1·32	$\bar{1}$·75	$\bar{7}$·22	405
0·90	6,000	0·840	4·93	1·40	$\bar{1}$·81	$\bar{7}$·23	413
1·00	6,094	0·827	4·94	1·48	$\bar{1}$·86	$\bar{7}$·24	420
1·2	6,269	0·804	4·97	1·64	$\bar{1}$·96	$\bar{7}$·25	430
1·4	6,437	0·783	4·99	1·78	0·06	$\bar{7}$·26	439

Pressures are given in dynes per sq. cm.

† G. Münch, *Ap. J.* **106**, 217 (1947).
‡ B. Strömgren, *Festschrift für Elis Strömgren* (Copenhagen), p. 218 (1940); *Publ. Copenhagen Obs.*, No. 138 (1944).

4. Ionization in the photosphere

The degree of ionization of an element in an equilibrium enclosure at temperature T is given by Saha's equation

$$\left(\frac{xN_e}{1-x}\right)_T = 2(2\pi mRT)^{3/2}h^{-3}e^{-I/RT}B_{p+1}(T)/B_p(T). \qquad (26)$$

In this equation $x/(1-x)$ is the ratio of the numbers of atoms in the $(p+1)$th and pth stages of ionization, I is the pth ionization potential, and $B_p(T)$ is the partition function of the pth stage of ionization. If most of the atoms in this stage are in the ground state, $B_p(T)$ is nearly equal to the statistical weight of this ground state. The ratio of the statistical weights of the ground states is written ϖ. Table XXVII contains values of I and ϖ for the first and second stages of ionization of the lighter elements.

TABLE XXVII
Ionization Potentials and Ratios of Statistical Weights

Stage of ionization		First		Second		Stage of ionization		First		Second	
Atomic number	Element	I volts	ϖ	I volts	ϖ	Atomic number	Element	I volts	ϖ	I volts	ϖ
1	H	13·59	$\frac{1}{2}$	..		15	P	10·9	$\frac{9}{4}$*	19·65	$\frac{9}{3}$
2	He	24·58	2	54·39	$\frac{1}{2}$	16	S	10·35	$\frac{4}{9}$*	23·4	$\frac{9}{4}$*
3	Li	5·39	$\frac{1}{2}$*	75·62	2	17	Cl	13·0	$\frac{3}{2}$	23·80	$\frac{4}{9}$
4	Be	9·32	2	18·20	$\frac{1}{2}$	18	A	15·75	6	27·6	$\frac{3}{2}$
5	B	8·31	$\frac{1}{6}$	25·12	2	19	K	4·34	$\frac{1}{2}$*	31·8	6
6	C	11·24	$\frac{2}{3}$*	24·38	$\frac{1}{6}$	20	Ca	6·11	2*	11·87	$\frac{1}{2}$
7	N	14·55	$\frac{9}{4}$	29·61	$\frac{2}{3}$	21	Sc	6·7	$\frac{3}{2}$*	12·9	$\frac{2}{3}$*
8	O	13·61	$\frac{4}{9}$	35·14	$\frac{9}{4}$	22	Ti	6·84	$\frac{4}{3}$*	13·7	$\frac{3}{2}$*
9	F	17·42	$\frac{3}{2}$	34·98	$\frac{4}{9}$	23	V	6·74	$\frac{25}{28}$*	14·2	$\frac{28}{25}$*
10	Ne	21·56	6	41·08	$\frac{3}{2}$	24	Cr	6·77	$\frac{6}{7}$*	16·7	$\frac{25}{6}$*
11	Na	5·14	$\frac{1}{2}$*	47·29	6	25	Mn	7·43	$\frac{7}{6}$*	15·7	$\frac{6}{7}$*
12	Mg	7·64	2	15·03	$\frac{1}{2}$	26	Fe	7·89	$\frac{6}{5}$*	16·23	..
13	Al	5·98	$\frac{1}{6}$	18·83	2	27	Co	7·87	$\frac{3}{4}$*	17·2	..
14	Si	8·14	$\frac{2}{3}$*	16·34	$\frac{1}{6}$	28	Ni	7·64	$\frac{10}{21}$*	18·5	..

The * indicates that there are appreciable numbers of atoms in the excited states.

In the photosphere there is a departure from thermodynamic equilibrium, but the degree of ionization may be found by considering the balance between ionization and recombination. Let there be $N_e f(v)\, dv$ electrons per c.c. with velocities between v and $v+dv$. The number of recombinations per c.c. per second between these electrons and Nx ions per c.c. may be set equal to

$$N_e f(v)\, dv \times Nx\{\alpha(v)+\beta(v)J(v)\}.$$

In this expression $h\nu = I+\tfrac{1}{2}mv^2$, and three-body recombinations (the reverse of ionizations by collision) are ignored, but allowance is made for recombinations stimulated by radiation, as was done in the case of line transitions in Section 4.1 of Chapter VI. Now let $\psi(\nu)$ be the probability that an ion (in the lower stage considered) captures a quantum in a radiation field of unit intensity, so that $\psi(\nu)$ is the atomic absorption coefficient divided by $h\nu$. Then the number of ionizations per c.c. per second resulting from the capture of quanta with energies between $h\nu$ and $h(\nu+d\nu)$ is

$$N(1-x)\psi(\nu)\times 4\pi J(\nu)\,d\nu.$$

In thermodynamic equilibrium the ν, $d\nu$ captures balance the ν, $d\nu$ ionizations, where $h\,d\nu = mv\,dv$ on account of the relation $h\nu = I + \tfrac{1}{2}mv^2$, and $f(v)$ is Maxwell's distribution $M(v, T)$, where

$$M(v, T) = 4\pi(2\pi RT)^{-3/2}m^{3/2}v^2 e^{-\frac{1}{2}mv^2/RT}.$$

Hence

$$\psi(\nu)\times 4\pi B(\nu, T) = \left(\frac{xN_e}{1-x}\right)_T \times M(v, T)\frac{h}{mv}\{\alpha(v)+\beta(v)B(\nu, T)\}, \quad (27)$$

a result which must be true for all v. Substituting for $\{xN_e/(1-x)\}_T$ and $M(v, T)$ gives

$$\frac{\alpha(v)}{\beta(v)} = \frac{2h\nu^3}{c^2}, \tag{28}$$

$$\frac{\psi(\nu)}{v\alpha(v)} = \frac{\varpi m^2 c^2}{(h\nu)^3}. \tag{29}$$

The first of these equations is similar to equation (66) of Chapter VI, which gives the relation between the Einstein transition coefficients. Equation (29) can be reduced to a relation between the atomic continuous coefficient $\kappa(\nu)$ and the recombination coefficient $\alpha(v)$. Since $\kappa(\nu) = \psi(\nu)h\nu$, equation (29) gives

$$\kappa(\nu) = \varpi(mc/h\nu)^2 v\alpha(v), \tag{30}$$

a relation due to Milne.

The total number of captures per c.c. per second irrespective of v depends on the temperature, and may be written $N_e N x\alpha(T)$, where $\alpha(T)$ is defined by

$$\alpha(T) = \int_0^\infty \{\alpha(v)+\beta(v)B(\nu, T)\}M(v, T)\,dv,$$

the integrand being given by equation (27). Hence

$$\alpha(T) = \left(\frac{1-x}{xN_e}\right)_T \int_{\nu_0}^\infty \psi(\nu)\times 4\pi B(\nu, T)\,d\nu. \tag{31}$$

Now Kramers' law for hydrogen-like atoms gives

$$\kappa(\nu) = f_c \frac{2\pi e^2 \nu_0^2}{mc^4} \lambda^3, \qquad \lambda < \lambda_0.$$

In this case $$\alpha(T) = \frac{8\pi^2 e^2 h^2}{\varpi m c^3 (2\pi m)^{\frac{3}{2}}} \frac{\nu_0 f_c}{(RT)^{\frac{1}{2}}} \times z e^z E_1(z),$$

where $z = h\nu_0 / RT$. For a hydrogen-like atom of principal quantum number n, and charge Ze, we have $\nu_0 = 2\pi m e^4 Z^2 / h^3 n^2$. Since $z e^z E_1(z)$ is nearly equal to unity in practical cases, the recombination coefficient $\alpha(T)$ is proportional to $Z^2 T^{-\frac{3}{2}}$. Inserting numerical values

$$\alpha(T) = 6 \cdot 66 \times 10^{-12} Z^2 T^{-\frac{1}{2}} n^2 f_c / \varpi.$$

In a steady state, not necessarily thermodynamic equilibrium, the total number of ionizations per c.c. per second must be equal to the total number of recombinations. Hence

$$\int_{\nu_0}^{\infty} N(1-x)\psi(\nu) \times 4\pi J(\nu) \, d\nu = \int_{0}^{\infty} N_e N x f(\nu) \{\alpha(\nu) + \beta(\nu) J(\nu)\} \, d\nu. \qquad (32)$$

We suppose that collisions set up a Maxwellian distribution of electron velocities at the local temperature T: then $f(\nu) = M(\nu, T)$. Then, ignoring the fact that in equation (32) the small term $\beta(\nu)$ appears multiplied by $J(\nu)$ instead of $B(\nu, T)$, as in equation (27), we have

$$\alpha(T) \frac{xN_e}{1-x} = \int_{\nu_0}^{\infty} \psi(\nu) \times 4\pi J(\nu) \, d\nu.$$

With $\alpha(T)$ given by (31), we find

$$\frac{xN_e}{1-x} \Big/ \left(\frac{xN_e}{1-x} \right)_T = \int \psi(\nu) J(\nu) \, d\nu \Big/ \int \psi(\nu) B(\nu, T) \, d\nu, \qquad (33)$$

where T is the local temperature defined by the distribution of the electron velocities.

This innocent-looking equation is not easy to apply in practice, because all ionization potentials are so high that the ionizing radiation is in the ultra-violet, where knowledge of $J(\nu)$ is poor. A further difficulty is that the variation of $\psi(\nu)$ with ν is seldom known accurately. The latter point is, however, not fatal since, as Pannekoek pointed out, $h\nu_0 / RT$ is always large (if the ion is at all well represented in the atmosphere) so that

$$\int_{\nu_0}^{\infty} \nu^m \exp(-h\nu/RT) \, d\nu = (RT/h)\nu_0^m e^{-h\nu_0/RT} \qquad (34)$$

to a high degree of accuracy, and ν_0^m occurs in both numerator and denominator. Then in the case of geometrical dilution, or

$$J(\nu) = \omega B(\nu, T'),$$

equation (33) reduces to

$$\frac{xN_e}{1-x} \Big/ \left(\frac{xN_e}{1-x}\right)_T = \omega \, \frac{T'}{T} \exp\left\{\frac{h\nu_0}{RT} - \frac{h\nu_0}{RT'}\right\}. \tag{35}$$

At the surface of the star the electron velocity temperature is T_0, but the effective temperature of the radiation is $T_e = 2^{\frac{1}{4}}T_0$. This statement does not imply that the frequency distribution of the outgoing radiation is $B(\nu, T_e)$: it only implies that the intensity integrated over all frequencies is $B(T_e)$. But if we assume that $I_1(\nu) = B(\nu, T_e)$, so that $J = \frac{1}{2}B(\nu, T_e)$, then at the surface of the photosphere we have from (34) and (35)

$$\frac{xN_e}{1-x} \Big/ \left(\frac{xN_e}{1-x}\right)_{T_0} = \frac{1}{2}\frac{T_e}{T_0} \exp\left\{\frac{h\nu_0}{RT_0} - \frac{h\nu_0}{RT_e}\right\}. \tag{36}$$

More generally, at any point in the photosphere where the electron velocity temperature is T and the radiation 'effective temperature' T_1, that is $J = \frac{1}{2}B(\nu, T_1)$, we have

$$\frac{xN_e}{1-x} \Big/ \left(\frac{xN_e}{1-x}\right)_T = \frac{1}{2}\frac{T_1}{T} \exp\left\{\frac{h\nu_0}{RT} - \frac{h\nu_0}{RT_1}\right\}. \tag{37}$$

This modification of Saha's formula is due to Pannekoek, and has been used by Russell who adopted $T = 0\cdot86T_1$ as a mean value for stellar atmospheres.

The following treatment takes more account of the frequency distribution of the photospheric radiation. According to equation (13) of Chapter IV

$$J(\nu) = B(\nu, T) + \frac{2b_\nu - 3a_\nu}{3 + 2\sqrt{3}} e^{-\sqrt{3}\tau_\nu},$$

where $a_\nu = B(\nu, T_0)$ and $b_\nu = \frac{3}{8}(\bar{k}/k_\nu)(h\nu/RT_0)a_\nu$. This value of $J(\nu)$ can be inserted in (33) and integrated. Since a_ν, b_ν and $B(\nu, T)$ vary much more rapidly with ν than does $\psi(\nu)$ or τ_ν, the approximation (34) can be used and equation (33) then gives

$$\frac{xN_e}{1-x} \Big/ \left(\frac{xN_e}{1-x}\right)_T = 1 + \frac{2b_\nu/a_\nu - 3}{3 + 2\sqrt{3}} \frac{T_0}{T} \exp\left\{-\sqrt{3}\tau_\nu + \frac{h\nu_0}{RT} - \frac{h\nu_0}{RT_0}\right\}. \tag{38}$$

This formula gives much smaller corrections to Saha's equation in practical cases than the formula (37) of Pannekoek does. For example, consider the case where $h\nu_0/RT_0 = 18$. The computation of (37) requires no further datum, but for (38) a value of $\bar{k}/k_{\nu_0}$ is required. Two cases

$\bar{k} = k_{\nu_0}$ and $\bar{k} = 0\cdot1k_{\nu_0}$ (which correspond roughly to hydrogen in early type stars and to metals in the solar photosphere respectively) are shown in Table XXVIII.

It is seen that the correction to Saha's formula is small in the case of metals in the photosphere, the correction being greater or less than unity according as $\frac{1}{4}(\bar{k}/k_{\nu_0})(h\nu_0/RT_0)$ is greater or less than unity. In Strömgren's extensive calculations on the photosphere, and in most later calculations, no correction to Saha's equation has been applied.

TABLE XXVIII

Corrections to Saha's Formula

$$\frac{xN_e}{1-x}\Big/\left(\frac{xN_e}{1-x}\right)_T \text{ for } h\nu_0/RT_0 = 18.$$

τ	Pannekoek's equation (37)	Equation (38)	
		$k_{\nu_0} = \bar{k}$	$k_{\nu_0} = 10\bar{k}$
0·0	7·23	2·62	0·714
0·1	6·62	1·70	0·974
0·3	5·78	1·18	1·000
0·5	5·20	1·06	1·000
1·0	4·31	1·01	1·000

5. Calculation of the profiles of absorption lines. The principal lines of neutral and ionized calcium in the Sun

The line absorption spectrum of the model atmosphere of Section 3.2 may be calculated from the physical theory of line absorption and the theory of line formation. When the variation of the physical parameters with optical depth is known, Strömgren's method† for the treatment of arbitrary variations in η may be used. The actual calculation is divided into two parts—the determination of η as a function of optical depth, and η as a function of $\nu-\nu_0$.

5.1. *Variation of η with depth*

Consider a metal atom with abundance a relative to all other metal atoms present, and let A be the hydrogen to metal ratio. Then from equation (54) of Chapter VII we have

$$\eta = \frac{N}{N_a}\frac{a}{A}\frac{\alpha(\nu)_D}{km_H}, \qquad (39)$$

where N is the number of atoms in the state from which the absorption takes place, N_a being the total number of metal atoms of the kind considered. If only two stages of ionization (neutral and once ionized) are

† Chapter VII, Section 6.3.

present, and if the atoms and ions absorb from their ground states, we have for the neutral stage

$$\eta_1 = (1-x_a)\frac{a}{A}\frac{\alpha(\nu)_D}{k_1\,m_H},$$ (40)

and for the ionized stage

$$\eta_2 = x_a\frac{a}{A}\frac{\alpha(\nu)_D}{k_2\,m_H},$$ (41)

where k_1 and k_2 are the values of k_λ for the two lines. Now in the wings of the line, that is, outside the Doppler core, we have

$$\alpha(\nu)_D = \frac{\pi e^2}{mc}f\frac{\delta}{\pi}\frac{1}{(\nu-\nu_0)^2}.$$ (42)

So far as the variation of η with depth is concerned, we only have to consider the behaviour of $(1-x_a)\delta_1/k_1$ and $x_a\,\delta_2/k_2$.

As an example we consider the variation of η with depth for the principal lines of neutral and ionized calcium in the model solar atmosphere of Table XXVI.

5.11. *Ionization*

We have shown in Section 4 that the ionization is given with sufficient accuracy by Saha's equation without any correction. Thus

$$\log\frac{x}{1-x} = -5040I/T+\tfrac{5}{2}\log T-0.48+\log 2\varpi-\log p_e,$$ (43)

where I is in volts and p_e in dyne cm.$^{-2}$ From Table XXVII we have $I = 6.11$ volts and $\varpi = 2$ for the ionization of Ca to Ca$^+$. Table XXIX gives $\log\{x/(1-x)\}$ for the model solar atmosphere of Section 3.2.

TABLE XXIX

Ionization of Ca *to* Ca$^+$ *in the Solar Photosphere*

τ	$\log\dfrac{x}{1-x}$	τ	$\log\dfrac{x}{1-x}$
0·01	2·84	0·32	2·73
0·02	2·62	0·36	2·76
0·04	2·55	0·40	2·79
0·06	2·54	0·50	2·86
0·08	2·53	0·60	2·91
0·10	2·54	0·70	2·94
0·12	2·55	0·80	2·97
0·14	2·56	0·90	3·00
0·16	2·58	1·00	3·02
0·18	2·60	1·2	3·03
0·20	2·62	1·4	3·05
0·24	2·66	2	3·07
0·28	2·69	3	3·08

5.12. *Damping*

The damping constant δ is the sum of the half-widths due to radiation damping and collision damping, or $\delta = \delta_n + \delta_c$. The natural damping constant δ_n does not vary with depth, and has the value $(\gamma_k + \gamma_j)/4\pi$, where γ_k and γ_j are defined in terms of the Einstein coefficient by equation (68) of Chapter VI. In the case of principal lines $\gamma = 0$ for the lower state, and when there is only one downward transition from the upper state γ_k is simply equal to A_{k1} for that state.

For the resonance line $\lambda 4,227$ A of Ca the transition is $4\,^1S$- $4\,^1P^0$, and the $4\,^1P^0$ state has no other down-ward transition. According to Hartree and Hartree† the value of A_{k1} is $2 \cdot 81 \times 10^8$ sec.$^{-1}$, so that

$$\delta_n = A_{k1}/4\pi = 0 \cdot 222 \times 10^8 \text{ sec.}^{-1}$$

On the other hand the H and K lines of Ca$^+$ form part of a more complicated scheme shown in Fig. 34. The probability of either transition $4\,^2P^0 \to 4\,^2S$ is $1 \cdot 66 \times 10^8$ sec.$^{-1}$, and that of

$$4\,^2P^0 \to 3\,^2D \quad \text{is} \quad 0 \cdot 15 \times 10^8 \text{ sec.}^{-1}$$

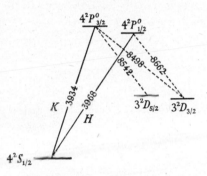

FIG. 34. Energy-level diagram for the H and K lines of ionized calcium.

Hence $\gamma_k \; (= \sum A_{kj})$ for either of the states $4\,^2P^0_{\frac{3}{2}}$ or $4\,^2P^0_{\frac{1}{2}}$ is $1 \cdot 81 \times 10^8$ sec.$^{-1}$, and we have

$$\delta_n = \gamma_k/4\pi = 0 \cdot 144 \times 10^8 \text{ sec.}^{-1}$$

The collision-damping half-width δ_c, due to phase collisions between the line-absorbing atoms and neutral hydrogen, may be calculated from Lindholm's theory by equations (58), (59), and (60) of Chapter VI. For any atom of mass m_a

$$\delta_c = 7 \cdot 814 \times 10^{15} C^{2/5} \left(1 + \frac{m_H}{m_a} \right)^{3/10} p\,\theta^{7/10}, \qquad (44)$$

and for calcium, in particular, we have $\delta_c = 7 \cdot 87 \times 10^{15} C^{2/5} p \theta^{7/10}$. The effect of collisions with electrons or ions is unimportant for the model solar atmosphere under consideration, since the electron pressure is not much more than 10^{-4} of the gas pressure.

Determination of the van der Waals interaction constant. The value of C is related to the mean square radius of the upper state of the broadened line by

$$C = (\alpha e^2/h)\overline{r_k^2}, \qquad (45)$$

† See D. R. Hartree and W. Hartree, *Proc. Roy. Soc.* A, **164**, 167 (1938).

TABLE XXX

*Radiation and Collision Damping Constants for Principal Lines of
Neutral and Ionized Calcium*

Line	A_{k1}	δ_n	$\overline{r_k^2}$	C	δ_c
Ca λ4,227 A	$2 \cdot 81 \times 10^8$	$0 \cdot 22 \times 10^8$	$69a_0^2$	$4 \cdot 46 \times 10^{-32}$	$2 \cdot 27 \times 10^3 p\theta^{7/10}$
Ca$^+$ H and K	$1 \cdot 66 \times 10^8$	$0 \cdot 14 \times 10^8$	$23a_0^2$	$1 \cdot 49 \times 10^{-32}$	$1 \cdot 46 \times 10^3 p\theta^{7/10}$

where α is the polarizability of the hydrogen atom. With $\alpha = 6 \cdot 63 \times 10^{-25}$, we have $\alpha e^2/h = 2 \cdot 31 \times 10^{-17}$. The mean square radius in the excited state is given by the quantum mechanical formula

$$\overline{r^2} = \int_0^\infty Rr^2R \cdot r^2 \, dr, \tag{46}$$

where R is the normalized radial wave function.† In the case of hydrogen it may be shown that

$$\overline{r^2} = \frac{n^2}{2Z^2}\{5n^2 + 1 - 3l(l+1)\}, \tag{47}$$

the unit of length being the radius of the first Bohr orbit,

$$a_0 = h^2/4\pi^2 me^2 = 0 \cdot 529 \times 10^{-8} \text{ cm.}$$

Equation (47) may be applied to hydrogen-like atoms if n and Z are replaced by an effective quantum number and an effective nuclear charge. Let χ be the ionization energy of the upper state of the line in Rydberg units (one Rydberg unit equals 13·59 volts), then equation (47) applies with $n = Z/\sqrt{\chi}$, where $Z = 1, 2,$ or 3 for neutral, singly, or doubly ionized atoms. Thus

$$\overline{r^2} = \frac{5Z^2/\chi + 1 - 3l(l+1)}{2\chi}, \tag{48}$$

where χ is, of course, a function of l, the azimuthal quantum number.

If the normalized radial wave function is available, we may calculate $\overline{r^2}$ from equation (46) by numerical quadrature. In self-consistent field results the quantity $P = rR$ is tabulated, and we have

$$\overline{r^2} = \int_0^\infty P^2 r^2 \, dr. \tag{49}$$

† See D. R. Hartree, *Reports on Progress in Physics*, **11**, 113 (1946/7) for a list of atomic calculations.

From the self-consistent field calculations for Ca and Ca$^+$ by Hartree and Hartree (loc. cit.) we find the function $P^2 r^2$ shown in Fig. 35. Numerical quadrature gives $69 \cdot 2 a_0^2$ for the mean square radius of the excited state of the line $\lambda 4,227$ A, and $22 \cdot 6 a_0^2$ for the excited states of the H and K lines. The Coulomb approximation (48) cannot be used for the line

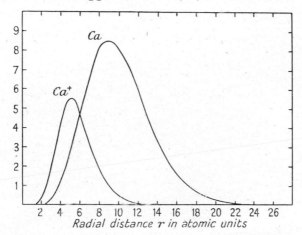

FIG. 35. Variation of $P^2 r^2$ ($= R^2 r^4$) with radial distance for a $4p$ electron in the ^1P state of neutral calcium (larger curve), corresponding to the upper state of the resonance line $\lambda 4,227$ A, and for a $4p$ electron in the ^2P state of ionized calcium (smaller curve), corresponding to upper states of the H and K lines. The area beneath each curve is the mean square radius of the atom in the excited state of the line concerned. The curves are based on the self-consistent field calculations of Hartree and Hartree.

$\lambda 4,227$ A, the neutral Ca atom not being hydrogen-like, but the formula should apply to the ionized atom. For $\lambda 3,934$ A we have $\chi = 0 \cdot 64$ Rydbergs, and with $Z = 2$ equation (48) gives $20 \cdot 6 a_0^2$ for the mean square radius of the excited state of the ionized atom. This is in good agreement with the value $22 \cdot 6 a_0^2$ derived from equation (49). But it should be noted that in calculating the interaction between an ionized calcium atom and a neutral H atom, we have taken no account of the fact that the charge on the Ca$^+$ atom introduces polarization of the H atom, which then acts on the Ca$^+$ atom. It is considered that this effect does not introduce any serious error in the determination of the interaction constant. At all events C only appears in equation (44) raised to a fairly low power, namely 2/5, so that great accuracy in the value of C is not necessary.

From the values of $x/(1-x)$ shown in Table XXIX, the values of δ for neutral and ionized calcium in Table XXXI, and the values of $\bar{k}$ shown in Table XXVI we can calculate *relative values of* η as a function of

TABLE XXXI

Half-Widths of Principal Lines of Neutral and Ionized Calcium in the Solar Photosphere

τ	$\delta = \delta_n + \delta_c$		τ	$\delta = \delta_n + \delta_c$	
	Ca	Ca+		Ca	Ca+
	Multiply by 10^8			Multiply by 10^8	
0·01	0·27	0·17	0·32	1·34	0·86
0·02	0·46	0·30	0·36	1·42	0·91
0·04	0·59	0·38	0·40	1·49	0·96
0·06	0·69	0·44	0·50	1·62	1·04
0·08	0·78	0·50	0·60	1·74	1·12
0·10	0·84	0·54	0·70	1·82	1·17
0·12	0·88	0·57	0·80	1·88	1·21
0·14	0·96	0·62	0·90	1·93	1·24
0·16	1·01	0·65	1·00	1·96	1·26
0·18	1·06	0·68	1·2	2·04	1·32
0·20	1·12	0·72	1·4	2·10	1·35
0·24	1·20	0·77	2	2·30	1·48
0·28	1·28	0·82	3	2·35	1·49

depth (assuming that in each case k has the same variation with τ that $\overline{k}$ has): we simply compute $(1-x)\delta_1/\overline{k}$ and $x\delta_2/\overline{k}$. Table XXXII shows these values of η normalized to unity at $\tau = 0\cdot4$.

TABLE XXXII

Variation of η with Optical Depth in the Solar Photosphere for the Principal Lines of Neutral and Ionized Calcium

τ	η		τ	η	
	Ca	Ca+		Ca	Ca+
0·01	1·42	1·24	0·32	1·17	1·01
0·02	1·77	1·29	0·36	1·08	1·00
0·04	2·08	1·20	0·40	1·00	1·00
0·06	2·05	1·14	0·50	0·80	0·97
0·08	2·00	1·11	0·60	0·68	0·92
0·10	1·97	1·09	0·70	0·60	0·87
0·12	1·90	1·07	0·80	0·52	0·78
0·14	1·82	1·05	0·90	0·44	0·69
0·16	1·70	1·04	1·00	0·38	0·63
0·18	1·60	1·03	1·20	0·30	0·52
0·20	1·52	1·02	1·4	0·24	0·43
0·24	− 1·38	1·02	2	0·20	0·35
0·28	1·28	1·01	3	0·12	0·22

5.2. *Residual intensity*

At a given depth, say $\tau = 0\cdot 4$, η will pass from very small values in the far wings of the line to very large values at the centre. Corresponding to each value of η at the reference depth there will be a set of values of η at all other depths, which may be obtained by multiplying the values in a Table such as XXXII (the master table) by a constant (the place constant) which gives the required value of η at the reference depth.

The residual intensity is calculated for coherent scattering by the method set out in Chapter VII, Section 6.32. When $\epsilon = 0$ equation (99) is

$$r = \frac{1+\tfrac{2}{3}\sqrt 3}{\tfrac{1}{4}(x_0/n)+\tfrac{2}{3}\sqrt 3}\,\frac{\tfrac{1}{4}(x_0/n)\bar\lambda+\tfrac{2}{3}\sqrt 3\,\overline{\sqrt\lambda}}{1+\tfrac{2}{3}\sqrt 3\,\overline{\sqrt\lambda}}. \tag{50}$$

To compute $\bar\lambda$ and $\overline{\sqrt\lambda}$, we have first to find n, the value of $k/\bar k$. Next, if η_0 is the value of η at the reference depth, we form the quantity $\lambda_0 = 1/(1+\eta_0)$, and $\sqrt{\lambda_0}$. We then calculate the division points τ_j in the numerical quadrature for $\bar\lambda$ and $\overline{\sqrt\lambda}$. The two sets of values of τ_j for the evaluation of $\bar\lambda$ and $\overline{\sqrt\lambda}$ are

$$\frac{1}{n}\sqrt{\lambda_0}\times 0\cdot 028,\ 0\cdot 151,\ 0\cdot 400,\ 0\cdot 846,\ 1\cdot 767,$$

$$\frac{1}{n}\sqrt{\lambda_0}\times 0\cdot 014,\ 0\cdot 076,\ 0\cdot 200,\ 0\cdot 423,\ 0\cdot 884,$$

respectively. These are the values of τ at which η must be extracted from the *master table* and multiplied by the *place constant*. Let

$$\lambda_j = 1/(1+\eta_j)$$

be the value of λ at $\tau = \tau_j$, then we have

$$\bar\lambda = \sum \alpha_j \lambda_j, \qquad \overline{\sqrt\lambda} = \sum \alpha_j\sqrt{\lambda_j},$$

the weights α_j being given in Table XXIII.

We now calculate the residual intensity in the K line of Ca$^+$ in the Sun, at a place within the line where $\eta_0 = 10$. From Chapter IV we take $n = 0\cdot 68$ at wave-length 3,934 A. Now

$$\lambda_0 = 1/11 = 0\cdot 0909, \qquad \sqrt{\lambda_0} = 0\cdot 3015,$$

and we have $(1/n)\sqrt{\lambda_0} = 0\cdot 443$. The division points τ_j for the calculation of λ and $\sqrt\lambda$ together with the numerical details are given in the following table.

TABLE XXXIII
Numerical Data for Calculating $\bar{\lambda}$ and $\overline{\sqrt{\lambda}}$

τ	η/η_0	η	λ	α	$\alpha\lambda$
0·012	1·25	12·5	0·0741	0·119	0·0088
0·066	1·13	11·3	0·0813	0·239	0·0194
0·177	1·03	10·3	0·0885	0·284	0·0251
0·374	1·00	10·0	0·0909	0·239	0·0216
0·782	0·80	8·0	0·1111	0·119	0·0132

τ	η/η_0	η	$\sqrt{\lambda}$	α	$\alpha\sqrt{\lambda}$
0·006	1·22	12·2	0·275	0·119	0·0327
0·034	1·26	12·6	0·271	0·239	0·0645
0·088	1·10	11·0	0·289	0·284	0·0822
0·187	1·03	10·3	0·292	0·239	0·0697
0·391	1·00	10·0	0·302	0·119	0·0360

We now have

$$\bar{\lambda} = \sum \alpha\lambda = 0\cdot0881,$$

$$\overline{\sqrt{\lambda}} = \sum \alpha\sqrt{\lambda} = 0\cdot2851.$$

The remainder of the calculation is as follows:† the quantity x_0 in equation (50) is given by

$$x_0 = \frac{h\nu/RT_0}{1-e^{-h\nu/RT_0}}. \qquad (51)$$

For the K line of Ca^+ we have $h\nu = 3\cdot151$ volts. With $T_0 = 4,830°$ equation (51) gives $x_0 = 7\cdot570$, and since $n = 0\cdot68$, $\tfrac{1}{4}x_0/n = 2\cdot783$. Then from (50)

$$r = \frac{2\cdot155}{3\cdot938}\,\frac{2\cdot783\bar{\lambda}+1\cdot155\overline{\sqrt{\lambda}}}{1+1\cdot155\overline{\sqrt{\lambda}}} = 0\cdot237.$$

When η is small, $\lambda_0 = \sqrt{\lambda_0} = 1$, and the division points in the numerical quadrature for $\bar{\lambda}$ and $\overline{\sqrt{\lambda}}$ are simply $1/n \times 0\cdot028$ etc., and $1/n \times 0\cdot014$ etc., respectively. Neglecting η^2, equation (50) may be written in the form

$$r = 1-A\eta, \qquad (52)$$

η being the value at the reference depth. For the K line we have $r = 1-0\cdot437\eta$. This enables us to compute intensities in the far wings of the line.

5.3. *The line profile and its equivalent width*

From equations (41) and (42) the actual value of η for the ionized element is

$$\eta = x\,\frac{a}{A}\,\frac{e^2}{mc}\,\frac{f\delta\lambda_0^4}{km_H c^2}\,\frac{1}{(\lambda-\lambda_0)^2}. \qquad (53)$$

† We wish to thank Mr. E. R. Hill for making available some calculations on the equivalent widths of lines of neutral and ionized calcium in the Sun.

For the K line $\lambda 3,934$ A of Ca^+, $f = \frac{2}{3}$, and from Table XXV we take $\log a = \overline{2} \cdot 30$ for the relative abundance of calcium, the hydrogen to metal ratio being given by $\log A = 3 \cdot 8$. At the reference depth $\tau = 0 \cdot 4$ we have $x = 1 \cdot 00$, $\delta = 0 \cdot 96 \times 10^8$, and $\log \overline{k} = \overline{1} \cdot 54$. The absorption coefficient k_λ is equal to $n\overline{k}$, where $n = 0 \cdot 68$ for the K line. Equation (53) then gives $\log \eta = 2 \cdot 06 - 2 \log(\lambda - \lambda_0)$, expressing $\lambda - \lambda_0$ in angstroms. This gives

$$\lambda - \lambda_0 = B\eta^{-\frac{1}{2}}$$

with $B = 10 \cdot 7$. The values of η chosen at the reference depth in the last section correspond to the distances from the centre of the line shown in Table XXXIV.

The equivalent width of the line is defined by the equation

$$W_\lambda = \int (1 - r) \, d\lambda. \tag{54}$$

Thus W_λ is the width of a rectangular profile which absorbs the same total energy as the actual line. To compute W_λ we proceed as follows: Let r^* be the residual intensity for Eddington's standard case η constant, where η is the value at the reference depth in the actual atmosphere, and let W^* be the equivalent width of the standard line. Now, from equation (24) of Chapter VII,

$$1 - r^* = \frac{\eta}{1 + \eta + \frac{2}{3}q}, \tag{55}$$

where $q^2 = 3(1 + \eta)$. With $\lambda - \lambda_0 = B\eta^{-\frac{1}{2}}$ we have $W^* = Bw^*$, where

$$\tfrac{1}{2}w^* = \int\limits_{\eta=\infty}^{0} (1 - r^*) \, d\eta^{-\frac{1}{2}} = \sqrt{3} \int\limits_{q=\sqrt{3}}^{\infty} \frac{dq}{(q+2)(q-3)^{\frac{1}{2}}}.$$

This gives $\tfrac{1}{2}w^* = \sqrt{3} \ln \sqrt{3}$, and $W^* = \sqrt{3} \, B \ln 3$. The equivalent width of the actual line is now given by

$$W = W^* + \int (r^* - r) \, d\lambda. \tag{56}$$

The advantage gained by introducing W^* lies in the fact that the second term in equation (56) is only a small correction to W^* if the reference depth is skilfully chosen.

TABLE XXXIV

Profile of the K Line $\lambda 3,934$ A

η	0·1	0·2	0·3	1	3	10	30
$\lambda - \lambda_0$ angstroms	33·9	24·0	18·2	10·7	5·8	3·4	1·8
r	0·960	0·920	0·885	0·702	0·455	0·237	0·128
r^*	0·959	0·919	0·885	0·725	0·524	0·326	0·198

The calculated equivalent width of the K line is 21·8 angstroms. This refers to the integrated light from the disk. Observed values of W for the centre of the solar disk are given in Table XXXV. The measurement is made difficult by the presence of many absorption lines in the wings of the line. The mean of the observations gives $W = 17$ angstroms.

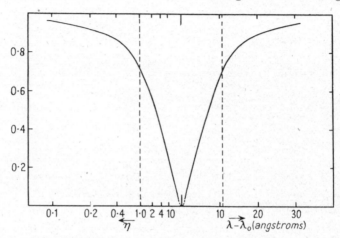

FIG. 36. Computed profile of the K line λ3,934 A of ionized calcium in the Sun. The ordinate gives the residual intensity of the line averaged over the disk of the Sun. The abscissa to the right of the centre of the line gives the distance from the centre in angstroms; to the left of the centre are given values of η (at the reference depth $\tau = 0.4$ in the solar atmosphere) for several points in the line. The equivalent width is the width of the rectangular profile shown. This profile absorbs the same total energy as the actual line.

Considering the difficulty of measurement and the approximate abundance of calcium adopted, the agreement between observed and computed values is satisfactory. The method could be used to derive a revised value of the calcium abundance, but the hydrogen to metal ratio and other uncertain factors are involved.

5.4. *Comparison of the equivalent widths of lines of neutral and ionized calcium*

The abundance of calcium enters in the same way into the equivalent widths of the lines of the neutral and ionized element, so that the ratio of the equivalent widths is independent of this uncertain factor. A comparison of the calculated equivalent widths with observation is therefore a comparison of the computed ionization of calcium with observation. Such a comparison was made by Woolley,† who used it to obtain an independent value of the temperature of the Sun, but a better

† R. v. d. R. Woolley, *M.N.* **93**, 691 (1933).

use of the comparison is made if one regards the temperature as well established and determines the electron pressure at the reference depth. The comparison of equivalent widths is then a determination of the absolute value of k_λ. This idea was put forward in another form by Milne,[†] who used the position of the maximum strength of lines of ionized elements in the spectral sequence to determine an astrophysical value of the absorption coefficient. It should be noted that centre-to-limb observations (see Chapter V) do not test the absolute value of k_λ, but only the form of its variation with λ.

The equivalent width depends partly on the abundance of the atoms forming the line, and partly on their distribution with depth. If we want to compare the abundances of two kinds of atom which are not distributed in the same way, we shall have to take care to make the comparison at a particular depth. We can do this by computing a reference profile in which we plot $1-r$ as a function of $\eta^{-\frac{1}{2}}$, η being the value at the reference depth used in computing r. We can in fact form a *reference equivalent width w* defined by

$$w = \int (1-r)\, d\eta^{-\frac{1}{2}}.$$

If two lines due to atoms with abundances a_1 and a_2 at the reference depth are treated in this way, the ratio of the actual equivalent widths W_1 and W_2 is given by

$$\left(\frac{W_1}{W_2}\right)^2 = \left(\frac{w_1}{w_2}\right)^2 \left(\frac{af\delta\lambda_0^4}{k_\lambda}\right)_1 \bigg/ \left(\frac{af\delta\lambda_0^4}{k_\lambda}\right)_2.$$

Applying this equation to the lines of a neutral and ionized element, if W and W^+ are the equivalent widths, the equation for the ionization at the reference depth is

$$\frac{x}{1-x} = \left(\frac{w}{w^+}\right)^2 \left(\frac{W^+}{W}\right)^2 \left(\frac{f\delta\lambda_0^4}{k_\lambda}\right) \bigg/ \left(\frac{f\delta\lambda_0^4}{k_\lambda}\right)^+. \tag{57}$$

TABLE XXXV

Observed Equivalent Widths at the Centre of the Disk

Observer	Ca⁺ λ3,934 A	Ca λ4,226 A	W^+/W
Allen	15·0 A	1·23 A	12·2
Mulders	15·9	1·20	13·2
Houtgast	19·2	1·43	13·4

† E. A. Milne, *Phil. Trans. Roy. Soc.* A, **228**, 421 (1929).

For $\lambda 3{,}934$ A of Ca^+ and $\lambda 4{,}226$ A of neutral Ca we find by numerical quadrature, as in Section 5.3, $\frac{1}{2}w^+ = 1{\cdot}017$ and $\frac{1}{2}w = 1{\cdot}023$. The experimental values of W^+ and W at the centre of the solar disk, according to several observers, are shown in Table XXXV.† Adopting $W^+/W = 13$, and $k_\lambda/k_\lambda^+ = 1{\cdot}080$ by interpolation in Table VIII, equation (57) gives

$$\log \frac{x}{1-x} = 2{\cdot}99.$$

From Table XXIX the calculated value of $\log x/(1-x)$ at the reference depth $\tau = 0{\cdot}4$ is $2{\cdot}79$. This corresponds to $W^+/W = 10{\cdot}3$, and the difference between this and the observed value appears real. The difference amounts to a factor of $0{\cdot}63$ in the right-hand side of equation (57), but it is not likely that the factor is to be found in the ratio

$$\frac{f\delta\lambda_0^4}{k_\lambda} \bigg/ \left(\frac{f\delta\lambda_0^4}{k_\lambda}\right)^+.$$

On the other hand, the difference could arise through the ionization equation. Since $xp_e/(1-x) \propto T^{5/2}e^{-I/RT}$, we have

$$\Delta \ln \frac{x}{1-x} = \frac{\Delta T}{T}\left(\frac{5}{2}+\frac{I}{RT}\right)-\frac{\Delta p_e}{p_e}.$$

Now $\Delta \ln x/(1-x) = 0{\cdot}20/\log e = 0{\cdot}46$, so that either the temperature at $\tau = 0{\cdot}4$ is too small by $150°$ K., or the tabular value of p_e too large, and therefore that of $\bar{k}$ too small, by 50 per cent. A third of this correction could be due to blanketing, according to Section 1.22 of Chapter V.

6. The curve of growth

A curve giving the relation between the equivalent width and the number of atoms producing a given line is called a curve of growth. In the laboratory the growth of an absorption line can be studied by actually varying the amount of matter producing the line, but in stellar spectra there is no means of doing this. Instead, the stellar curves of growth are built up in practice from relative intensities of lines in a multiplet within which the ratio of the number of oscillators is known.

The general features of an ideal curve of growth may be shown as follows. Writing $v = (\nu-\nu_0)/b$, where b is the Doppler half-width $(\nu_0/c)\sqrt{(2RT/M)}$, we have from equation (114) of Chapter VI,

$$\eta = \eta_0\left(e^{-v^2}+\frac{a}{\sqrt{\pi}}\frac{1}{v^2}\right), \qquad (58)$$

† The observational uncertainties are such that we do not attempt to distinguish between the equivalent width at the centre of the Sun and the mean equivalent width.

where
$$\eta_0 = \frac{\pi e^2}{mc} f \frac{1}{b\sqrt{\pi}} \frac{N}{k\rho}. \tag{59}$$

The ratio N/ρ is the number of absorbing atoms per gramme of stellar atmosphere, and the quantity a is equal to δ/b, that is the half-width of the line, due to radiation damping and collisions, divided by the Doppler half-width. For a given distribution of atoms with depth, a definite value of η at some reference depth produces a certain value of the residual intensity r. The equivalent width in frequency units is

$$W_\nu = \int_0^\infty (1-r)\, dv = b \int_{-\infty}^\infty (1-r)\, dv, \tag{60}$$

and it is also given by
$$2b \int_{r_c}^1 v(r)\, dr,$$

where r_c is the central intensity of the line. We now consider the two cases, weak and strong lines:

(i) If the line is so weak that the Doppler core absorption is predominant, the wings having little effect, we take the first term $\eta = \eta_0 e^{-v^2}$ in equation (58). Since $1-r = A\eta$ for small η, the equivalent width is given by

$$W_\nu = bA\eta_0 \int_{-\infty}^\infty e^{-v^2}\, dv = bA\sqrt{\pi}\, \eta_0. \tag{61}$$

For weak lines, the equivalent width is therefore proportional to $Nf/k\rho$.

(ii) When the line is so strong that the Doppler core does not contribute sensibly to the equivalent width, we can neglect e^{-v^2} in equation (58), so that

$$v = \left(\frac{a}{\sqrt{\pi}} \frac{\eta_0}{\eta}\right)^{\frac{1}{2}}.$$

Accordingly
$$W_\nu = 2b\left(\frac{a\eta_0}{\sqrt{\pi}}\right)^{\frac{1}{2}} \int_{r_c}^1 \frac{dr}{\eta^{\frac{1}{2}}}. \tag{62}$$

Now in the case of strong lines r_c is effectively zero: we have already pointed out that r is the same function of η for all lines for a given distribution of atoms with depth, so that the integral in equation (62) is always the same. Hence for strong lines we have $W^2 \propto a\eta_0$, or $W^2 \propto Nf\delta/k\rho$. Thus the ideal curve of growth is the curve of the equivalent widths of a set of lines having the same distribution of both η_0 and δ with depth, but having increasing values of η_0 at a reference depth.

Theoretical curves of growth may be constructed† by actually calculating

$$W_\nu = b \int\limits_{-\infty}^{\infty} (1-r)\, dv,$$

using tabular values of the Doppler modification of the line-absorption coefficient, and some standard form for $1-r$ as a function of η. Actual curves of growth are usually built up from all the multiplets which can be found in the region of the spectrum observed. The method is due to Minnaert. For the lines of each multiplet, $\log(W/\lambda)$ is plotted against the logarithm of the relative intensities of the multiplet lines, the intensities being theoretical intensities or experimental intensities obtained from absorption spectra. Each multiplet gives a segment of the curve of $\log(W/\lambda)$ plotted against $\log(Nf\lambda/k_\lambda\rho)$. The results from many multiplets are united into a single curve by sliding the segments along the axis of $\log(Nf\lambda/k_\lambda\rho)$. All the points from a single multiplet should be very nearly on an ideal curve, as the lines are formed by a group of lower states with almost the same excitation potential, and the lines have the same value of δ. It might be possible to find a group of multiplets arising from the same lower state, or from a set of states of the same element, with nearly the same ionization potential and for which δ happened to be nearly the same for all the multiplets; then the points from these should again lie near to an ideal curve. In practice, however, the material is too meagre to admit of such a selection, and multiplets with all kinds of distribution with depth (including those of the neutral and ionized element!) and with various values of δ are usually combined. The resultant composite curve is therefore not precisely identical with any ideal curve of growth. For this reason, and on account of observational uncertainties, no purpose can be served by attempting to distinguish between actual distributions of η with depth, and the standard case η constant. As it is not possible to assign different values of δ to different multiplets, the actual curve of growth is supposed to refer to a mean δ. Modern work‡ recognizes the desirability of restricting the number of multiplets used in constructing mean curves of growth.

In the case of the Sun, complete data are available from which the curve of growth can be put together from the weakest lines, in which W is proportional to N, to the strongest lines, in which W^2 is proportional to N. The quantity N referred to is really Nf, the number of oscillators,

† M. H. Wrubel, *Ap. J.* **109**, 66 (1949); **111**, 157 (1950).
‡ K. O. Wright, *Dom. Ap. Obs. Publ.* **8**, 281 (1950).

and these statements are only true for lines close together in wave-length since $Nf\lambda/k_\lambda\rho$ is involved. The first solar curve of growth was constructed by Minnaert,† and led to the conclusion that the mean δ was about nine times the classical value (it is now recognized that δ is not constant with depth, being given by $\delta = \delta_n + \delta_c$, where δ_n is roughly

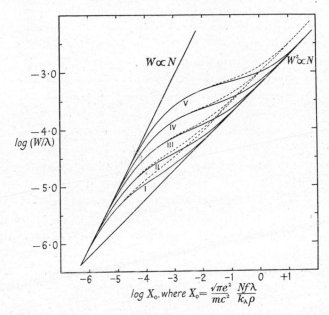

Fig. 37. Theoretical curves of growth for a stellar atmosphere in which η and δ are constant with depth, based on Wrubel's calculations for a region of the spectrum where $hc/\lambda RT_0 = 4k_\lambda/\bar{k}$, T_0 being the boundary temperature of the star. The numbered curves correspond to different values of V/c, where V, the most probable velocity of agitation of the atoms, is made up of thermal agitation and turbulence $(V^2 = 2RT/M + V_t^2)$. The values of $\log(V/c)$ are: I, $-5\cdot4$; II, $-5\cdot0$; III, $-4\cdot6$; IV, $-4\cdot2$; V, $-3\cdot8$; the corresponding velocities in kilometres per second being $1\cdot2$, $3\cdot0$, $7\cdot5$, $18\cdot9$, and $47\cdot5$ respectively. The full curves correspond to $\delta/\nu = 1\cdot6\times10^{-7}$, and the dashed curves to $\delta/\nu = 4\times10^{-7}$. On the classical theory of radiation damping $\delta/\nu = 2\pi e^2/3mc^2\lambda$, giving $\delta/\nu = 1\cdot2\times10^{-8}$ for $\lambda5{,}000$ A, so that the curves correspond to a damping constant about ten times the classical value.

equal to the classical damping constant and δ_c is due to collisions). Other empirical curves of growth have been constructed, notably by Menzel, Baker, and Goldberg,‡ using theoretical intensities and Allen's equivalent widths, and by Wright,§ who used intensities from laboratory measurements instead of theoretical values. The curves commence

† M. Minnaert and G. F. W. Mulders, *Zs. f. Ap.* **1**, 192 (1930); **2**, 165 (1931).
‡ D. H. Menzel, J. G. Baker, and L. Goldberg, *Ap. J.* **87**, 81 (1938).
§ K. O. Wright, ibid. **99**, 249 (1944).

with $W \propto N$ for small N, and pass through a point of inflexion, after which they conclude with $W^2 \propto N$ for large N.

Curves of growth constructed from equivalent widths in stellar spectra are usually less complete than the curve for the solar spectrum, and do not show the entire sequence from $W \propto N$ to $W^2 \propto N$ as well as does the solar curve of growth. An important series of early measurements by Struve and Elvey[†] led to stellar curves of growth for some F-type super-giant stars in which the gradient $\Delta \log W / \Delta \log N$ of the curve of growth formed from multiplets of Fe I, Fe II, Ti II, Cr I, Cr II, and Sc II was steeper than the gradient in some A-type stars (α Lyrae; $A0$ V; α Canis Majoris, $A1$ V; α Cygni, $A2$ I), although the equivalent width of the lines in the F stars (ϵ Aurigae, $F0$ I; α Persei, $F5$ I) is greater than in the A stars mentioned. In addition the $A0$ star 17 Leporis, for which a curve of growth had been determined by Hynek,[‡] also showed the same gradient effect. We have, in fact, $W \propto N$ in 17 Lep, and $W^2 \propto N$ in the other A stars, with ϵ Aur and α Per being intermediate: yet W is greatest in 17 Lep (in the mean of the lines examined). This can only be due to a greater Doppler half-width of the lines—far larger than the expected thermal Doppler half-width. This was attributed by Struve and Elvey to turbulence of the same kind as that supposed by McCrea[§] to account for the support of the solar chromosphere. The Doppler half-width b is then given by $\nu_0 V/c$, where

$$V^2 = 2RT/M + V_t^2,$$

where M is the mass of the atom, and V_t is the most probable velocity of masses of gas in turbulent motion with a Maxwellian distribution. Struve and Elvey found $V_t = 67$ km./sec. in 17 Leporis, 20 km./sec. in ϵ Aurigae, and 7 km./sec. in α Persei. It has been pointed out by Plaskett[||] that the turbulence cannot resemble granulation, but must be small-scale turbulence, because the outflowing light must pass in unit optical depth successively through several moving masses of gas having different velocities, to produce the effect required to explain Struve and Elvey's curves of growth.

Turbulent velocities derived from the curve of growth have been found to disagree with velocities found from the line contours themselves. Thus Struve[††] found $V_t = 30$ km./sec. from line contours in δ Canis

† O. Struve and C. T. Elvey, *Ap. J.* **79**, 409 (1934).
‡ J. A. Hynek, ibid. **78**, 54 (1933).
§ W. H. McCrea, *M.N.* **89**, 718 (1929).
|| H. H. Plaskett, ibid. **107**, 138 (1947).
†† O. Struve, *Ap. J.* **104**, 138 (1946).

Majoris, whereas the curve of growth constructed for this star by Miss Steel[†] gave $V_t = 5$ km./sec. A similar effect has been found for η Aquilae by Schwarzschild,[‡] and for ϵ Aurigae by Wright and van Dien.[§] According to current theory,[||] the convection zone beneath the stellar atmosphere supplies energy to large-scale eddies in the photosphere. The energy supplied to these large eddies flows into a hierarchy of eddies of smaller and smaller size, being finally dissipated in the smallest eddies by viscosity. Eddies of all sizes affect the line contours, but the large eddies broaden the lines without increasing their equivalent width. The smaller eddies have a greater effect on the total absorption, and hence on the curve of growth. This suggests that nearly all the turbulence in the outer layers of δ Canis Majoris must be in the form of large eddies.

Struve has remarked[††] that curves of growth conceal a lot of information—the data from individual multiplets and individual lines: and that in combining all the information into a single curve 'important physical information is buried . . . where it can never be brought to light'. One might amplify this by pointing out that where multiplets from neutral and ionized atoms are combined into a single curve, information about the electron pressure is at once discarded. The curve of growth remains, however, a convenient device for extracting information from an extensive series of measurements of equivalent width without special calculations on the individual profiles: it is a means for deducing, somewhat roughly, relative abundances from observed equivalent widths without a full-scale calculation after the manner of Section 5 of this chapter.

　† H. R. Steel, ibid. **102**, 429 (1945).
　‡ M. Schwarzschild, B. Schwarzschild, and W. S. Adams, ibid. **108**, 225 (1948).
　§ K. O. Wright and E. van Dien, *J.R.A.S.* (Canada), **43**, 15 (1949).
　|| For a summary of the physical theory of turbulence see S. Chandrasekhar, *Ap. J.* **110**, 329 (1949). See also Su-shu Huang, ibid. **112**, 418 (1950), and M. H. Wrubel, ibid. **112**, 424 (1950).
　†† O. Struve, ibid. **98**, 134 (1943).

CONVECTION

1. Schwarzschild's criterion for convection in a stellar atmosphere

SUPPOSE that an atmosphere is in radiative equilibrium, so that at every optical depth the temperature gradient has the value $(dT/d\tau)_{\text{rad}}$. Now consider a small volume of gas at a certain depth τ which becomes displaced to a new optical depth $\tau + \Delta\tau$. If the movement of the gas is adiabatic, the temperature is increased by the amount $(dT/d\tau)_{\text{ad}} \Delta\tau$, the adiabatic gradient multiplied by the element of optical depth through which the gas is displaced. In moving through $\Delta\tau$ the gas arrives at a place where the temperature of its surroundings has changed by $(dT/d\tau)_{\text{rad}} \Delta\tau$. Consider the case where $\Delta\tau$ is negative, so that the gas has risen. If it arrives at a place where it is hotter than its surroundings, it is lighter than the gas around it and will therefore receive assistance in rising farther from hydrostatic forces, but if it is cooler than its surroundings its upward rise will be checked. It is hotter or cooler according as $(dT/d\tau)_{\text{ad}}$ is less than or greater than $(dT/d\tau)_{\text{rad}}$. In the former case, an upward displacement once commenced will continue, and in the latter case any displacement will be damped by hydrostatic restoring forces. In this latter case radiative equilibrium will control the temperature gradient, but if there are no restraining forces, upward and downward movement will occur, and will transport heat from the interior outwards by convection.

The condition for no convection to occur is therefore

$$\left(\frac{dT}{d\tau}\right)_{\text{rad}} < \left(\frac{dT}{d\tau}\right)_{\text{ad}}.$$

Now in radiative equilibrium we have approximately $T^4 = T_0^4(1 + \frac{3}{2}\tau)$ so that

$$\frac{1}{T}\left(\frac{dT}{d\tau}\right)_{\text{rad}} = \frac{3}{8 + 12\tau}.$$

On the other hand, for adiabatic movement $T^\Gamma p^{1-\Gamma}$ is constant (where Γ is, in the simplest case, the ratio of the specific heats), so that

$$\left(\frac{dT}{d\tau}\right)_{\text{ad}} = \frac{\Gamma - 1}{\Gamma}\frac{T}{p}\frac{dp}{d\tau}.$$

Hence the condition for no convection to occur is

$$\frac{3}{8+12\tau} < \frac{\Gamma-1}{\Gamma}\frac{1}{p}\frac{dp}{d\tau}.$$

But the equation of hydrostatic equilibrium is $\bar{k}\,dp = g\,d\tau$. Then if $\bar{k}$ is independent of τ, $p = (g/\bar{k})\tau$ and $(1/p)(dp/d\tau) = (1/\tau)$. The condition for no convection is, in this case,

$$\frac{3\tau}{8+12\tau} < \frac{\Gamma-1}{\Gamma}.$$

This will be satisfied for all values of τ if $\Gamma > \frac{4}{3}$. For a monatomic gas $\Gamma = \frac{5}{3}$, and it was supposed by Schwarzschild that convection could not occur in a stellar atmosphere, and that the temperature gradient would be determined by radiative equilibrium.

There are, however, two cases in which the Schwarzschild criterion decides in favour of convection. Considering these cases in the order in which the criteria actually apply; going downwards in the solar atmosphere the first occurs when $\bar{k}$ is not independent of τ. Suppose that $\bar{k} = \kappa p^n$. Then

$$\frac{1}{p}\frac{dp}{d\tau} = \frac{1}{(n+1)\tau},$$

so that the condition for radiative equilibrium is

$$\frac{3(n+1)\tau}{8+12\tau} < \frac{\Gamma-1}{\Gamma}.$$

With $\Gamma = \frac{5}{3}$, this inequality is no longer satisfied at all depths: for example, with $n = 1$, the inequality is not satisfied when $\tau > 2$. According to current theory $\bar{k}$ increases rapidly with τ so that convection is able to destroy radiative equilibrium at quite small optical depths (that is, below $\tau = 1.5$ approximately). Secondly, in a dissociating gas Γ takes very small values approaching the value unity, so that convection would not be forbidden by the Schwarzschild criterion even if $\bar{k}$ were independent of p (and therefore of τ). On account of the great abundance of hydrogen, the value of Γ for the solar mixture of elements falls well below the Schwarzschild limit $\frac{4}{3}$ in the zone where hydrogen is substantially, but not quite completely, ionized.

2. Convection in the solar atmosphere

In the Sun, convection has been supposed to be responsible for the granulation. When the seeing is exceptionally good, a mottled structure can be seen and photographed on the Sun's disk. The size of the granules has been given as 5″ by Plaskett,† 2″ by ten Bruggencate,‡ and 1″ by Keenan.§ The last-mentioned investigation supposes that the larger diameters given by earlier writers refer to aggregations of the smallest granules. The contrast between the bright grains and the dark areas is given as 10 per cent. by Unsöld and 15 per cent. by Keenan. Accurate observations of the size and contrast are only obtained with great difficulty, as objects as small as 1″ in apparent diameter would be quite difficult to photograph accurately on an average night. By day, seeing is usually much worse than the night seeing, on account of local currents set up in the Earth's atmosphere by the solar heating of objects close to the observatory, and by more general thermal disturbance of the Earth's atmosphere. Despite these difficulties, Grotrian and ten Bruggencate‖ have been able to observe the mean life of the granules, using a very ingenious method. They find the value 190 sec.

Convection has another connexion with solar observation, as has been mentioned in Chapter V: for if convection proceeds on a sufficient scale and comes close enough to the solar surface, it will modify the radiative temperature gradient and affect the darkening of the limb. The first work on this subject was done by Plaskett,† who deduced a temperature gradient (differing from the radiative gradient) from an analysis of limb darkening observations.

Two leading ideas on the nature of solar convection have been suggested. According to Plaskett, convection takes place in a more or less regular cellular structure, similar to that observed by Bénard in small-scale convection: and according to Siedentopf,†† it takes place through upward moving granules pushing their way through downward moving matter.

3. Adiabatic change in a dissociating gas

Let one gramme of an element occupy a volume v and let there be $n(1-y)$ neutral atoms, ny ions, and ny electrons in this volume; and let the energy of ionization be χ ergs per ion pair. Then the total energy in ergs per gramme is

$$E = n(1+y)\tfrac{3}{2}RT + ny\chi. \tag{1}$$

In an adiabatic change $dE + p\,dv = 0$, or

$$p\,dv + \tfrac{3}{2}n(1+y)R\,dT + n\,dy(\tfrac{3}{2}RT + \chi) = 0. \tag{2}$$

† H. H. Plaskett, *M.N.* **96**, 402 (1936).
‡ P. ten Bruggencate, *Zs. f. Ap.* **19**, 59 (1939).
§ P. C. Keenan, *Ap. J.* **89**, 604 (1939).
‖ W. Grotrian and P. ten Bruggencate, *Zs. f. Ap.* **12**, 323 (1936).
†† H. C. Siedentopf, *A.N.* **247**, 297 (1933); **249**, 53 (1933); **255**, 157 (1935).

Now the equation of state is $pv = \mathbf{R}(1+y)T$, which combined with (2) gives

$$\frac{dv}{v} + \frac{3}{2}\frac{dT}{T} + \left(\frac{\chi}{RT} + \frac{3}{2}\right)\frac{dy}{1+y} = 0, \tag{3}$$

and by differentiation of the equation of state we obtain

$$\frac{dp}{p} + \frac{dv}{v} = \frac{dy}{1+y} + \frac{dT}{T}. \tag{4}$$

Lastly the equation of ionization is $py^2/(1-y) = K(T)$ or

$$\frac{dp}{p} + \frac{2y}{1-y^2}\frac{dy}{y^2} = \left(\frac{\chi}{RT} + \frac{5}{2}\right)\frac{dT}{T}. \tag{5}$$

From these equations any two of the differentials dp, dv, dy, and dT may be eliminated, leaving one relation between the remaining pair, appropriate to adiabatic change.

A point of interest is that although pv^g is constant when T is constant, g is not the ratio of the specific heats. To see this, eliminate $dy/(1+y)$ from (3) and (4); then

$$\left(\frac{\chi}{RT} + \frac{3}{2}\right)\frac{dp}{p} + \left(\frac{\chi}{RT} + \frac{5}{2}\right)\frac{dv}{v} = \frac{\chi}{RT}\frac{dT}{T}, \tag{6}$$

so that at constant T, pv^g is constant, where

$$g = \frac{\dfrac{\chi}{RT} + \dfrac{5}{2}}{\dfrac{\chi}{RT} + \dfrac{3}{2}}. \tag{7}$$

On the other hand γ, the ratio of the specific heats, is given by

$$\gamma = \frac{\left(\dfrac{\partial E}{\partial T}\right)_p}{\left(\dfrac{\partial E}{\partial T}\right)_v} = \frac{\frac{5}{2}(1+y) + \left(\dfrac{\chi}{RT} + \dfrac{5}{2}\right)T\left(\dfrac{\partial y}{\partial T}\right)_p}{\frac{3}{2}(1+y) + \left(\dfrac{\chi}{RT} + \dfrac{3}{2}\right)T\left(\dfrac{\partial y}{\partial T}\right)_v}, \tag{8}$$

and in general γ is not equal to g.

The quantity of interest is $(\Gamma-1)/\Gamma$, where Γ, called by Unsöld the effective value of the ratio of the specific heats, is defined by

$$\frac{\Gamma-1}{\Gamma} = \left(\frac{d\ln T}{d\ln p}\right)_{\text{ad}}.$$

Eliminating dy and dv from equations (2), (3), and (5) we find

$$\frac{\Gamma-1}{\Gamma} = \frac{1 + \frac{1}{2}y(1-y)\left(\dfrac{\chi}{RT} + \dfrac{5}{2}\right)}{\frac{5}{2} + \frac{1}{2}y(1-y)\left(\dfrac{\chi}{RT} + \dfrac{5}{2}\right)^2}. \tag{9}$$

The value of this quantity for a mixture of elements is given by Unsöld†
as follows: let ν_i be the fraction, by numbers, of atoms of the ith kind,
and let $\bar{y} = \sum \nu_i y_i$, and $\overline{y^2} = \sum \nu_i y_i^2$. Then $(\Gamma-1)/\Gamma$ is given by the
expression

$$\frac{1+\bar{y}+\dfrac{\bar{y}+\bar{y}^2}{2\bar{y}+\bar{y}^2-\overline{y^2}}\sum \nu_i y_i(1-y_i)\left(\dfrac{\chi_i}{RT}+\dfrac{5}{2}\right)}{\tfrac{5}{2}(1+\bar{y})+\sum \nu_i y_i(1-y_i)\left(\dfrac{\chi_i}{RT}+\dfrac{5}{2}\right)^2-\dfrac{\left[\sum \nu_i y_i(1-y_i)\left(\dfrac{\chi_i}{RT}+\dfrac{5}{2}\right)\right]^2}{2\bar{y}+\bar{y}^2-\overline{y^2}}}.$$

$$(10)$$

4. The convection zone

In an atmosphere in which $\bar{k}$ is independent of τ the convection zone
is the region in which $\Gamma < \tfrac{4}{3}$. More generally, it is the zone in which

$$\frac{\Gamma-1}{\Gamma} < \frac{d\ln T}{d\ln p}.$$

Since hydrogen is so abundant in stellar atmospheres, it dominates the
value of Γ in a mixture of elements. Consider a pure hydrogen atmosphere
at the solar temperature. At the surface hydrogen is mainly neutral
and $y \approx 0$ so that $\Gamma \approx \tfrac{5}{3}$. Although $\bar{k}$ varies with p, at small depths
radiative equilibrium is stable, but farther down convection sets in.
At great depths hydrogen is mainly ionized so that $1-y \approx 0$, and once
again $\Gamma \approx \tfrac{5}{3}$. At these depths the variation of $\bar{k}$ with p is probably small,
because most of the variation at small depths is due to the influence of
negative ions. There is, accordingly, a lower limit to the convection
zone which is, generally speaking, the zone in which hydrogen is partly
ionized.

The position of the top of the convection zone can be located from the
circumstances of the solar atmosphere, calculated for radiative equilibrium, shown in Table XXXVI. In this table $(\Gamma-1)/\Gamma$ is calculated
for pure hydrogen by means of equation (9) and also for a mixture
of H, He, and a representative metal in the proportion 6,000 : 1,000 : 1.
The ionization potentials χ_i are taken as 13·59 volts, 24·58 volts, and
7·90 volts respectively, but the ionization of the metal mixture is taken
from Strömgren's tables.

From Table XXXVI it is seen that the addition of helium and the
metals hardly produces any change in $(\Gamma-1)/\Gamma$ when only two significant

† A. Unsöld, *Physik der Sternatmosphären*, Berlin, 1938, p. 382.

figures are kept, and that the top of the convection zone occurs between $\tau = 1\cdot 0$ and $\tau = 1\cdot 5$.

TABLE XXXVI

The Top of the Convection Zone

τ	θ	T	$\log y_{\mathrm{H}}$	Pure hydrogen equation (9)	Mixture equation (10)	$\dfrac{d \log T}{d \log p}$
				$(\Gamma-1)/\Gamma$		
1·0	0·827	6,090	$\overline{4}$·26	0·38	0·39	0·31
1·5	0·775	6,500	$\overline{4}$·77	0·38	0·38	0·44
2·0	0·736	6,850	$\overline{3}$·07	0·35	0·36	0·59

Since hydrogen ionization increases going upwards from the photosphere into regions of very low pressure, one might expect a second zone located in the chromosphere where Γ falls below $\frac{4}{3}$. But the temperature in the chromosphere is not controlled by radiative equilibrium, and is influenced by conduction inwards from the corona, so that there is actually a reversal of the temperature gradient in the high chromosphere and the temperature increases outwards. Now if the temperature is constant (or increases with height) the gas on rising expands and falls in temperature relative to its surroundings if $\Gamma > 1$: so that rising gas is denser than its surroundings and falls back. Hence there is no second convection zone in the chromosphere.

An account must be given of an objection to the low values of Γ given in Section 3 which was raised by Eddington and later withdrawn. The argument supposes that the rising gas is actually able to change its state of ionization: but it can only do this through the recombination of ions and electrons, and as each recombination releases a photon, the photons must somehow be removed from the gas, or they would be reabsorbed by atoms to form new ion pairs. The granule is too large to radiate away the photons released in the interior without reabsorption. This objection of Eddington's was met by M. Schwarzschild, who showed that collisions were sufficiently frequent to break down the high energy quanta into kinetic energy, and so allow the ionized gas to convert its ionization energy into thermal energy, as required by the argument of Section 3. We must note that even if this were not so, the variation of $\bar{k}$ with p is sufficient to allow a limited convection zone: but Eddington himself accepted M. Schwarzschild's analysis and the point is now only of historical interest.

5. Theory of convective movement

An equation can be constructed which expresses the condition that the sum of the heat fluxes at any point, due to convection and radiation, is a constant. Let us suppose that at any depth a fraction α_1 of the surface area is occupied by upward moving matter, all of which has the same temperature T_1, density ρ_1, and velocity ξ_1: and that the fraction $\alpha_2 = 1-\alpha_1$ is occupied by matter with T_2, ρ_2 and downward velocity ξ_2. Let us count upward velocities as positive, so that ξ_1 is positive and ξ_2 negative. The condition that there is no secular transport of mass is $\alpha_1\rho_1\xi_1+\alpha_2\rho_2\xi_2 = 0$.

The density of the atmosphere is $\rho = \alpha_1\rho_1+\alpha_2\rho_2$. We suppose that $\bar{k}$ is the same for both streams, and set $d\tau = -\bar{k}\rho\,dx$. Now let convection carry the fraction $\beta(\tau)$ of the net outward flux of energy F, so that radiation must carry the fraction $1-\beta(\tau)$, and

$$F[1-\beta(\tau)] = \frac{\alpha_1\rho}{\rho_1}\frac{4\pi}{3}\frac{dB(T_1)}{d\tau}+\frac{\alpha_2\rho}{\rho_2}\frac{4\pi}{3}\frac{dB(T_2)}{d\tau}. \qquad (11)$$

Consider now the flux carried by convection. Since both streams are at the same pressure, and since $\alpha_1\rho_1\xi_1 = -\alpha_2\rho_2\xi_2$,

$$F\beta(\tau) = \alpha_1\rho_1\xi_1\int_{T_2}^{T_1} C_p\,dT, \qquad (12)$$

where C_p is the specific heat at constant pressure.

Introduce a temperature defined by $T^4 = \alpha_1 T_1^4+\alpha_2 T_2^4$, and let $T_1 = T(1+\alpha_2\gamma)$: this defines γ. If γ is a small quantity then

$$T_2 = T(1-\alpha_1\gamma).$$

Now $\qquad \dfrac{\rho}{\rho_1} = 1+\alpha_2\gamma\left\{1+\dfrac{T}{1+y}\left(\dfrac{\partial y}{\partial T}\right)_p\right\} = 1+\alpha_2\gamma Q,$

and $\rho/\rho_2 = 1-\alpha_1\gamma Q$. Also, since $B(T) = (\sigma/\pi)T^4$, we have

$$4\pi\frac{dB(T_1)}{d\tau} = 16\sigma T_1^3\frac{dT_1}{d\tau} = 16\sigma T^3(1+3\alpha_2\gamma)\left\{(1+\alpha_2\gamma)\frac{dT}{d\tau}+\alpha_2\,T\frac{d\gamma}{d\tau}\right\},$$

with a similar expression for $dB(T_2)/d\tau$.

Substituting in equation (11) and collecting terms we get

$$F[1-\beta(\tau)] = \tfrac{16}{3}\sigma T^3\frac{dT}{d\tau}+\text{terms of order }\gamma^2. \qquad (13)$$

Introducing the quantity γ into equation (12)

$$F\beta(\tau) = \alpha_1\rho_1\xi_1.C_p\gamma T. \qquad (14)$$

Adding the last two equations we obtain

$$F = \tfrac{16}{3}\sigma T^3 \frac{dT}{d\tau} + \alpha_1 \rho_1 \xi_1 . C_p \gamma T.$$
(15)

Since $F = 2\sigma T_0^4$, this may be expressed as

$$T_0^4 = \tfrac{8}{3}T^3 \frac{dT}{d\tau} + \frac{\alpha_1 \rho_1 \xi_1}{2\sigma} C_p \gamma T.$$
(16)

It is convenient to give expressions for $\beta(\tau)$ and $1-\beta(\tau)$ for reference. They are

$$\beta(\tau) = \frac{\alpha_1 \rho_1 \xi_1}{2\sigma T_0^4} C_p \gamma T,$$
(17)

$$1-\beta(\tau) = \frac{8}{3}\frac{T^3}{T_0^4}\frac{dT}{d\tau}.$$
(18)

Returning to equation (16) we can reconstruct Schwarzschild's inequality which was set up in Section 2 by general arguments: for, since ξ and γ are positive quantities, we must have $T_0^4 > \tfrac{8}{3}T^3(dT/d\tau)$. But $(dT/d\tau)_{\mathrm{rad}} = 3T_0^4/8T^3$ so that the temperature gradient must satisfy the inequality

$$\frac{dT}{d\tau} < \left(\frac{dT}{d\tau}\right)_{\mathrm{rad}}.$$
(19)

A second equation can be formed by considering the heat balance of the moving gas. Let E be the internal energy of one gramme of the gas at a given instant, and let the gas do work dW and lose by conduction or radiation the amount of heat $q\,dt$ in time dt. Then

$$\frac{dE}{dt} + \frac{dW}{dt} + q = 0.$$

If the gas is moving parallel to the x-axis with a velocity ξ, the equation becomes

$$\frac{dE}{dx} + \frac{dW}{dx} + \frac{q}{\xi} = 0.$$

Let
$$\frac{dE}{dx} + \frac{dW}{dx} \equiv L\frac{dT}{dx} + M\frac{dp}{dx},$$

then $L = C_p$, the specific heat at constant pressure. To evaluate M we observe that in adiabatic motion $L\,dT + M\,dp = 0$ so that

$$\frac{M}{L} = -\frac{T}{p}\left(\frac{d\ln T}{d\ln p}\right)_{\mathrm{ad}} = -\frac{T}{p}\frac{\Gamma-1}{\Gamma}.$$

The equation therefore reduces to

$$C_p\left(\frac{dT}{dx} - \frac{T}{p}\frac{\Gamma-1}{\Gamma}\frac{dp}{dx}\right) + \frac{q}{\xi} = 0.$$
(20)

Convection is only possible if heat is *lost* to the surroundings by *upward* moving matter, that is if q/ξ is positive (both x and ξ being positive upwards). Now q/ξ will be positive if

$$\frac{dT}{dx} - \frac{T}{p}\frac{\Gamma-1}{\Gamma}\frac{dp}{dx}$$

is negative. But

$$\left(\frac{dT}{dx}\right)_{\text{ad}} = \frac{T}{p}\frac{\Gamma-1}{\Gamma}\frac{dp}{dx}.$$

Hence a condition for convection to occur is that $dT/dx - (dT/dx)_{\text{ad}}$ should be negative. Since both quantities are negative this is

$$\left|\frac{dT}{dx}\right| > \left|\left(\frac{dT}{dx}\right)_{\text{ad}}\right|. \tag{21}$$

Taking this condition together with equation (19) we see that the actual temperature gradient must satisfy the inequality

$$\left|\left(\frac{dT}{dx}\right)_{\text{rad}}\right| \geqslant \left|\frac{dT}{dx}\right| > \left|\left(\frac{dT}{dx}\right)_{\text{ad}}\right|, \tag{22}$$

and that the *convection zone* is the zone in which

$$\left|\left(\frac{dT}{dx}\right)_{\text{rad}}\right| > \left|\left(\frac{dT}{dx}\right)_{\text{ad}}\right|.$$

The condition (21) places an upper limit on $\beta(\tau)$, namely

$$\beta(\tau) < 1 - \frac{8}{3}\frac{T^4}{T_0^4}\frac{1}{p}\frac{dp}{d\tau}\frac{\Gamma-1}{\Gamma}. \tag{23}$$

6. Siedentopf's model

We now consider for definiteness rising granules which are spherical and have a radius a. If there is no internal motion a radial temperature gradient will be set up, and the mean heat lost to the surroundings per gramme per sec. is[†]

$$q = \frac{10\sigma T^4}{\bar{k}\rho_1^2 a^2}\gamma(1-2\gamma). \tag{24}$$

But as the temperature difference between the centre of the sphere and the boundary is $\frac{5}{4}\gamma T$, that is to say a little larger than the mean difference between the upward and downward moving matter, internal convection will be set up. This will be aided by obstruction at the interface, and the sphere may lose heat as if it were well mixed, in which case the heat lost per gramme per sec. is

$$q = \frac{12\sigma T^4}{a\rho}\gamma. \tag{25}$$

[†] R. v. d. R. Woolley, *M.N.* **103**, 193 (1943). There is a misprint in the equation (2.3) in that paper, a γ being omitted.

According to Siedentopf the reaction to the movement of the sphere is approximately equal to $4\pi a^2 \rho \xi^2$. This gives an equation for the acceleration

$$\xi \frac{d\xi}{dx} = g\gamma Q - \frac{3\xi^2}{a}. \tag{26}$$

In addition we need an expression for $dp/d\tau$. It can be shown† in the case of cylindrical flow ($\xi\rho$ constant) that $dp/d\tau$ is close to the hydrostatic value $g/\bar{k}$ provided that $|\xi_1 \xi_2|$ is small compared with $\mathbf{R}T$, which is a good approximation with likely values of the velocities. In what follows we shall assume $dp/d\tau = g/\bar{k}$.

If we now bring together the equations and suppose for simplicity that $\alpha_1 = \alpha_2 = \frac{1}{2}$, that $Q = 1$, and that $d\xi/d\tau$ may be neglected, we find from equations (16), (20), (25), and (26):

$$\rho C_p \xi \left\{ \frac{dT}{d\tau} - \frac{T}{p} \frac{\Gamma-1}{\Gamma} \frac{g}{k} \right\} = -\frac{12\sigma T^4 \gamma}{k\rho a}, \tag{27}$$

$$T_0^4 = \tfrac{8}{3} T^3 \frac{dT}{d\tau} + \frac{\rho C_p T}{4\sigma} \xi\gamma, \tag{28}$$

$$\xi^2 = \tfrac{1}{3} a g \gamma. \tag{29}$$

There are now three equations between the four quantities a, ξ, γ, and $dT/d\tau$, so that the equations are insufficient to determine the scale on which convection will occur. A solution can be made if we take any one of the quantities—for example a, the size of the granules—from observation.

Before proceeding to a numerical solution of the equations with an assumed value of a, we may examine some limiting factors. A very small granule cools more quickly and experiences more resistance than a larger one, so that there is probably a minimum size for survival, which may determine the actual size of the granule. Apart from this there is an upper limit to ξ set by h, the depth in km. of the convection zone: for if we reckon x upwards from the bottom of the convection zone, the solution of equation (26) with $Q = 1$ and γ constant, and with the condition $\xi = 0$ at $x = 0$, is

$$\xi^2 = \tfrac{1}{3} a g \gamma (1 - e^{-3x/a}),$$

and

$$\xi_{\max}^2 = \tfrac{1}{3} a g \gamma (1 - e^{-3h/a})$$

which cannot exceed $g\gamma h$: hence $\xi^2 < g\gamma h$ whatever the value of a. There is also an upper limit to ξ imposed by (23).

† R. v. d. R. Woolley, *M.N.* **101**, 59 (1941).

7. Numerical application of the equations

Equations (27), (28), and (29) reduced to a cubic equation for ξ, namely

$$A\xi^3 + B\xi = C, \tag{30}$$

where

$$A = \frac{9\rho C_p}{32 a g \sigma T^2}, \qquad B = \frac{36 \sigma T^4}{\bar{k} \rho^2 a^2 g C_p}$$

and

$$C = \frac{3T_0^4}{8T^3} - \frac{T}{p} \frac{\Gamma - 1}{\Gamma} \frac{g}{k}.$$

We can solve equation (30) by using values of T and p as functions of τ taken from the theory of radiative equilibrium. The solutions will give not only ξ and γ but also values of $dT/d\tau$, which will not agree with the values of $dT/d\tau$ with which we started. We therefore proceed by iteration. Table XXXVII shows solutions for ξ, γ, and $\beta(\tau)$ computed for $\tau = 3$ and for $\tau = 5$ for a number of values of a. In forming the equations a mixture of H:He in the proportions of 6:1 was adopted, and the initial values of T and p used were: at $\tau = 3$, $T = 7{,}400°$, $\log p = 5.13$; and at $\tau = 5$, $T = 8{,}270°$, $\log p = 5.20$.

TABLE XXXVII

First Approximations to Convection

a (cm.): $\times 10^8$	$\tau = 3$			$\tau = 5$		
	ξ (km./s.)	γ	$\beta(\tau)$	ξ (km./s.)	γ	$\beta(\tau)$
1·4	5·52	0·24	0·66	5·25	0·22	0·86
1·0	4·73	0·24	0·58	4·61	0·23	0·79
0·7	3·88	0·24	0·47	3·94	0·25	0·73
0·5	3·02	0·20	0·30	3·31	0·24	0·58

Table XXXVII shows that the velocities ξ are not excessively sensitive to the values of a chosen, and that for a given value of a, the velocity does not change much between $\tau = 3$ and $\tau = 5$.

The atmosphere tabulated in Table XXXVIII is self-consistent with convection for $a = 0.7 \times 10^8$ cm. at $\tau = 3$ and $\tau = 5$; that is to say, if the temperatures and pressures shown in the table are used, and if a is placed at 7×10^7 cm. (which subtends 1″ of arc at the Earth), then the values of β agree with values of $dT/d\tau$ in the table.

In this table $(dT/d\tau)_{\text{rad}} = 3T_0^4/8T^3$, with $T_0 = 4{,}830°$. The values of β are practically equal to $1 - \dfrac{dT}{d\tau} \Big/ \left(\dfrac{dT}{d\tau}\right)_{\text{rad}}$. It will be seen that the values of γ are consistent with the observed contrast (10 to 15 per cent.).

TABLE XXXVIII

Self-Consistent Convective Atmosphere with Granules 1″ of Arc

τ	T	$\dfrac{dT}{d\tau}$	$\dfrac{dT}{d\tau}\Big/\left(\dfrac{dT}{d\tau}\right)_{\mathrm{rad}}$	ξ $(km./s.)$	γ	β
1·5	6,500	..	..	..	..	..
2	6,800	500	0·80	..	..	..
3	7,200	360	0·72	3·35	0·18	0·27
4	7,520	250	0·59	..	..	..
5	7,700	155	0·42	3·93	0·24	0·58
6	7,830	..	..	..	..	..

We can now compute the darkening of the limb given by the temperature distribution shown in Table XXXVIII and compare it with the darkening given by radiative equilibrium. Table XXXIX shows values of $f(\alpha, p)$ and $F(\alpha, p)$ for $\lambda 5{,}010$ A (or $\alpha = 5{\cdot}917$). The function $F(\alpha, p)$ is defined by equation (11) of Chapter V.

TABLE XXXIX

$$f(\alpha,\ p)\ and\ F(\alpha,\ p)$$

$$\alpha = 5{\cdot}917\ (\lambda 5{,}010\ \text{A})$$

p	2·143	1·875	1·667	1·500	1·200	1·000	0·750	0·500
$f(5{\cdot}917, p)$	83·95	76·52	70·34	65·35	56·42	50·44	42·69	34·86
$F(5{\cdot}917, p)$	77·73	72·03	67·66	63·26	55·14	49·76	42·47	34·84

To compute $F(\alpha, p)$ it is necessary to adopt values of T down to $\tau = 10$: these are not critical. The values $T = 7{,}900°$ at $\tau = 7$, $T = 7{,}950°$ at $\tau = 8$, $T = 7{,}980°$ at $\tau = 9$, and $T = 8{,}000°$ at $\tau = 10$ were taken in compiling Table XXXIX.

Quadratic expressions $a + bp + cp^2$ may be fitted to $f(\alpha, p)$ and to $F(\alpha, p)$, (i) over the range $p = 2{\cdot}143$ to $p = 0{\cdot}750$, which corresponds to $\cos\theta = 1$ and $\cos\theta = 0{\cdot}350$ if $k_\lambda/\bar{k} = 0{\cdot}7$, and (ii) over the range $p = 1{\cdot}500$ to $p = 0{\cdot}500$ which corresponds to $\cos\theta = 1$ and $\cos\theta = 0{\cdot}333$ if $k_\lambda/\bar{k} = 1$. The results are given in Table XL.

TABLE XL

Quadratic Expressions for the Functions $f(\alpha, p)$ and $F(\alpha, p)$

$k_\lambda/\bar{k} = 0{\cdot}7$	$f(\alpha, p)$	$19{\cdot}00 + 32{\cdot}28p - 0{\cdot}92p^2$
	$F(\alpha, p)$	$17{\cdot}46 + 36{\cdot}16p - 3{\cdot}75p^2$
$k_\lambda/\bar{k} = 1{\cdot}0$	$f(\alpha, p)$	$18{\cdot}61 + 33{\cdot}17p - 1{\cdot}34p^2$
	$F(\alpha, p)$	$18{\cdot}50 + 34{\cdot}10p - 2{\cdot}84p^2$

The quadratic formulae reproduce the tabular values with errors which are always less than one-half per cent., and usually only one or two parts per thousand. The corresponding quadratic expansions in $\cos\theta$ for the limb-darkening ratio are shown in Table XLI, together with Chalonge and Kourganoff's values derived from observations.

TABLE XLI

Darkening of the Limb at $\lambda 5{,}010$ A

		a_λ	b_λ	c_λ
Radiative equilibrium	$k_\lambda/\bar{k} = 0{\cdot}7$	$0{\cdot}291$	$0{\cdot}741$	$-0{\cdot}032$
	$k_\lambda/\bar{k} = 1{\cdot}0$	$0{\cdot}285$	$0{\cdot}761$	$-0{\cdot}046$
Convection (Table XXXVIII)	$k_\lambda/\bar{k} = 0{\cdot}7$	$0{\cdot}276$	$0{\cdot}857$	$-0{\cdot}133$
	$k_\lambda/\bar{k} = 1{\cdot}0$	$0{\cdot}292$	$0{\cdot}809$	$-0{\cdot}101$
Observed (from Chalonge and Kourganoff's analysis, Table XIII)	.	$0{\cdot}259$	$0{\cdot}872$	$-0{\cdot}134$

Table XLI shows that whether the value of $k_\lambda/\bar{k}$ is $0{\cdot}7$ or $1{\cdot}0$ the temperature distribution modified by convection gives a much better fit with the observations than does the radiative temperature distribution. Attention may be drawn to the high negative value of c_λ given by the convective distribution, since the high negative values of c_λ are found at all wavelengths (Chapter V). There seems therefore some support from the observed darkening of the limb for convection with velocities of order 3 or 4 km./sec.

XI

THE SOLAR CORONA

1. Introduction. General description of the corona

VERY little attention was paid by astronomers to the striking features of total eclipses of the Sun—the corona and the prominences –until the middle of the nineteenth century. It was not until the advent of photography that it was admitted by all astronomers that the prominences belonged to the atmosphere of the Sun rather than to that of the Moon. The word *corona* was first used in its present astronomical sense by Baily describing the eclipse of 1842, though the word was employed long ago by Seneca for haloes round the Sun arising in the Earth's atmosphere, or, as we should now say, meteorological corona. Baily's description brings out so many important features of the corona that it may still be quoted with profit.

The dark body of the Moon was suddenly surrounded with a Corona . . . similar to that which painters draw round the heads of Saints. . . . The breadth of the Corona measured from the circumference of the Moon appeared to me to be nearly half the Moon's diameter. The light was most dense close to the border of the Moon and became gradually and uniformly more attenuate as the distance therefrom increased, assuming the form of diverging rays, which at the extremity were more divided, and of unequal length; so that in no part of the Corona could I discover the regular and well-defined shape of a ring at its *outer* margin. . . . Its colour was quite white . . . and the rays had a vivid and flickering appearance.

The intensity of the corona falls off so rapidly with distance from the limb that it is impossible to photograph the whole corona with a single exposure: if the outer corona is well defined the inner corona is greatly over-exposed, and on this account drawings compiled from photographs differently exposed are employed to show detail of the streamers in both inner and outer corona. The drawings also show structure in the inner corona, namely, arches and plumes. Such drawings, however, fail to give the correct impression of the distribution of light as they cannot sufficiently emphasize the brightness of the inner corona. But they do convey a good impression of the irregularity of the corona, and a warning against theories of the corona which assume, for example, spherical symmetry.

The corona changes its form with the solar cycle. Hansky classified the forms of the corona according to three types, Equatorial, Polar, and Intermediate. In the *Equatorial* type the streamers are entirely in the equatorial direction, and short plumes are abundant at both poles; in the *Polar* type the streamers extend in all directions and the polar plumes are absent. Ludendorff attempted to give precision to the idea by constructing isophotes of the corona and calculating a rough value of the ellipticity. He agreed with Mitchell that the corona takes its shape from the lengths and position angles of its longest streamers. It can have no constant shape, but no doubt varies from day to day depending on the location of the Sun's activity. The equatorial type of corona occurs a year or two before sunspot minimum, and the polar type a year or two before sunspot maximum.

Notwithstanding the irregular character of the corona, attempts have been made to represent the intensity as a function of the distance from the centre of the Sun; but in no case has it been possible to represent the intensity of both inner and outer corona by a single (inverse) power of the radius, or a single exponential.†

The total light of the corona has been measured on a number of occasions by a variety of methods. The results do not agree with one another. The smallest observed value was 0·17 times the light of the full Moon obtained by K. Schwarzschild in 1905; and the value 1·1 in the same units has twice been obtained, by Abney and Thorpe in 1893, and by Turner in 1898. The mean of the most reliable determinations is equal to 0·47 of the light of the full Moon or $1·00 \times 10^{-6}$ of the light of the Sun.‡ It is doubtful if the observations are sufficiently precise to show whether there is any variation of the total light of the corona with the sunspot cycle or not.

The light of the corona is partly polarized. As long ago as 1879 Schuster§ calculated the proportions of polarized and unpolarized light that would be seen (looking as we do along a chord passing through the corona) given any law of radial distribution of scattering particles, and given the ratio of scattered light to unpolarized light emitted by the corona. Schuster showed how the inverse problem of determining the amount of scattering in the corona from the observed polarization could be solved if a law of distribution of the particles with radial distance was assumed.

2. The coronal spectrum

The corona exhibits a continuous spectrum crossed by weak absorption lines (the same Fraunhofer lines as appear in the normal solar spectrum)

† Dyson and Woolley, *Eclipses of the Sun and Moon* (Oxford), p. 116.
‡ Ibid., p. 125.
§ A. Schuster, *M.N.* **40**, 35 (1879).

and by some very characteristic emission lines. The colour of the *continuous spectrum* was established as white by Ludendorff, who showed that the magnitude difference between the spectrum of the corona of 1923 September 10 and that of the full Sun was constant to within a tenth of a magnitude between wave-lengths 3,820 A and 4,840 A. Grotrian, examining the spectrum of the corona of 1929 May 9, confirmed Ludendorff's result and extended it from 3,400 A to 6,500 A, the range of magnitude difference again being less than $0^{m}\cdot1$.

Grotrian interpreted the weak *Fraunhofer spectrum* by dividing the coronal light into two parts—a continuous spectrum showing no absorption lines at all; and another spectrum showing the solar absorption lines. In the inner corona the continuous spectrum was found to be much stronger than the Fraunhofer spectrum, but in the outer corona the latter had gained relative to the former: at a distance of 3′ from the limb the continuous spectrum was six times as strong as the Fraunhofer spectrum and only twice as strong at 20′ from the limb.

The *bright line spectrum* of the corona is seen up to 5′ from the limb. There is, however, no reason to suppose that the material emitting the bright lines does not extend farther out than this, as, according to Grotrian, the intensity of the bright line spectrum falls off in the same way as the continuous spectrum from the maximum, which is just over 1′ from the limb, to as far out as he was able accurately to photometer the bright line spectrum (about 3′). The strongest lines are at λ5,303 A and λ3,388 A. These lines, together with about a dozen other bright lines emitted by the corona, defied all efforts to identify them until recently. They have been observed in no laboratory sources whatever, and in only one celestial object, the star RS Ophiuchi, which suddenly increased its brightness from $11^{m}\cdot0$ to $4^{m}\cdot3$ and is subject to repeated outbursts. The bright coronal emission line at λ5,303 A is at least one angstrom unit wide.

In 1882 Huggins attempted to photograph the corona in daylight, but met with no success. The difficulty lies in the elimination of light scattered from the disk of the Sun by the Earth's atmosphere and the instrument. This scattered light overpowers the corona. The problem received attention from Hale and Deslandres, who attempted to use the spectroheliograph, but without success. In about 1930 it was considered impossible to photograph the corona, but about this time the problem was taken up by Lyot. He reduced scattering in the Earth's atmosphere by going to an altitude of 2,870 metres on the Pic du Midi, and took extraordinary precautions to minimize the scattering of light in the instrument. Lyot found that the edge of the camera diffracted a large quantity of light, and he masked off this edge. He also chose lenses that were particularly free from scratches and bubbles, as these cause trouble. With Lyot's coronograph, which employs dispersion so that monochromatic light is used, the inner corona can be photographed in light of wave-length 5,303 A and 6,374 A. Similar coronographs have been installed in Switzerland and in Colorado.

3. The nature of the corona

The view was proposed by Minnaert† in 1930 that the coronal spectrum was made up of three parts: polarized light scattered by particles of atomic dimensions, showing the Rayleigh blue; polarized light scattered by electrons, and white in colour; and a continuous emission from the corona, unpolarized and red in colour so as to balance the Rayleigh blue and give a white colour to the whole spectrum. On Minnaert's theory the polarization increases from red to violet, and for this he claimed some observational support. An alternative theory proposed by Grotrian‡ in 1931 attributed the continuous spectrum to scattering by electrons, moving so fast as to obliterate the Fraunhofer lines with shifts due to Doppler effect, and attributed the Fraunhofer spectrum to scattering by dust particles of dimensions at least 3μ. Both spectra are white. The light scattered by electrons is polarized, and Grotrian supposed the light scattered by dust not to be polarized. On his theory, therefore, the degree of polarization is independent of the wave-length; and observational support for this was obtained at the eclipse of 1936 June 9 by Dufay and Grouiller. Grotrian's theory was faced with a difficulty over the existence of dust particles in the corona, as small solid objects should attain temperatures of nearly 4,000° in the corona. It was, therefore, hard to resist the conclusion that dust would volatilize.

Observations conducted by Allen§ at the total eclipse of 1940 October 1 showed no difference between the polarization in red and blue light, and also indicated that the ratio of polarized to unpolarized light was substantially equal to the ratio of the Fraunhofer spectrum to the continuous spectrum. These results accordingly confirmed Grotrian's theory. In addition, Allen‖ removed the difficulty connected with the volatilization of dust by showing that the dust could be located not in the corona itself, but in the space between the Sun and the Earth.

† M. G. J. Minnaert, *Zs. f. Ap.*, **1**, 209 (1930).
‡ W. Grotrian, ibid. **3**, 199 (1931).
§ C. W. Allen, *M.N.* **101**, 281 (1941).
‖ C. W. Allen, ibid. **106**, 146 (1946).

The Fraunhofer spectrum of the corona is seen by small-angle scattering of ordinary photospheric sunlight by interplanetary dust particles whose presence and approximate abundance are indicated by the zodiacal light.

The spectrum of the corona proper is therefore a white spectrum, showing no absorption lines, together with a peculiar emission spectrum.

4. Distribution of electron density

If the light from the corona is due to electron scattering of sunlight, the concentration of electrons in the corona can be deduced from the observed brightness of the corona relative to the solar disk.

4.1. *Electron scattering in the Corona*

According to J. J. Thomson the scattering coefficient for free electrons is independent of wave-length. We can therefore consider the total intensity I integrated over all frequencies.

Let $I\,d\omega$ be the flow of radiation in a given direction within the element of solid angle $d\omega$. The amount of radiation (initially unpolarized) which *each* electron scatters into a solid angle $d\omega'$ in a direction making an angle Θ with the direction of incidence is given by the classical theory as

$$\frac{8\pi}{3}\left(\frac{e^2}{mc^2}\right)^2 I\,d\omega\left\{\tfrac{3}{4}(1+\cos^3(\Theta))\frac{d\omega'}{4\pi}\right\}, \tag{1}$$

the factor $\{...\}$ being the probability of scattering into directions within $d\omega'$. The scattered light is polarized, as in Rayleigh scattering, the ratio of the intensity of the two components being $1:\cos^2\Theta$, the stronger component having its electric vector in the plane containing the incident ray and the scattered ray; (1) gives the sum of the energy scattered by both components. Integrating over all directions of scattering the total energy scattered per electron is

$$\frac{8\pi}{3}\left(\frac{e^2}{mc^2}\right)^2 I\,d\omega. \tag{2}$$

Consider the scattering of sunlight by electrons at the point P in the corona (Fig. 38). The incident radiation at P lies within a cone of semi-vertical angle ϕ so that the apparent disk of diameter AB subtends at P a solid angle

$$\Omega = 2\pi(1-\cos\phi) = 2\pi[1-\sqrt{\{1-(R/r)^2\}}].$$

Neglecting the darkening of the limb of the Sun, the total amount of radiation scattered per unit volume at P will be given by

$$\frac{8\pi}{3}\left(\frac{e^2}{mc^2}\right)^2 2\pi I_\odot[1-\sqrt{\{1-(R/r)^2\}}]N_e, \tag{3}$$

N_e being the electron concentration at the point P, and $I_{\odot}$ the emergent intensity at the surface of the Sun. In (3) we have set $I = I_{\odot}$ since the

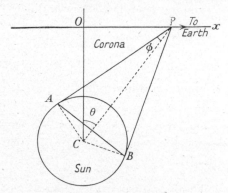

FIG. 38.   The scattering of sunlight by coronal electrons.
$$AC = R_{\odot}, \qquad OC = \rho, \qquad PC = r.$$

electron scattering only reduces the photospheric intensity by a negligibly small amount. Let ϵ be the radiation scattered per unit volume at P into unit solid angle along the x-axis towards the earth. If the scattered radiation (3) is isotropic we have

$$\epsilon = \frac{8\pi}{3}\left(\frac{e^2}{mc^2}\right)^2 \tfrac{1}{2}I_{\odot}[1-\sqrt{\{1-(R/r)^2\}}]N_e. \tag{4}$$

4.2. *The intensity of coronal light, and the electron density*

To find the intensity $I_K(\rho)$ of scattered radiation emerging from the corona at an apparent distance ρ from the centre of the Sun we have to integrate the equation

$$\frac{dI_K}{dx} = -\alpha I_K + \epsilon, \tag{5}$$

where α is the volume scattering coefficient given by $\alpha = \sigma_e N_e$ with

$$\sigma_e = \frac{8\pi}{3}\left(\frac{e^2}{mc^2}\right)^2 = 0\cdot 66 \times 10^{-24} \text{ cm.}^2$$

The 'absorption' term αI_K in equation (5) is negligibly small compared with the 'emission' ϵ so that the emergent intensity is obtained by integrating ϵ along the x-axis throughout the corona.

It is convenient to measure distances in terms of the solar radius as unit. Equation (5) then gives

$$\frac{I_K(\rho)}{I_{\odot}} = \tfrac{1}{2}\sigma_e R_{\odot} \int\limits_{x=-\infty}^{\infty} \{1-\sqrt{(1-1/r^2)}\}N_e \, dx, \tag{6}$$

where
$$r^2 = \rho^2 + x^2.$$

Now the integrand in equation (6) involves N_e at every point of the path of integration, and hence at all radial distances from the centre of the Sun, and the determination of N_e from observed coronal intensities involves the solution of an integral equation. Equation (6) may be written

$$\frac{I_K(\rho)}{I_\odot} = \tfrac{1}{2}\sigma_e R_\odot \int_\rho^\infty \{1 - \sqrt{(1-1/r^2)}\} N_e(r)\, \frac{2r\,dr}{\sqrt{(r^2-\rho^2)}},$$

which is an Abelian integral equation. The solution of this equation is well known, but instead of proceeding with the solution we demonstrate the essential features of the problem by considering the inverse problem of finding the emergent intensity of coronal light for a given variation of electron density with radial distance. Let N_e be given by a sum of terms in powers of $1/r$, such as

$$N_e = \frac{a}{r^m} + \frac{b}{r^n}, \tag{7}$$

and write
$$1 - \sqrt{(1-1/r^2)} = \frac{1}{2r^2} + \frac{1}{8r^4} + \cdots \sim \frac{1}{2r^2}.$$

We now have

$$\frac{I_K(\rho)}{I_\odot} \sim \tfrac{1}{2}\sigma_0 R_\odot \int_\rho^\infty \left(\frac{a}{r^m} + \frac{b}{r^n}\right) \frac{dr}{r\sqrt{(r^2-\rho^2)}}.$$

With $r = \rho \sec\theta$ we readily obtain

$$\frac{I_K(\rho)}{I_\odot} \sim \frac{A}{\rho^{m+1}} + \frac{B}{\rho^{n+1}}, \tag{8}$$

where
$$A = \tfrac{1}{2}\sigma_e R_\odot . a \int_0^{\frac{1}{2}\pi} \cos^m\theta\, d\theta = \tfrac{1}{2}\sigma_e R_\odot . a\, \frac{m!}{\{(\tfrac{1}{2}m)!\}^2}\frac{\pi}{2^{m+1}},$$

and B is given by a similar expression. Comparing (7) and (8) we see that the powers of the terms in $1/r$ for N_e are one less than the powers in the corresponding terms of the series in $1/\rho$ for $I_K(\rho)/I_\odot$.

If the observed variation of coronal light with apparent distance ρ can be described by an empirical relation of the form (8), a determination of the indices enables one to deduce the variation of electron density with radial distance. But before making such a deduction it is necessary to subtract from the apparent coronal light that fraction of it which shows the Fraunhofer lines. This fraction is not scattered by the electrons in the corona and is therefore not true coronal light.

Suppose that microphotometer tracings are made of a Fraunhofer line in the apparent coronal spectrum, and of the same line in the normal solar spectrum, photographed with the same spectrograph. In the figure DF/AC is the (measured) central intensity r_c of the line in the corona, and RS/PQ is the central intensity $r_\odot$ of the line in the solar spectrum. If the position of the point B on AC is such that

$$DE/AB = RS/PQ,$$

then AB/BC is the ratio of the intensity of spurious light to true light in the corona, namely I_F/I_K. We have in fact

$$\frac{I_F}{I_K} = \frac{1 - r_c}{r_c - r_\odot}.$$

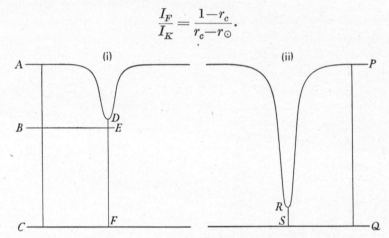

FIG. 39. A Fraunhofer line as it would appear (i) in the coronal spectrum, and (ii) in the solar spectrum.

It is found empirically that

$$\left.\begin{aligned}
\frac{I_F(\rho)}{I_\odot} &= \frac{0 \cdot 0532}{\rho^{2 \cdot 5}} \times 10^{-6}, \\[2mm]
\frac{I_K(\rho)}{I_\odot} &= \left(\frac{1 \cdot 425}{\rho^7} + \frac{2 \cdot 565}{\rho^{17}}\right) \times 10^{-6},
\end{aligned}\right\} \tag{9}$$

from which may be deduced

$$N_e = \left(\frac{1 \cdot 55}{r^6} + \frac{2 \cdot 99}{r^{16}}\right) \times 10^8, \tag{10}$$

an allowance having been made for limb darkening. These figures were deduced by Baumbach[†] from observations taken at a number of eclipses: the distinction between I_F and I_K was made by Allen,[‡] and independently

† S. Baumbach, *Astronomische Nachrichten*, **263**, 122 (1937).
‡ C. W. Allen, *M.N.* **107**, 426 (1947).

by van de Hulst.† According to the latter, a further reduction‡ of eclipse data suggests a variation of electron density with the sunspot cycle, and leads to a distinction between the polar and equatorial radii of the corona at minimum phase. At maximum phase the corona is taken to be symmetrical. The results of this work are compared with Baumbach's results, as modified by Allen, in Table XLII.

TABLE XLII

The Electron Density in the Corona as a Function of Height

r unit equals $R_\odot$	van de Hulst			Baumbach– Allen
	Maximum phase	Minimum phase		
		Equatorial	Polar	
1	403×10^6	227×10^6	174×10^6	454×10^6
1·03	316	178	127	346
1·06	235	132	87·2	227
1·1	160	90	53·2	154
1·2	70·8	39·8	16·3	68·5
1·3	37·6	21·2	5·98	36·6
1·5	14·8	8·30	1·41	14·1
1·7	7·11	4·00	0·542	6·48
2·0	2·81	1·58	0·196	2·42
2·0	0·665	0·374	0·040	0·500
3·0	0·313	0·176	0·017	0·213
4·0	0·090	0·050	0·004	0·038
5·0	0·044	0·025	..	0·010
6·0	0·029	0·016	..	0·0033

Support to the identification of I_F and I_K is given by observations of polarization of coronal light. Broadly speaking the observed polarization matches the polarization computed on the assumption that I_F is unpolarized, but some discrepancies are in evidence. The reader is referred to van de Hulst (1950).

5. The high temperature of the corona

The first suggestion of a high coronal temperature was made by Grotrian§ who pointed out in 1931 that if the electrons which scattered the photospheric light obliterated the Fraunhofer lines through the Doppler effect, the electrons must have high velocities, and that the temperature corresponding to a Maxwellian distribution of the electron velocities would be of the order of one million degrees. The second observational fact which confirms the high temperature is the great width of the line at λ5,303 A. According to Lyot,‖ the intensity of this line

† H. C. van de Hulst, *Ap. J.* **105**, 471 (1947).
‡ Idem, *B.A.N.* **11**, 135 (1950).
§ W. Grotrian, *Zs. f. Ap.* **3**, 220 (1931).
‖ B. Lyot, *L'Astronomie*, **51**, 211 (1937).

falls to e^{-1} of the maximum value at wave-lengths 0·46 A on either side of the centre of the line. Now the Doppler core of the emission coefficient is of the same form as equation (111) of Chapter VI. Since this is nearly equal to

$$\exp\left\{-\frac{Mc^2}{2RT}\left(\frac{\lambda-\lambda_0}{\lambda_0}\right)^2\right\},$$

the intensity falls to e^{-1} of the central value, where

$$\frac{\lambda-\lambda_0}{\lambda_0} = \frac{2RT}{Mc^2}. \qquad (11)$$

As we shall see shortly, the line at λ5,303 A is attributed to Fe, for which which $M = 55\cdot8m_{\mathrm{H}}$ or $9\cdot1\times10^{-23}$ gm. Accordingly with

$$(\lambda-\lambda_0)/\lambda_0 = 0\cdot46\div5303,$$

or $8\cdot6\times10^{-5}$, equation (11) gives $T = 2,300,000°$ K. More recent determinations have given higher temperatures in some active areas (for example, 6·5 million degrees has been observed by Waldmeier).†

TABLE XLIII

Emission Lines in the Spectrum of the Corona and their Identification According to Edlén

Wave-length λ (A)	Identification		Ionization* potential (volts)
3,328	Ca XII	$^2P_{\frac{3}{2}}-^2P_{\frac{1}{2}}$	589
3,388	Fe XIII	$^3P_2-^1D_2$	325
3,601	Ni XVI	$^2P_{\frac{1}{2}}-^2P_{\frac{3}{2}}$	455
3,987	Fe XI	$^3P_1-^1D_2$	261
4,086	Ca XIII	$^3P_2-^3P_1$	655
4,231	Ni XII	$^2P_{\frac{3}{2}}-^2P_{\frac{1}{2}}$	318
5,116	Ni XIII	$^3P_2-^3P_1$	350
5,303	Fe XIV	$^2P_{\frac{1}{2}}-^2P_{\frac{3}{2}}$	355
6,375	Fe X	$^2P_{\frac{3}{2}}-^2P_{\frac{1}{2}}$	233
6,702	Ni XV	$^3P_0-^3P_1$	422
7,892	Fe XI	$^3P_2-^3P_1$	261
10,747	Fe XIII	$^3P_0-^3P_1$	325
10,798	Fe XIII	$^3P_1-^3P_2$	325

* The ionization potential refers to ionization of the element from the next lower stage. For example to ionize Fe XIII to Fe XIV requires 355 volts.

Further evidence for the high temperature of the corona is given by the emission lines, which have been found to be due to highly ionized atoms with ionization potentials averaging about 400 volts. It was found

† M. Waldmeier, *Ast. Mitt. Stern. Zürich*, No. 149 (1947).

by Grotrian in 1939 that the wave numbers of coronal lines at λ6,374 A and λ7,892 A coincided with doublet and triplet separations in the ground terms of Fe X (ionization potential 233 volts) and Fe XI (261 volts), and shortly afterwards Edlén† identified most of the remaining lines, the line at λ5,303 A corresponding to the doublet separation in the ground term of Fe XIV (355 volts). That the ionization of the corona indicates a temperature of about a million degrees will be shown in Section (6) of this chapter.

Other indications of high temperature are given by solar radio noise, and by the extension of the corona. *Solar noise* observations indicate that, although there are disturbances which are probably non-thermal, there is a level of noise intensity below which the radiation on any wavelength does not fall—the thermal component or the *quiet* solar noise. At 200 Mc./s. the refractive index is such that most of the radiation which reaches the earth originates in the corona, and the intensity of quiet radiation on this frequency gives a temperature a little less than a million degrees. As regards the *extension of the corona* it is roughly equal to that which would be exhibited by an atmosphere of the solar mixture of elements at a temperature of a million degrees in hydrostatic equilibrium under solar gravity. The form of the corona (especially of the streamers) is so irregular that it hardly admits the supposition that it is really in hydrostatic equilibrium, but the extension nevertheless is easier to understand if the corona is at the high temperature. Lastly we may mention high-energy phenomena (especially the appearance of high excitation lines of He and He+) in the chromosphere, which indicate that it also is hotter than the photosphere.

There are no observations which indicate that the temperature of the corona is less than that of the photosphere. The reversal of the temperature gradient must be reconciled with the flow of heat outwards from the Sun, but there is no difficulty (other than that of accounting for a nonradiative source of heat in the corona) provided the optical depth in the corona is sufficiently small. We now demonstrate this point.

5.1. *The effect of a high-temperature region overlying the photosphere*

Consider an atmosphere stratified in plane parallel layers and divided into two parts as shown in the figure. In the lower part $\tau > \tau_0$ the temperature is controlled by radiation alone so that

$$B(T) = 3H\tau + \text{constant},$$

† B. Edlén, *Arkiv Mat. Ast. Fys.* **28**, B, 1 (1942).

and in the upper part $\tau < \tau_0$ the temperature has a fixed value of $T = T_1$ maintained by a non-radiative source of heat. Suppose that in the lower part k is independent of frequency so that $J(\tau)$, given by the ratio j/k, is equal to $B(T)$, the integrated Planck function. It would be inappropriate to make such a supposition in the corona: instead one supposes that the emission j is equal to j_0 in the upper region. From equation (26) of Chapter I the inward intensity at the interface $\tau = \tau_0$ is given by

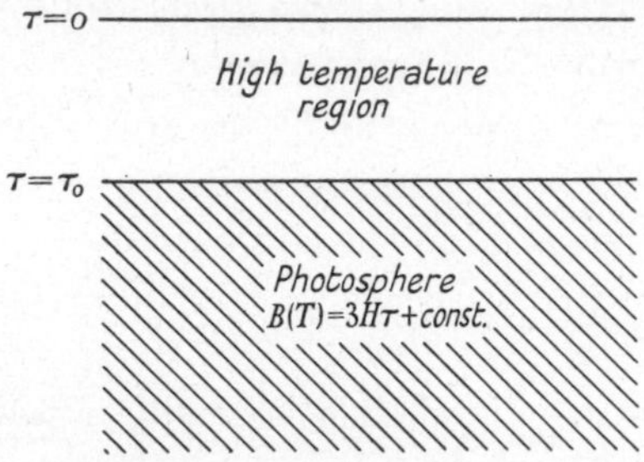

FIG. 40. The photosphere with an over-lying region of high temperature.

$$I(\tau_0, \varphi) = \int_0^{\tau_0} e^{-(\tau_0-\tau)\sec\varphi}(j_0/k)\sec\varphi\, d\tau,$$

and the flux inwards at this boundary is given by

$$2\pi \int_0^{\frac{1}{2}\pi} I(\tau_0, \varphi)\sin\varphi \cos\varphi\, d\varphi = 2\pi(j_0/k)\{E_3(0) - E_3(\tau_0)\}.$$

But

$$E_3(\tau_0) = \tfrac{1}{2} - \tau_0 + \tfrac{1}{2}\tau_0^2(\tfrac{3}{2} - \gamma - \ln\tau_0) + \ldots,$$

so that the value of $E_3(0) - E_3(\tau_0)$ when τ_0 is small is simply τ_0. Accordingly, the inward flux at $\tau = \tau_0$ for small τ_0 is

$$2\pi(j_0/k)\tau_0 = 2\pi j_0 \int \rho\, dx = \pi J_0.$$

Hence in the first approximation of Chapter I the temperature distribution in the lower part of the atmosphere is given by

$$B(T) = \tfrac{1}{2}B(T_e)\{1 + \tfrac{3}{2}(\tau - \tau_0) + 2J_0/B(T_e)\}, \tag{12}$$

where T_e is the effective temperature of the photosphere.

From equation (12) it is seen that the equation

$$B(T) = \tfrac{1}{2}B(T_e)\{1 + \tfrac{3}{2}(\tau - \tau_0)\}$$

is little disturbed if $J_0/B(T_e)$ is small. If, for example, it was numerically of order 10^{-2} the disturbance in $B(T)$ would be very hard to detect by observation. Later in the present chapter we give estimates of the emission from the whole corona in its continuous spectra. Of these, only the free-free continuum has any part in the visible spectrum, the emission from the entire corona in this spectrum being 6×10^{25} ergs per second. Hence πJ_0 is equal to $\frac{1}{2} \times 10^3$ ergs cm.$^{-2}$ sec.$^{-1}$ But $\pi B(T_e)$ is

6×10^{10} ergs cm.$^{-2}$ sec.$^{-1}$, so that $2J_0/B(T_e)$ is of order 10^{-8} and the disturbance to the temperature distribution in the photosphere is negligible. Hence none of the observations which indicate radiative equilibrium in the photosphere are in any way irreconcilable with the very high temperature of the corona, as the high temperature only leads to a small value of J_0.

6. Ionization in the corona

In thermodynamic equilibrium the degree of ionization of any element can be found from Saha's relation. This does not apply in the corona where the agitation temperature is very high compared with the temperature appropriate to the energy density of the radiation. The ionization equilibrium in the corona is therefore set up by radiative processes of strength appropriate to the low radiation temperature, and by collision processes at the high coronal temperature.

Consider the secular equilibrium between the pth and the $(p+1)$th stages of ionization of an atom in the corona. Ionization of the atom from the pth stage takes place by radiation capture, and also when the atom experiences an inelastic collision with an electron. The reverse processes of recombination by which the atom returns to the pth stage are (i) the capture of an electron by the $(p+1)$th ionized atom resulting in the emission of a quantum; (ii) a three-body super-elastic collision between the $(p+1)$th ionized atom and two electrons in which one of the electrons is captured and the other gets away with the energy of ionization. Now let there be $N(1-x)$ ions per unit volume in the pth stage, with the remainder Nx in the $(p+1)$th stage. If N_e be the electron density, the number of transitions per unit volume per second will be as follows:

$N(1-x)Q$ photo-electric ionizations,

$\alpha(Nx)N_e$ photo-electric recombinations,

$N(1-x)N_e S_{12}$ ionizations by inelastic collisions with electrons,

$(Nx)N_e^2 S_{21}$ collision recombinations (three-body).

The quantity Q depends on the radiation field $\Big($for a line† Q is given by

$\dfrac{\pi e^2}{mc} f \dfrac{4\pi J_\nu}{h\nu}\Big)$, whilst α, S_{12}, and S_{21} depend on the temperature as judged by the agitation of the particles.

† For transitions to the continuum f would be replaced by f_c (see Chapter VI) and $J_\nu/h\nu$ by a suitable average.

In thermodynamic equilibrium, that is when $J_\nu = B(\nu, T)$, the processes balance separately, the number of photo-electric ionizations being equal to the number of radiative recombinations, and the number of inelastic collisions being equal to the number of super-elastic collisions. With $Q = Q_T$ we have

$$N(1-x)Q_T = \alpha(Nx)N_e, \tag{13}$$

$$N(1-x)N_e S_{12} = (Nx)N_e^2 S_{21}, \tag{14}$$

and, from Saha's relation,

$$\left(\frac{xN_e}{1-x}\right)_T = 2(2\pi m RT)^{\frac{3}{2}}h^{-3}\varpi e^{-I/RT}, \tag{15}$$

where ϖ is the ratio of the statistical weights of the two states, and I is the ionization potential. From equations (13) and (14)

$$\frac{S_{12}}{S_{21}} = \frac{Q_T}{\alpha} = \left(\frac{xN_e}{1-x}\right)_T. \tag{16}$$

But in a steady state which is not necessarily that of thermodynamic equilibrium

$$N(1-x)(Q+N_e S_{12}) = NxN_e(\alpha+N_e S_{21}).$$

Hence

$$\frac{xN_e}{1-x} = \frac{Q+N_e S_{12}}{\alpha+N_e S_{21}}. \tag{17}$$

Since the corona is optically thin it is not able to build up a population of high-frequency quanta, and the value of Q is consequently very far below the equilibrium value Q_T. Neglecting Q in the numerator of equation (17), we have

$$\frac{x}{1-x} = \frac{S_{12}}{\alpha+N_e S_{21}}. \tag{18}$$

Now S_{12} is given by equation (101) of Chapter VI where it is called $S(T)$. We have

$$S_{12} = \frac{12\pi e^4 b}{(2\pi m RT)^{\frac{1}{2}}}\frac{RT}{I^2}e^{-I/RT}, \tag{19}$$

where b is a constant which replaces the oscillator strength of the line; and the ionization potential I replaces $h\nu$. The value of α for Fe XIV at 10^6 degrees according to Hill[†] is $3 \cdot 4 \times 10^{-12}$ cm.^{3} sec.$^{-1}$ With this value of α it can be verified by means of equations (16) and (19) that for $N_e \sim 10^8$ per c.c., $\alpha \gg N_e S_{21}$. Equation (18) may therefore be written

$$\frac{x}{1-x} = \frac{S_{12}}{\alpha}. \tag{20}$$

Thus *the degree of ionization is independent of electron pressure.* The

† E. R. Hill, *Aust. J. Sci. Res.* A, **4**, 437 (1951).

physical explanation of this result is that both ionization (by electron impact) and recombination are proportional to the electron pressure, so that in a balance between the two processes the electron pressure cancels.

Table XLIV gives values of the ionization at 10^6 degrees with $b = \frac{1}{2}$ and $\alpha = 3 \cdot 4 \times 10^{-12}$.

TABLE XLIV

Ionization in the Corona by Electron Impact

I/RT	I (volts)	$x/(1-x)$
3·0	258	4·41
3·5	301	1·94
4·0	344	0·93
4·5	387	0·44
5·0	430	0·21
5·5	473	0·106
6·0	516	0·053

With the help of equation (20) we could calculate the population of various ions in the corona (for example, Fe XII, Fe XIII, Fe XIV, etc.), assuming the relative abundances of the elements to be the same as in the photosphere. But it is possible to extract a good value of the hydrogen to metal ratio from the coronal observations themselves. This is because the ratio of the intensities of the coronal emission lines to the coronal continuum measures the relative populations of metallic ions and electrons, and most of the electrons are liberated from protons so that the electron population is easily related to the hydrogen population. The individual ion (such as Fe XIV producing λ5,303 A) has to be related to the total number of ions produced by the element with the help of equation (20) before an electron to element population ratio can be deduced.

Table XLV gives the abundance ratio of atoms to electrons in the corona as found by Woolley and Allen† from the observed intensities of coronal lines relative to the coronal continuum I_K. If it is assumed that hydrogen and helium are present in the ratio 6:1 and that substantially all the coronal electrons are due to the ionization of these two elements, there will be eight electrons to every six hydrogen nuclei if both H and He are fully ionized. This gives H = 0·75 in the table.

TABLE XLV

Atoms per Electron in the Corona

H	Fe	Ni	Ca	A
0·75	$4 \cdot 7 \times 10^{-5}$	$1 \cdot 9 \times 10^{-6}$	$1 \cdot 6 \times 10^{-6}$	8×10^{-8}

† R. v. d. R. Woolley and C. W. Allen, *M.N.* **108**, 292 (1948).

7. Heat loss in the corona

Although in most astrophysical cases radiation is a much more efficient means of transporting heat than conduction, this is not so across the inner boundary of the corona. The reason for this is that coronal emission of radiation falls far short of the value $k_\nu B(\nu, T)$, corresponding to thermodynamic equilibrium at the agitation temperature; but conduction depends precisely upon that agitation.

7.1. *Conduction*

The amount of heat transferred per sq. cm. per sec. by a simple gas is given by Chapman and Cowling† as

$$\epsilon = CT^{\frac{5}{2}}\left(\frac{dT}{dh}\right),\qquad(21)$$

where

$$C = \frac{75}{16}\left(\frac{R}{\pi m}\right)^{\frac{1}{2}}\frac{R^3}{e^4}\,T^{\frac{5}{2}}/A_2(2).$$

$A_2(2)$ has the value $4\ln(4RT/e^2N^{\frac{1}{3}})-2$, or about 50 in the low corona. If there is a magnetic field equation (21) applies to conduction along the lines of force, conduction across them being negligible.

In the case of a mixture of ions and electrons C has one-half of this value, and under coronal conditions $C = 0{\cdot}5\times10^{-6}$. When the rate of heat conduction inwards is constant, the solution of equation (21) will be

$$\epsilon h = \tfrac{2}{7}CT^{\frac{7}{2}}+\text{constant}.\qquad(22)$$

Now if H be the distance in which T drops from T_c' ($=10^6$ degrees) to negligible values

$$\epsilon = \frac{2}{7}\frac{C}{H}\,T_c^{\frac{7}{2}}.\qquad(23)$$

Assuming that the hot corona is 4×10^9 cm. above the highest layer at substantially photospheric temperature (corresponding to a distance which subtends $1'$ of arc at the Earth) then H along the lines of force may be taken as 8×10^9 cm. With $T_c = 10^6$ degrees equation (23) gives

$$\epsilon = 1{\cdot}8\times10^4 \text{ ergs cm.}^{-2}\text{ sec.}^{-1}$$

Over the whole solar surface of $6{\cdot}1\times10^{22}$ sq. cm. the amount of heat conducted is $1{\cdot}1\times10^{27}$ ergs per sec., which is about $2{\cdot}8\times10^{-7}$ of the outward solar flux.

7.2. *Loss by radiation*

To estimate the heat loss by radiation we break up the spectrum into line emission, continuous emission due to bound-free transitions, and continuous emission due to free-free transitions.

† S. Chapman and T. G. Cowling, *Mathematical Theory of Non-uniform Gases* (Cambridge).

The *line emission* may be calculated from the number of excitations by electron impact. In the case of permitted transitions, if there are N_p ions of a certain kind per c.c. and the oscillator strength of a transition from the ground state is f, the number of excitations per c.c. per second is given by equation (100) of Chapter VI as

$$N_p\,N_e\frac{12\pi e^4 f}{(2\pi m RT)^{\frac{1}{2}}}\,\frac{1}{h\nu}\,\{e^{-y}-y\,E_1(y)\},$$

where $y = h\nu/RT$, ν being the frequency of the line. Now if we put $p = N_p/N_e$ and suppose that p is independent of position in the corona (which is a legitimate supposition if the corona is isothermal and the ionization independent of electron pressure as in Section 6), the total number of quanta emitted in the line is given by

$$Q = \frac{12\pi e^4}{(2\pi m RT)^{\frac{1}{2}}}\frac{fp}{h\nu}\,\{e^{-y}-y\,E_1(y)\}\int N_e^2\,dv. \qquad (24)$$

The integral is taken over the entire volume of the corona. Taking the Baumbach–Allen values for N_e given by equation (10), and assuming that the base of the corona occurs at $r = 1.015$ solar radii, we find

$$\int N_e^2\,dv = 3.2\times 10^{49},$$

the solar radius being 6.96×10^{10} cm.

According to Woolley and Allen[†] the most important contribution from amongst the *permitted transitions* comes from the principal doublet of Mg X, for which $\lambda = 610$ A, $f = 0.2$, and $p = 1.2\times 10^{-5}$. Hence, from equation (24),

$$Q = 33\times 10^{35} \text{ quanta sec.}^{-1},$$

the corresponding energy being 1.05×10^{26} ergs per second.

The most important contribution to the heat loss by *forbidden transitions* is made by the line at $\lambda 5,303$ A due to Fe XIV. The effective cross-section of this line for excitation by electron impact is given by Woolley and Allen as $S = 2.3\times 10^{-17}$ cm.^{2} The number of excitations per c.c. per second is then $pN_e^2 S(8RT/\pi m)^{\frac{1}{2}}$. From Table XLV the number of Fe atoms per electron is 4.7×10^{-5}, and of these Fe atoms the fraction 0.4 are in the Fe XIV stage of ionization, so that we have $p = 2\times 10^{-5}$. Accordingly

$$Q = 9\times 10^{36} \text{ quanta sec.}^{-1}$$

The quantum energy is relatively low (2.34 volts, or 3.7×10^{-12} ergs), and the energy emitted in the line is 3.4×10^{25} ergs per second. This is the

† R. v. d. R. Woolley and C. W. Allen, *M.N.* **108**, 292 (1948); **110**, 358 (1950).

energy emitted as a consequence of excitation by electron impact, as distinct from photospheric sunlight scattered in the line. The remaining lines in the optical emission spectrum of the corona (principally the strong Fe XIII pair at λ10,747 A and λ10,798 A) raise the figure to approximately 1×10^{26} ergs per second.

We now consider the *bound-free continuous emission*. If α is the recombination coefficient of a particular ion, the number of recombinations per c.c. per second of the type

$$N^{s+1} + e \rightarrow N^s + h\nu$$

(where s is the positive charge on the ion) is $\alpha N_e N^{s+1}$, or $\alpha N_e^2 p_{s+1}$. For hydrogen $\alpha = 5\cdot 4 \times 10^{-15}$ and $p_{s+1} = 0\cdot 75$, so that the number of quanta released per second by recombination with protons is $1\cdot 1 \times 10^{35}$ per second, the corresponding energy being $2\cdot 4 \times 10^{24}$ ergs per second. Proceeding similarly with other elements it is found that a total of 2×10^{35} quanta, giving an energy 6×10^{24} ergs, are emitted per second in bound-free continua.

Lastly we come to the *free-free continuum*. If there are N_p ions of a certain kind with an ionic charge Z, the energy emitted per c.c. per sec. in the free-free spectrum of these ions† is equal to

$$N_e N_p Z B T^{\frac{1}{2}} \text{ ergs cm.}^{-3} \text{ sec.}^{-1},$$

where
$$B = \frac{128\pi^3 e^6 R^{\frac{1}{2}}}{(6\pi m)^{\frac{3}{2}} h c^3}.$$

The emission from the whole corona is therefore

$$\left(\sum p Z^2\right) B T^{\frac{1}{2}} \int N_e^2 \, dv \quad (p = N_p/N_e).$$

Since $\sum p Z^2$ has the value $1\cdot 27$, the total emission is $5\cdot 8 \times 10^{25}$ ergs per second.

To summarize the conclusions of the preceding paragraphs, the total heat loss by radiation is made up as follows:

Permitted transitions $10\cdot 5 \times 10^{25}$ ergs per sec.
Forbidden transitions   10
Bound-free continua   0·6
Free-free continua   5·8
Total 27×10^{25} ergs per sec.

According to these calculations the heat loss by radiation ($2\cdot 7 \times 10^{26}$) is somewhat less than the heat loss by conduction ($1\cdot 1 \times 10^{27}$), but the figures are rather uncertain. The total power which must be supplied

† G. G. Cillié, *M.N.* **92**, 820 (1932).

to the corona to maintain it at 10^6 degrees is given roughly by these figures as $1\cdot4\times10^{27}$ ergs per second, or about 10^{-7} of the solar output.

8. The corona as a source of radio noise

When the aerial of a sensitive radar receiver operating on frequency of say 200 megacycles per second (Mc./s.) is directed towards the Sun electromagnetic radiation of solar origin is detected. Observations indicate that the *radio noise* consists of a steady component of intensity on which is superimposed variable components which are connected with sunspots and other solar activity. The steady component is termed the thermal component of the radiation. The discussion in this section is only concerned with the thermal component, that is the radiation from the *quiet Sun*.

Before investigating the emission of radio-frequency radiation from the corona we consider the refraction of a beam of parallel rays of radio frequency ν incident upon the corona from outside. Since the refractive index in an ionized region decreases with increasing electron density, each ray will experience a continuous change in direction. When there is spherical symmetry in the distribution of electron density the ray paths are symmetrical about the radius vector from the centre of the Sun to the 'point of reflection'. Let ϕ be the angle between the direction of the ray and the radius vector, then, according to Bouguer's rule, $\mu r \sin\phi$ is constant along the ray path. If μ_0 and r_0 be the refractive index and radius vector when $\varphi = \frac{1}{2}\pi$, we have
$$\mu r \sin\phi = \mu_0 r_0.$$

For a given frequency of radiation the depth of penetration into the corona depends upon the distance ρ between the direction of the ray outside the corona (where $\mu = 1$) and the ray directed towards the centre of the Sun; we have in fact $\rho = \mu_0 r_0$. The ray path in polar coordinates (r, θ) is determined by the geometrical equation
$$\frac{1}{r}\frac{dr}{d\phi} = \cot\phi,$$

and the equation of refraction
$$\mu r \sin\phi = \rho.$$

The equation of the ray path will therefore be
$$\frac{dr}{d\theta} = \pm r\sqrt{\{(\mu r/\rho)^2 - 1\}}, \tag{25}$$

where the plus and minus signs refer to the incoming and outgoing portions of the path. The ray directed towards the centre of the Sun is, of course, a straight line extending down to the level of reflection where $\mu = 0$. All other rays are reflected at greater radial distances than the direct ray.

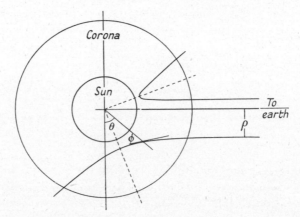

FIG. 41. Ray paths in the corona for a given radio frequency.

When we come to consider the problem of the emission of radiation from the corona, it appears that radiation of frequency ν emerging from the corona in the direction of the Earth, and at a distance ρ from the centre of the solar disk, can only be due to the emission of radiation along the curve (25) from all elements of volume on the curve. In particular, radiation emerging from the corona at the centre of the apparent disk is due to the emission of radiation in both outward and inward directions. Since the radiation travelling towards the Sun is reflected at a level where the refractive index is reduced to zero by the increasing electron density, and since there is no energy with frequency ν propagated in the region of higher electron density, the emission region in the corona extends down to the reflection level $\mu = 0$. For other rays with emergence parameter ρ the concluding remark of the preceding paragraph applies.

The refractive index μ and coefficient of absorption κ (per unit length of path, *not* per unit mass of atmosphere) are given by the well-known complex relation in magneto-ionic theory[1]

$$(\mu - i\chi)^2 = 1 + \frac{1}{\alpha + i\beta},$$

where $\chi = \dfrac{\kappa c}{p}, \qquad \alpha = -\dfrac{mp^2}{4\pi e^2 N_e}, \qquad \beta = \dfrac{mpq}{4\pi e^2 N_e},$

p being the angular frequency of the wave (equal to $2\pi\nu$), and q is the collision frequency. When β/α is small

$$\mu^2 - \chi^2 = 1 + \frac{1}{\alpha}, \qquad 2\mu\chi = \frac{\beta}{\alpha^2},$$

from which we obtain

$$2\mu^2 = \left(1 + \frac{1}{\alpha}\right) + \left\{\left(1 + \frac{1}{\alpha}\right)^2 + \frac{\beta^2}{\alpha^4}\right\}^{\frac{1}{2}}, \qquad (26)$$

$$2\chi^2 = -\left(1 + \frac{1}{\alpha}\right) + \left\{\left(1 + \frac{1}{\alpha}\right)^2 + \frac{\beta^2}{\alpha^4}\right\}^{\frac{1}{2}}. \qquad (27)$$

The collision frequency is given† by

$$q = N_e \left\{\frac{\pi}{2m(RT)^3}\right\}^{\frac{1}{2}} e^4 A_1(2),$$

where R is Boltzmann's constant, and

$$A_1(2) = \ln\{1 + (4RT/e^2 N_e^{\frac{1}{3}})^2\}.$$

The logarithmic term is a slowly varying function of N_e and T and may be treated as constant in the corona. With $T = 10^6$ and $N_e = 10^8$, $A_1(2) = 30 \cdot 9$, and $\beta/p = 1 \cdot 31 \times 10^{-17}$. For all values of p shown in Table XLVI (which covers most of the solar-noise spectrum) β is much smaller than α^2. From equation (26) it follows that μ becomes almost zero when $-1/\alpha$ approaches unity.

If we take the base of the corona at $r = 1 \cdot 015$, then according to equation (10) $N_e = 4 \times 10^8$. Thus for 2,000 Mc./s. radiation, μ remains sensibly equal to unity in the corona, which is therefore a non-deviating region for this frequency. On the other hand, for 20 Mc./s., μ is almost zero where $N_e = 5 \times 10^6$, which is fairly high in the corona. On 200 Mc./s. the condition μ almost zero is met at the base of the corona. Accordingly radiation of frequency 200 Mc./s. or less originates in the corona.

TABLE XLVI

Values of $-\dfrac{1}{\alpha} = \dfrac{4\pi e^2 N_e}{mp^2}$ *in the Corona*

Frequency (Mc./s.)	20	200	2,000
p	$1 \cdot 26 \times 10^8$	$1 \cdot 26 \times 10^9$	$1 \cdot 26 \times 10^{10}$
$N_e = 10^7$	$2 \cdot 14$	$0 \cdot 0214$	$0 \cdot 0002$
10^8	$21 \cdot 4$	$0 \cdot 214$	$0 \cdot 0021$
10^9	214	$2 \cdot 14$	$0 \cdot 0214$
Value of N_e which makes $\alpha = -1$	$5 \cdot 0 \times 10^6$	$5 \cdot 0 \times 10^8$	$5 \cdot 0 \times 10^{10}$

† S. F. Smerd and K. C. Westfold, *Phil. Mag.* (7) **40**, 831 (1949).

8.1. *The equation of transfer for radio-frequency radiation*

The problem of finding the intensity of radiation of frequency ν emerging from the corona at a given apparent distance from the centre of the disk is similar to the problem of finding the emergent intensity of radiation from a star in the visible part of the spectrum. But in the previous problem the refractive index of stellar material for visible light was taken as unity, so that we need to generalize the equation of transfer to include the case of transfer along a ray in a refracting medium.

Let P, P' be two points on a ray in a medium with varying refractive index, and let two elementary surfaces of area $d\sigma$, $d\sigma'$ be drawn normal to the ray at P and P'. The distance between P and P' is supposed so large relative to the dimensions of $d\sigma$ and $d\sigma'$ that all pencils of rays passing through a point in $d\sigma$ and filling $d\sigma'$ have substantially the same solid angle $d\omega$. Similarly $d\omega'$ is the solid angle of every pencil of rays passing through a point in $d\sigma'$ and filling $d\sigma$. Then if μ_ν and μ_ν' are the refractive indices at P and P' it is a consequence of Snell's laws of refraction that

$$\mu_\nu^2 \, d\sigma d\omega = \mu_\nu'^2 \, d\sigma' d\omega'.$$

Hence, if I_ν and I_ν' are the specific intensities at P and P' for radiation of frequency ν filling $d\sigma$ and refracted to pass through $d\sigma'$, then in the absence of absorption and emission we have†

$$\frac{I_\nu}{\mu_\nu^2} = \frac{I_\nu'}{\mu_\nu'^2}. \tag{28}$$

Let ds be an element of length along a ray and let $\partial/\partial s$ denote differentiation along the ray *in the absence of absorption or emission*. Equation (28) may then be written

$$\frac{\partial}{\partial s}\left(\frac{I_\nu}{\mu_\nu^2}\right) = 0,$$

or

$$\frac{1}{\mu_\nu^2}\frac{\partial I_\nu}{\partial s} - 2\frac{I_\nu}{\mu_\nu^3}\frac{\partial \mu_\nu}{\partial s} = 0. \tag{29}$$

Now if κ_ν be the coefficient of *absorption per unit length of path* in the medium, the flow of radiation $I_\nu \, d\sigma d\omega$ loses an amount $\kappa_\nu I_\nu \, d\sigma d\omega ds$ in passing along a length ds of the path, and gains $\eta_\nu \, d\sigma d\omega ds$ in the same distance, η_ν being the *emission per unit volume* per unit solid angle in the direction of the path. Hence

$$\frac{dI_\nu}{ds} = \frac{\partial I_\nu}{\partial s} - \kappa_\nu I_\nu + \eta_\nu.$$

† Cf. E. A. Milne, *Handbuch der Astrophysik*, **3**/1, 74–79 (Berlin, Julius Springer).

But the emission in a refracting medium in thermodynamic equilibrium at temperature T is
$$\eta_\nu = \mu_\nu^2 \kappa_\nu B(\nu, T).$$

Hence
$$\frac{1}{\kappa_\nu}\frac{d}{ds}\left(\frac{I_\nu}{\mu_\nu^2}\right) = -\frac{I_\nu}{\mu_\nu^2} + B(\nu, T). \tag{30}$$

In deriving equation (30) we have assumed that there is no scattering, and that absorption is balanced by thermal emission. This may be shown to be correct for the damping of electromagnetic waves by collisions; indeed Martyn† has shown that Lorentz damping by collisions is equivalent to Kramers–Gaunt absorption due to free-free transitions.

Let τ_ν be the optical depth measured along the ray backwards from its emergence so that $d\tau_\nu = -\kappa_\nu\, ds$. Equation (30) may be written

$$\frac{d}{d\tau_\nu}\left(\frac{I_\nu}{\mu_\nu^2}\right) = \frac{I_\nu}{\mu_\nu^2} - B(\nu, T). \tag{31}$$

The solution for the intensity at any optical depth may be written

$$e^{-\tau_\nu}\left(\frac{I_\nu}{\mu_\nu^2}\right) = e^{-\tau}\left(\frac{I}{\mu^2}\right) + \int_{\tau_\nu}^{\tau} e^{-\tau\nu}B(\nu, T)\, d\tau_\nu,$$

where I and μ are the values of I_ν and μ_ν when $\tau_\nu = \tau$. The ray produced backwards will leave the corona, either because it enters the chromosphere, or because it is bent round and emerges from the corona as shown in Fig. 41. Let τ be the optical depth along the ray to the point where it emerges from the corona. At this point there is no incident radiation, and $\mu = 1$, so that $I/\mu^2 = 0$. At $\tau_\nu = 0$ we also have $\mu_\nu = 1$. Hence the intensity emerging from the corona at an apparent distance ρ from the centre of the disk is

$$I_\nu(\rho) = \int_0^{\tau} e^{-\tau\nu}B(\nu, T)\, d\tau_\nu. \tag{32}$$

When T is independent of τ_ν equation (32) gives
$$I_\nu(\rho) = B(\nu, T)(1 - e^{-\tau}). \tag{33}$$

In accordance with our usage in Chapter I we measure the distance s along the selected ray as positive outwards with the origin of s at the point of emergence. The optical depth at any point on the ray is then given by

$$\tau_\nu = -\int_0^{s} \kappa_\nu\, ds. \tag{34}$$

† D. F. Martyn, *Proc. Roy. Soc.* A, **193**, 44 (1948).

It is convenient to change the variable from the arc length s to the radius vector r by means of the equation

$$\left(\frac{ds}{dr}\right)^2 = 1 + r^2\left(\frac{d\theta}{dr}\right)^2, \tag{35}$$

with $r(d\theta/dr)$ given by equation (25). Since $r \to \infty$ as $s \to 0$ we have

$$\tau_\nu = \int_r^\infty \frac{\kappa_\nu\, dr}{\sqrt{\{1-(\rho/\mu_\nu r)^2\}}}.$$

Since the path is symmetrical about the radius vector to the point of reflection, the optical path along the entire curve will be given by

$$\tau = 2 \int_{r_0}^\infty \frac{\kappa_\nu\, dr}{\sqrt{\{1-(\rho/\mu_\nu r)^2\}}}. \tag{36}$$

8.2. *The radio-noise spectrum of the corona at the centre of the solar disk*

A guide to the general behaviour of the radio-noise spectrum may be had by considering the paths at (nearly) vertical incidence which are practically straight and are reflected at a level where $\mu = 0$, that is $\alpha = -1$. The value of τ in equation (36) is then $2\tau_1$, where

$$\tau_1 = \int_{r_0}^\infty \kappa\, dr, \tag{37}$$

κ being given by equation (27), and the lower limit of the integral being such that N_e at $r = r_0$ makes $\alpha = -1$. Now when $1+1/\alpha$ is not small we have

$$\kappa \doteqdot \frac{p}{c} \frac{\tfrac{1}{2}\beta}{\sqrt{(\alpha^3+\alpha^4)}}, \tag{38}$$

whilst for α nearly equal to -1,

$$\kappa < \frac{p}{c}\sqrt{(\tfrac{1}{2}\beta)}. \tag{39}$$

If we represent the electron density in the corona by $N_e = (N_e)_0\, e^{-h/H}$ for the sake of simplicity, the integral in equation (37) may be readily evaluated with the help of (38) and (39). If the frequency is such that the condition $\mu = 0$ is met before the electron density reaches its greatest value $(N_e)_0$ it may be shown that

$$\tau_1 \doteqdot \tfrac{2}{3}H\frac{\beta p}{c}, \tag{40}$$

but if the low value of μ is not reached in the corona (because N_e does not attain sufficiently high values) the optical thickness of the corona is given by

$$\tau_1 \doteq \tfrac{2}{3}H\frac{\beta p}{c}(1-\tfrac{3}{2}\xi_0^{\frac{1}{2}}+\tfrac{1}{2}\xi_0^{\frac{3}{2}}), \tag{41}$$

where ξ_0 is the value of $1+1/\alpha$ at the bottom of the corona, in other words

$$\xi_0 = 1 - \frac{4\pi e^2(N_e)_0}{mp^2}.$$

The spectrum of the radiation from the corona emerging at the centre of the disk is given by equation (33) with $\rho = 0$,

$$I_\nu(0) = B(\nu, T)(1-e^{-\tau}), \tag{42}$$

where $\tau\ (= 2\tau_1)$ is given by equation (40) when the frequency is such that the emission region does not quite extend down to the base of the corona, equation (40) being replaced by equation (41) for the higher frequencies. Table XLVII gives the spectral distribution (42) calculated for

$$H = 1 \cdot 5 \times 10^{10} \text{ cm.}, \qquad (N_e)_0 = 2 \cdot 3 \times 10^8.$$

TABLE XLVII

Coronal Radio-noise Spectrum
Intensity of Radiation at Centre of Disk in units of $B(\nu, T)$
$T = 10^6$ degrees

Frequency (Mc./s.)	20	50	100	200	500	1,000	2,000
Intensity . .	0·129	0·572	0·969	0·934	0·344	0·084	0·022

There is a maximum in the emission of coronal radiation from the centre of the disk of the Sun at a frequency near 100 Mc./s. The maximum arises in the following way: for very long wave-lengths the reflecting boundary occurs high in the corona and the optical depth to this point is small. As the wave-length decreases, the emission boundary moves downwards and the optical depth increases. Finally no such boundary occurs in the corona at all, but with increasing frequency the coefficient of absorption diminishes so that the optical thickness of the corona declines.

It should be noted that for frequencies greater than 200 Mc./s. all the coronal emission both forward and backward has been counted. Thus we assume a reflecting region beneath the corona but take no account of possible emission from such a region. This is discussed in the next chapter.

From equations (33) and (36) it is seen that the variation of $I_\nu(\rho)$ with ρ, that is the centre to limb variation of the emergent intensity in the frequency ν, is subject to two influences. According to equation (36), as ρ increases τ has a tendency to increase (and with it the intensity) due to an increase in the integrand, also a tendency to decrease due to an increase in the lower limit of the integral. Thus the behaviour of the intensity from centre to limb is a combination of both limb-brightening and limb-darkening, a phenomenon predicted by Martyn.[†] For the evaluation of the integral (36) along the various curved paths which occur, the reader is referred to the work of Smerd,[‡] and Jaeger and Westfold.[§]

9. Some unsolved problems of the corona

No definitive conclusion can, as yet, be made concerning the form of the corona and its variation with the sunspot cycle; the nature of the plumes and streamers; the support of the corona; and the source of the energy which maintains the high coronal temperature. It is possible that these are simply different aspects of the same problem, so that the explanation of all of these phenomena will be found at once.

As regards the *support* it was pointed out by Alfvén[||] that if the corona were in hydrostatic equilibrium it would have much the same extension as it is observed to have. In hydrostatic equilibrium at constant temperature the density would follow the law

$$\rho = \rho_0 \, e^{-(Mg/RT)h}.$$

The scale height H of the corona is therefore RT/Mg, where M is the mean molecular mass which is, in this case, one-half that of the hydrogen atom. With $T = 10^6$ and $g = 2 \cdot 74 \times 10^4$, the value of H is 6×10^9 cm., in fairly reasonable agreement with the effective scale height given by coronal electron densities (see Section 8.2). The irregular appearance of the corona, however, suggests very strongly that it is not supported by hydrostatic forces alone.

Turning to the *source of energy*, several suggestions have been made. (a) Matter in the form of solid particles falling into the Sun has been suggested by Vand[††] as a source of heat, and matter in the form of particles of atomic dimensions by Hoyle.[‡‡] The irregular form of the corona and the irregular distribution of temperature (indicated by the irregular distribution of the line at $\lambda 5,303$ A), as well as the variation

† D. F. Martyn, *Nature*, **158**, 632 (1946).
‡ S. F. Smerd, *Aust. J. Sci. Res.* A, **3**, 34 (1950).
§ J. C. Jaeger and K. C. Westfold, ibid. 376.
|| H. Alfvén, *Arkiv Mat. Ast. Fys.* **27** A, No. 25 (1941).
†† V. Vand, *Nature*, **151**, 728 (1943).
‡‡ H. Bondi, F. Hoyle, and R. A. Lyttelton, *M.N.* **107**, 184 (1947).

in the form of the corona with the sunspot cycle are obstacles to explanations of this kind. (b) Saha has suggested† that nuclear fission is responsible for Fe XIV ionization in the corona, but this was considered to be untenable by Woolley and Gascoigne;‡ however, these authors found that a modification of Saha's ideas, namely bombardment of the corona by short-lived radioactive elements, supposed to be brought up from the centre of the Sun by disturbances, could not be excluded by the arguments against fission. If this is the origin of the coronal heat, the radioactive sources must be distributed in such a way that (in units of the solar flux) they supply $10^{-7} \odot$ to the corona and not more than $10^{-2} \odot$ to the photosphere. (c) Perhaps the most attractive hypothesis is that the corona is heated by electric currents. The conductivity of coronal material along the lines of magnetic force is much greater than the corresponding conductivity in the photosphere, so that if electric potentials are set up in the photosphere (by differential rotation of the Sun, by movement of the granula across the lines of force of the general solar magnetic field, or by a change of magnetic flux in sunspots as suggested by Giovanelli,§ or in some other manner) there will be a discharge in the corona. There does not seem to be anything excessive about the figure $10^{-7} \odot$ for the energy released by the discharge.

† M. N. Saha, *Proc. Phys. Soc.* **57,** 271 (1945).
‡ R. v. d. R. Woolley and S. C. B. Gascoigne, *M.N.* **106,** 113 (1946).
§ R. G. Giovanelli, *Aust. J. Sci. Res.* A, **2,** 39 (1949).

XII

THE CHROMOSPHERE

1. Introduction

WHEN Young in 1871 observed the solar spectrum visually at a total eclipse, he saw the weaker Fraunhofer lines reverse sharply from dark to bright at second contact. Since the bright lines flash out at second contact, the emission spectrum at second (or third) contact is known as the *flash spectrum*. Lockyer gave the name *chromosphere* to the region, on account of its bright red appearance to the naked eye.

The chromosphere was first studied by attempting to identify the lines in slitless spectrograms of the flash. It was at first thought that the flash spectrum was a mere reversal of the Fraunhofer spectrum, but it was established by Dyson in 1906, with the help of slit spectrograms, that the flash spectrum is stronger in 'enhanced' lines (that is lines due to ionized as distinct from neutral metals) than the spectrum of the photosphere. At that time the theory of ionization equilibrium had not been developed and the result seemed to imply a reversal of the temperature gradient, which was regarded as anomalous. However, as soon as low pressure was recognized as a cause of high ionization (as a result of Saha's researches) an increase of ionization from photosphere to chromosphere was only to be expected. The situation is now further complicated by recognition of the high temperature of the corona, which necessitates a reversal of the temperature gradient somewhere between the photosphere and the corona. It is still debatable whether this reversal occurs low enough in the Sun's atmosphere to affect the flash spectrum or not, but the ionization in the flash spectrum does not require a temperature higher than that of the photosphere: the 'enhanced' lines can be adequately accounted for by the decrease in pressure.

It is not yet possible (1950) to give a theoretical account of the chromosphere comparable to that which can be given of the photosphere. The heat structure could only be worked out if the distribution of sources of heat were known, and the gravitational equilibrium could only be developed if the hydrodynamics of the chromosphere were fully understood: there is evidence that it is not in simple hydrostatic equilibrium. It is instead necessary to try to understand something of the chromosphere by making inferences from the observations. In the following sections accounts will be given of some of these observations and of the immediate deductions which have been made from them.

Mention must be made at the outset of the irregular structure of the chromosphere, which may easily be seen in eclipse photographs. It is, of course, necessary to replace the actual chromosphere by a model possessing spherical symmetry in order to make a mathematical attack on the subject, but we should always bear in mind the simplifying assumption that has been introduced.

2. The flash spectrum

Observations of the flash spectrum yield the relative intensities of the lines at any one apparent height above the limb (that is to say along the line of sight, tangent to a given height) and of the variation in the intensity of an emission line with height, called the decrement of the line. Many observers have catalogued the heights to which the various lines are seen to extend on a particular photograph: this clearly depends on the exposure and sensitivity of the plate and on a combination of the two first-mentioned factors, relative intensity and decrement.

The leading feature of the intensity observations is, as has already been mentioned, an increase in the intensity of lines of ionized elements relative to those of neutral elements as compared with the intensities in the Fraunhofer spectrum. This is illustrated in Table XLVIII, which shows the intensities of the lines of Mn and Mn$^+$ in the flash spectrum according to Cillié and Menzel,† as well as the intensities on Rowland's scale in the normal solar spectrum.

TABLE XLVIII

Lines in the Flash Spectrum due to Mn *and* Mn$^+$

Particle	Wave-length (A)	Rowland number	log(emission)	
			above 670 km.	above 900 km.
Mn	4,033	7	12·79	12·62
	4,031	9	12·89	12·72
Mn$^+$	3,489	4	13·28	13·21
	3,483	5	13·31	13·24
	3,474	4	13·43	13·38
	3,460	4	13·50	13·37
	3,442	6	13·67	13·51

Emission in ergs per c.c. per second.

From Table XLVIII it can be seen that although the lines of Mn are more intense than those of Mn$^+$ in the Fraunhofer spectrum (higher Rowland number), they emit less energy in the flash spectrum.

† G. G. Cillié and D. H. Menzel, *Harvard Circular*, **410** (1935).

Cillié and Menzel give the emission 'of a slice of the chromosphere 1 cm. in thickness', that is a volume bounded by two planes normal to the Sun's surface, 1 cm. apart, and a third plane passing through the observer and tangent to the Moon's edge. They actually observed the intensity of the line projecting above the Moon's limb and reduced the result to unit length along the tangent, without making any attempt to determine the variation with height in any one exposure: that is to say they record the amount of light coming from the semi-infinite area $ABCD$ in Fig. 42a, or $PQRLMN$ in Fig. 42b.

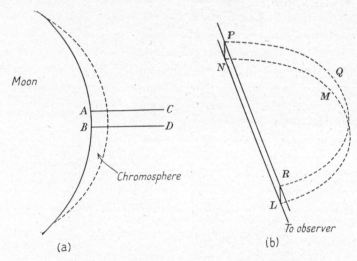

FIG. 42. 'A slice of the chromosphere 1 cm. in thickness.'

Let x denote height in the chromosphere. Then if the emission in ergs per c.c. per sec. $f(x)$ is of the form Ae^{-ax}, and if there is no self-absorption, Cillié and Menzel's emission $E(x)$ is given by

$$E(x) = \frac{(2\pi R)^{\frac{1}{2}}}{a^{\frac{3}{2}}} f(x),$$

where R is the radius of the Sun (provided that aR is large compared with unity). The value of a given for the Mn lines is $2\cdot36 \times 10^{-8}$ cm.$^{-1}$, and for the Mn^{+} lines is $1\cdot11 \times 10^{-8}$ cm.$^{-1}$ The emission from the 'slice' $E(x)$ can therefore be converted to the emission per c.c. $f(x)$, but the interpretation of these intensities is exceedingly complicated. In the first place it is not certain whether the lines are seen by mere scattering of photospheric light, or by some fluorescent process. Even if it is established that the former process is dominant, interpretation is made difficult by the presence of Fraunhofer lines in just those wave-lengths which are to be scattered, so that the amount of photospheric light available for scattering is uncertain. Finally it is not possible to deal adequately with self-absorption along the line of sight. The figures do, however, suggest that ionization in the chromosphere is reasonable compared with that in the photosphere, when allowance has been made for the decrease of electron pressure (by at least two powers of ten, at the heights shown in Table XLVIII).

The flash spectrum exhibits lines of He and He$^+$ which are not seen in the Fraunhofer spectrum. Their presence is remarkable on account of the high excitation potentials concerned. The strongest line is at λ4,471 A and is the transition $2\,^3P$–$4\,^3D$, the excitation potential of the lower state being 20·95 volts, while the He$^+$ line at λ4,686 A ($3\,^2D$–$4\,^2F$) has an excitation potential of 48·36 volts. (The ionization potential of He is 24·58 volts.) These potentials are small compared with the ionization potentials found in the corona (of order 400 volts) but are very high in comparison with the general level of excitation in the low chromosphere.

3. Scale heights

The increase of height in which the number of particles of a particular kind in an atmosphere falls to e^{-1} of an initial value is called the *scale height* of the particle at that point in the atmosphere. If the particles are distributed exponentially with height, the scale height is constant. In the chromosphere the distribution of most particles is well represented by a sum of two exponential terms: the scale height increases with height.

We first show that if the particle distribution is represented by two exponential terms, the number of particles in the line of sight is also represented by two terms with the same exponents. In Fig. 43, O is the centre of the Sun, and OH the normal to XX', the line of sight. Let $OH = R+h$, $OP = R+x$, where R is the radius of the Sun. Then if $HP = \xi$ we have

$$\xi^2 = (R+x)^2-(R+h)^2 = 2R(x-h),$$

provided both x and h are small compared with R.

Now suppose that the number of particles per c.c. at a height z is given by

$$n = Ae^{-az}+Be^{-bz}.$$

Then the number of particles per c.c. at H is $Ae^{-ah}+Be^{-bh}$, and the number in a column of unit cross-section along the line of sight XX' is

$$\int_{-\infty}^{\infty} (Ae^{-ax}+Be^{-bx})\,d\xi.$$

But $x = h + \xi^2/2R$, so that the number in the line of sight is

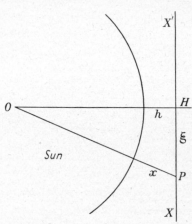

$$A\left(\frac{2\pi R}{a}\right)^{\frac{1}{2}}e^{-ah} + B\left(\frac{2\pi R}{b}\right)^{\frac{1}{2}}e^{-bh},$$

which is the required form

$$A'e^{-ah} + B'e^{-bh}.$$

Observations of chromospheric line emissions have often been reduced in this form. Unfortunately there is little agreement between various investigators except that all agree that the scale height increases with increasing height. Early reductions by Menzel[†] and by Mitchell and Miss Williams[‡] gave results for the number of atoms at a height H in kilometres which are in very good agreement, as is shown by the following comparison:

FIG. 43. The chromosphere viewed along XX'. The point O is the centre of the Sun with radius R, and $OH = R+h$, $OP = R+x$, $HP = \xi$.

Menzel (all atoms)	
From multiplet intensities . .	$\exp\left(-\dfrac{H}{4050}\right) + 59\exp\left(-\dfrac{H}{1500}\right)$
From microphotometer intensities.	$\exp\left(-\dfrac{H}{3580}\right) + 56\exp\left(-\dfrac{H}{1650}\right)$

Mitchell and Williams	
Ti II	$\exp\left(-\dfrac{H}{5000}\right) + 60\exp\left(-\dfrac{H}{2000}\right)$
Fe I	$\exp\left(-\dfrac{H}{3333}\right) + 50\exp\left(-\dfrac{H}{1667}\right)$

These figures agree in placing the scale height of metals in the low chromosphere at about 1,700 km. But this result has been considerably altered in further discussions by Cillié and Menzel,[§] and by Wildt[‖] who used Mitchell's plates and some others. There is disagreement about individual atoms: the average result for the scale height in kilometres in the low chromosphere is given in Table XLIX.

The scale height of an atmosphere at temperature T in hydrostatic

† D. H. Menzel, *Lick Obs. Publ.* **17**, Part 1 (1935).
‡ S. A. Mitchell and E. T. R. Williams, *Publ. Leander McCormick Obs.* **5**, 197 (1933).
§ G. G. Cillié and D. H. Menzel, loc cit.
‖ R. Wildt, *Ap. J.* **105**, 36 (1947).

TABLE XLIX
Scale Heights in the Low Chromosphere

	Cillié and Menzel	Wildt
Neutral metals	373	263
Ionized metals	446	251

equilibrium under the influence of gravity and no other force is RT/Mg, where R is Boltzmann's constant and M the mean molecular *mass*. If we suppose that there is too much movement and too much viscosity to allow the atoms to settle down in different concentrations, then the scale height is the same for all atoms and cannot be very different from the scale height for hydrogen alone on account of its high abundance (in the lower chromosphere we may suppose hydrogen atoms to be much more abundant than electrons). With $T = 5,040°$ the scale height for hydrogen atoms is 152 km. This is much lower than the scale heights first determined, and led to theories of support by radiation pressure,[†] and to a theory of turbulence developed by McCrea.[‡] However, the more recent determinations have removed most of the difference between the observed scale height and that given by the simplest theory.

No mention has here been made of the Balmer lines of hydrogen, which have been observed extensively. The interpretation of scale heights found from these lines is, however, made very difficult by the high excitation of the lower state of these lines (10·19 volts), and no attempt will be made here to go into the theory of the population of this state.

4. The low chromosphere

4.1. *Electron density*

The electron population of the low chromosphere has been deduced by Cillié and Menzel from the intensity of the Balmer continuum, and by Wildt[§] from the resolution of high members of the Balmer series.

According to Cillié,[||] if there are N_e electrons and N^+ protons per c.c., the number of electron captures per c.c. per sec. on the nth level of hydrogen is

$$N_e N^+ \frac{2^9 \pi^5}{(6\pi)^{\frac{3}{2}}} \frac{e^{10}}{m^2 c^3 h^3} \left(\frac{m}{RT}\right)^{\frac{3}{2}} \frac{1}{n^3} e^{\chi_n/RT} E_1(\chi_n/RT),$$

[†] See a discussion in Dyson and Woolley, *Eclipses of the Sun and Moon* (Oxford), chap. xii.
[‡] W. H. McCrea, *M.N.* **89**, 718 (1929).
[§] R. Wildt, *Ap. J.* **105**, 57 (1947).
[||] G. G. Cillié, *M.N.* **92**, 820 (1932).

where T is the temperature of agitation of the particles, and χ_n the energy required to ionize a hydrogen atom in the nth state. The Balmer continuum is an emission arising from captures in the state $n = 2$ with $\chi_n = 3\cdot40$ volts. The emission of energy in the spectral range ν to $\nu+d\nu$ in the Balmer continuum is then

$$N_e N^+ \frac{2^9\pi^5}{(6\pi)^{\frac{3}{2}}} \frac{e^{10}}{m^2c^3h^3}\left(\frac{m}{RT}\right)^{\frac{3}{2}}\tfrac{1}{8}e^{(\chi_2-h\nu)/RT}\,d\nu$$

$$= 2\cdot63\times10^{-33}N_e N^+ T^{-\frac{3}{2}}e^{(\chi_2-h\nu)/RT}\,d\nu \text{ erg cm.}^{-3}\text{ sec.}^{-1}$$

The emission at the head of the Balmer continuum ($\chi_2 = h\nu$) at a height of 900 km. is given by Cillié and Menzel as 63 ergs per second per unit frequency interval for their slice of the chromosphere 1 cm. thick. Since $a = 1\cdot54\times10^{-8}$ (observed), the emission per c.c. per sec., which is the above emission divided by $(2\pi R)^{\frac{1}{2}}a^{-\frac{3}{2}}$ or $3\cdot46\times10^{17}$, is $1\cdot82\times10^{-16}$ ergs per c.c. per second per unit frequency interval. We have therefore at 900 km.
$$\log N_e N^+ = 16\cdot84 + \tfrac{3}{2}\log T.$$

If $T = 5{,}040°$ this gives $\log N_e N^+ = 21\cdot39$. Further, if most of the electrons are liberated by protons we have $N_e = N^+$ and $\log N_e = 10\cdot7$ at a height of 900 km.

Wildt uses a result found by Inglis and Teller,[†] who examined the broadening of the Balmer series by Stark effect and gave a relation between the principal quantum number n of the last resolved Balmer line and c^*, the number of broadening charged particles per c.c., namely
$$\log c^* = 23\cdot26 - 7\cdot5\log n.$$

Wildt observes that $n = 37$ for the Balmer series and $n = 40$ for the Paschen series at a height of 500 km. With $n = 40$ we obtain
$$c^* = 1\cdot74\times10^{11} \text{ per c.c.}$$

The number c^* is the number of electrons plus the number of protons, so that
$$N_e = 8\cdot7\times10^{10} \text{ per c.c.,}$$

which is in excellent agreement with Cillié and Menzel's value, allowance being made for a small increase of electron population with decreasing height.

4.2. *Temperature*

According to the result quoted in the preceding section the emission per c.c. per second within ν to $\nu+d\nu$ in a given continuum is proportional to $e^{-h\nu/RT}$. From Menzel and Cillié[‡] we take the emission at $\lambda3{,}640$ A and $\lambda3{,}500$ A in two cases given in the following table.

† D. R. Inglis and E. Teller, *Ap. J.* **90**, 439 (1939).
‡ D. H. Menzel and G. G. Cillié, ibid. **85**, 94 (1937).

TABLE L

Region	Height	log(emission)	
		λ3,640 A	λ3,500 A
49 a	670 km.	12·15	12·02
49 b	900 km.	12·28	12·11

The corresponding temperatures are readily found to be 5,250° and 4,020° at 670 km. and 900 km. respectively.

The temperature in the low chromosphere has been deduced by Redman[†] from the profiles of lines in the flash spectrum. Redman found that the profiles were consistent with Gaussian distributions of the velocities of the emitting particles, the *average velocities* $\bar{v}$ are as follows:

Hydrogen . . 13·5 km./s.

Helium . . . 8·0 ,,

Lanthanum . . 1·6 ,,

Various other

heavy elements . 1·75 ,,

Now the velocity (in thermal equilibrium) is inversely proportional to the square of the mass, so that if the velocity of 13·5 km./s. for hydrogen were thermal, the other velocities would be

Helium . . . 6·8 km./s.

Ti, Cr, Fe . . 1·9 ,,

La, Ce, Nd, Sm . 1·1 ,,

and it is argued that the velocities are thermal. The corresponding temperature is found from $\bar{v} = \sqrt{(2RT/\pi m)}$, and the result is $T = 35,000°$.

The temperatures found by these two methods are irreconcilable. The higher value has been adopted by some writers on the chromosphere[‡] and rejected by others.[§] The scale height for hydrogen at 35,000° is 1,055 km.: this is much greater than the scale heights given by Cillié and Menzel and by Wildt, as discussed in Section 3, and no reason has been advanced to show why a scale height should be less than the hydrostatic value.

Wurm argues in favour of a low temperature from the non-appearance

† R. O. Redman, *M.N.* **102**, 140 (1942). Redman uses the *average line of sight velocity* $(2RT/\pi m)^{\frac{1}{2}}$, and Unsöld (*Zs. f. Ap.* **3**, 77 (1931)) the *most probable velocity* $(2RT/M)^{\frac{1}{2}}$. The two methods of reduction will, of course, give the same temperature.

‡ R. G. Giovanelli, *Aust. J. Sci. Res.* **1**, 275, 289, 305, 360 (1948); R. N. Thomas, *Ap. J.* **109**, 480 (1949).

§ K. Wurm, *Zs. f. Ap.* **25**, 109 (1948); R. v. d. R. Woolley and C. W. Allen, *M.N.* **110**, 358 (1950).

in the flash spectrum of the forbidden lines of oxygen and nitrogen. In those cases where an upper state is linked with the ground state by a forbidden transition under chromospheric conditions, the population of the upper state is mainly controlled by a balance between collision excitation (inelastic collisions) and the reverse process (super-elastic collisions), so that the population relative to the ground state is given to a high degree of accuracy by Boltzmann's equation (with the kinetic temperature of the electrons). Wurm takes as his criterion for the appearance or otherwise of a line the ratio of quanta emitted in the line to quanta of photospheric light scattered by electrons. When the ratio greatly exceeds unity, the line should be seen.

TABLE LI

Logarithm of the Ratio of Emission in Forbidden Lines to Electron Scattering

Ion	Wave-length (angstroms)	log(emission ratio)			
		$T_e = 5 \times 10^3$	10^4	2×10^4	4×10^4
O I	6,364	0·5	1·6	2·2	2·5
	5,577	−0·7	1·4	2·5	3·0
O II	$\begin{cases} 3,729 \\ 3,726 \end{cases}$	−2·7	−1·1	−0·2	1·8
O III	5,007	0·7	0·9	1·5	1·6
	4,363	−1·5	0·9	2·6	3·2
N II	5,755	−0·8	1·2	2·2	2·7

Table LI, after Wurm, shows that none of these forbidden lines should be seen if the electron temperature in the chromosphere is of order 5,000°, but that all (except possibly those of O II) should be present if the temperature is as high as 35,000°. The lines have not been observed. Of course there must be some layer in the chromosphere where the temperature attains the value 35,000° (since the photosphere below is at 5,000° and the corona above at 10^6 degrees) and it is argued from the non-appearance of the lines that the layers at the right temperatures to produce them are exceedingly thin, and the temperature gradient very steep—a conclusion which we shall see later is supported by other evidence.

4.3. *Ionization*

When both collisions and radiation are taken into account, the degree of ionization is given by equation (17) of Chapter XI, namely

$$\frac{xN_e}{1-x} = \frac{Q+N_e S_{12}}{\alpha+N_e S_{21}},$$

where
$$Q = 4\pi \int_{\nu_0}^{\infty} k_{\nu}(J_{\nu}/h\nu)\, d\nu.$$

In thermodynamic equilibrium at temperature T we have $J_{\nu} = B(\nu, T)$, and

$$\frac{Q_T}{\alpha(T)} = \frac{S_{12}}{S_{21}} = \left(\frac{xN_e}{1-x}\right)_T = K(T),$$

$K(T)$ being the Saha function $2(2\pi m RT)^{\frac{3}{2}} h^{-3} \varpi e^{-h\nu_0/RT}$. In the important case where the radiation is *dilute equilibrium radiation* of temperature θ, that is $J_{\nu} = \omega B(\nu, \theta)$, and the electron temperature T is not necessarily equal to θ, we have

$$\frac{x}{1-x} = \left(\frac{x}{1-x}\right)_T \times \frac{\omega\alpha(\theta)K(\theta) + N_e S_{12}}{K(T)\{\alpha(T) + N_e S_{21}\}}. \tag{1}$$

To illustrate this formula we calculate the degree of ionization of Mn to Mn^+, for which $h\nu_0 = 7\cdot43$ volts and $\varpi = 7/6$. For the low chromosphere we take $N_e = 10^{11}$, $\omega = \frac{1}{2}$, and $\theta = 5{,}040°$: and we suppose S_{12} given by equation (19) of Chapter XI with $b = \frac{1}{2}$, and

$$\alpha(T) = 4 \times 10^{-13}(T/5040)^{-\frac{1}{2}}.$$

Then with $T = 5{,}040°$ the collision terms are negligible and the ionization is half the Saha value, or $x/(1-x) = 405$. On the other hand, when $T = 30{,}240°$ the collision term in the numerator is larger than the radiative term (but the collision term in the denominator is negligible) so that the ionization is close to the 'coronal' value $S_{12}/\alpha(T)$. We have in fact

$$\frac{x}{1-x} = 1\cdot04 \times \frac{S_{12}}{\alpha(T)} = 2\cdot37 \times 10^4.$$

Now the ionization in the photosphere at $\tau = 0\cdot3$ ($T = 5{,}280°$, $\log p_e = 0\cdot78$) is given by $x/(1-x) = 18\cdot2$. The chromospheric ionization of Mn should therefore be about twenty times the photospheric ionization if the chromospheric temperature is $5{,}040°$, and about thirteen hundred times the photospheric ionization if it is $30{,}240°$.

Let us consider the lines shown in Table XLVIII. The relative number of atoms taking part in the formation of the lines in the photosphere is given by Adams and Russell's tables† in the form

$$\log(N'f\delta) = B \log A,$$

the quantity A depending on the Rowland number. N' refers to atoms in the lower state of the transition concerned, and not to the ground state. The emission per c.c. per unit frequency interval in the flash spectrum may be supposed proportional to $N'f\delta \times \lambda^2 I_{\lambda}(0)$, the light being

† H. N. Russell, W. S. Adams, and C. E. Moore, *Ap. J.* **68**, 1 (1928).

supposed to be scattered photospheric light. If we take the scale height a to be the same for Mn and Mn$^+$, the intensities in Table XLVIII are proportional to emissions per c.c., and if we further suppose that excitation is the same in the chromosphere and photosphere—which is supported by observations so far as they go—we can find the ratio of chromospheric to photospheric ionization from any pair of neutral and ionized lines in the table. Thus

$$\log\left(\frac{x}{1-x}\right)_{\mathrm{ch}} - \log\left(\frac{x}{1-x}\right)_{\mathrm{ph}}$$
$$= [B\log A]^+ - B\log A - \left\{\left[\log\frac{E}{\lambda^2 I_\lambda(0)}\right]^+ - \log\frac{E}{\lambda^2 I_\lambda(0)}\right\}.$$

This reduction is shown in the following table, the chromospheric ionization being taken at 670 km.

TABLE LII

Ratio of Chromospheric to Photospheric Ionization of Mn

Wave-length	Rowland number	$B\log A$	$\log E$	$\log \lambda^2 I_\lambda(0)$	$B\log A$ minus $\log\frac{E}{\lambda^2 I_\lambda(0)}$
Mn { 4,033	7	3·27	12·79	1·85	−7·67
4,031	9	3·55	12·89	1·85	−7·49
				Mean	−7·58
3,489	4	2·50	13·28	1·54	−9·24
3,483	5	2·99	13·31	1·54	−8·78
Mn$^+$ { 3,474	4	2·52	13·43	1·53	−9·38
3,461	4	2·54	13·50	1·52	−9·44
3,442	6	3·40	13·67	1·52	−8·75
				Mean	−9·12

$$\log(\mathrm{Mn}^+/\mathrm{Mn})_{\mathrm{ch}} - \log(\mathrm{Mn}^+/\mathrm{Mn})_{\mathrm{ph}} = 1\cdot 54$$

According to this calculation the chromospheric ionization of Mn is about thirty-five times the photospheric, in good agreement with the theoretical result for an electron temperature of 5,040°. The reduction is crude, but similar results may be obtained from the elements Cr and Fe. It seems unlikely that the logarithm of the ionization ratio is as high as 3·11, which is required by an electron temperature of 30,240°.

Miyamoto and Kawaguchi† have attempted to represent the calcium emission in the flash spectrum by a curve of growth. The emission as a function of height above the limb is characterized by two parameters,

† S. Miyamoto and I. Kawaguchi, *Pub. Ast. Soc. Japan*, **1**, 114 (1950).

a scale height α and a velocity v, the most probable velocity of the particles $(2RT/M)^{\frac{1}{2}}$. For Ca^+ they find $\alpha = 1\cdot6\times10^{-8}$ cm.$^{-1}$ and $v = 1\cdot5$ km./s., and the low value of v corresponds to $T \sim 6{,}000°$, in agreement with the argument from the ionization of Fe, Cr, and Mn. The method is not a powerful one for fixing the temperature of the flash spectrum, but it is of interest to note that an atmosphere with a constant scale height can show apparent variations in scale height due to the curve of growth.

The ionization of hydrogen, according to equation (1) is $\frac{1}{2}\{x/(1-x)\}_T$ for $T = \theta = 5{,}040°$, and is equal to $S_{12}/\alpha(T)$ for $T = 30{,}240°$. In the former case the numerical value is $2\cdot5\times10^7/N_e$, so that for all values of N_e greater than 10^9 hydrogen is almost entirely neutral. But if $T = 30{,}240°$ the value of $x/(1-x)$ is 554, and hydrogen is mainly ionized. There is an important difference in the optical depth in the Lyman continuum, which affects the number of quanta available to the ionosphere, discussed in Section 9.

5. The high chromosphere

5.1. *Conduction*

Chapman and Cowling have shown that the thermal conductivity of an electron gas in the absence of a magnetic field is

$$\lambda_1 = \frac{75}{16}\left(\frac{R}{\pi m}\right)^{\frac{1}{2}}\frac{R^3}{e^4}\,T^{\frac{5}{2}}/A_2(2), \qquad (2)$$

where $\qquad A_2(2) = 9\cdot2\ln(4RT/e^2N_e^{\frac{1}{3}})-2.$

In the chromosphere $A_2(2)$ is about 50. For a mixture of protons and electrons in equal numbers the conductivity is half the value given by equation (2), since the free path of the electrons is halved by the presence of the protons. Thus we write $\lambda_1 = \eta T^{\frac{5}{2}}$, where η has the numerical value 5×10^{-7}. In the presence of a magnetic field, the conductivity along the lines of force is unaltered but the conductivity normal to the lines of force is reduced, since the electrons are unable to travel in straight lines normal to the lines of magnetic force, but spiral around them. In the chromosphere the conductivity normal to the lines of force of the Sun's magnetic field is negligible, and the equation of conduction is

$$\epsilon = \eta\cos\theta\,T^{\frac{5}{2}}\frac{dT}{dh}, \qquad (3)$$

where ϵ is the quantity of heat conducted inwards per square cm. per second, h is measured vertically upwards, and θ is the angle between the magnetic field and the vertical.

If there were no heat lost by radiation ϵ would be constant from one height to another, otherwise ϵ will decrease with decreasing height (the source of heat being supposed located in the corona).

It is convenient to adopt a normalized height. On going inwards from the corona, at some height h_i above the photosphere the temperature (which drops exceedingly rapidly according to the equation of conduction) reaches the photospheric value, and the temperature drops no farther, as it is now maintained by photospheric radiation. We have now defined h_i: let h_c be the height of the bottom of the corona and let

$$y = \frac{h-h_i}{h_c-h_i}.$$

Then if ϵ_c is the quantity of heat conducted inwards at the bottom of the corona we set

$$\epsilon = \epsilon_c y^n,$$

where n has yet to be determined. Now the equation of conduction is

$$T^{\frac{5}{2}}\frac{dT}{dy} = \epsilon_c \frac{h_c-h_i}{\eta \cos \theta} y^n, \tag{4}$$

with the boundary conditions $T = T_i$ at $y = 0$, and $T = T_c$ at $y = 1$, the double boundary condition imposing a relation between the constants of the differential equation. If T_i/T_c is small compared with unity the solution of equation (4) is

$$(T/T_c)^{\frac{7}{2}} = y^{n+1}, \tag{5}$$

and the relation between the constants is

$$\epsilon_c = \tfrac{2}{7}(n+1)\frac{\eta \cos \theta}{h_c-h_i} T_c^{\frac{7}{2}}. \tag{6}$$

Taking the mean value of $\cos \theta$ to be $\tfrac{1}{3}$, and using $n = \tfrac{2}{5}$ as found in the next section, and with $h_c-h_i = 4 \times 10^9$ cm., $T_c = 10^6$, equation (6) gives
$$\epsilon = 1 \cdot 7 \times 10^4 \text{ erg cm.}^{-2} \text{ sec.}^{-1}$$

The distribution of pressure with height can readily be found (cf. Chapter IX) if the atmosphere is in hydrostatic equilibrium, or in more complicated cases if the laws governing the support of the atmosphere are understood. In the present case it is convenient to assume that

$$p_e = (p_e)_c y^s, \tag{7}$$

the suffix c indicating as usual the base of the corona. Then

$$N_e T = (N_e T)_c y^s,$$

and, from equation (5), $\quad N_e = (N_e)_c\, y^{s-\frac{2}{7}(n+1)}.$ (8)

In the next section we show that observations of radio-noise give one relation between the exponents s and n.

5.2. *Radio emission*

The absorption coefficient per centimetre of path (not per gramme of atmosphere) for radio waves of frequency f in a medium containing N_e electrons per c.c. is given† by

$$\kappa = \frac{4}{3}\left(\frac{2}{\pi}\right)^{\frac{1}{2}}\frac{e^6}{c(mR)^{\frac{3}{2}}}\frac{N_e^2}{f^2 T^{\frac{3}{2}}}\ln(3RT/2hf),$$ (9)

which approximates closely to

$$\kappa = aN_e^2\lambda^2 T^{-\frac{3}{2}},$$ (10)

where a has the numerical value $1\cdot4\times10^{-22}$.

We now calculate the optical depth of a medium in which κ has this value, T and N_e being given by equations (5) and (8). Now we have

$$\kappa = a\lambda^2(N_e^2\,T^{-\frac{3}{2}})_c\, y^{2s-(n+1)}.$$

Hence $\qquad \tau = \int \kappa\, dh$

$$= a\lambda^2(N_e^2\,T^{-\frac{3}{2}})_c(h_c - h_i)\int y^{2s-(n+1)}\, dy.$$ (11)

Reckoning optical depth from the base of the corona, the upper limit of the integral is unity and the lower limit y, so that

$$\tau = C\lambda^2\frac{1}{n-2s}\{y^{-(n-2s)}-1\},$$ (12)

where $\qquad C = a(h_c - h_i)(N_e^2\,T^{-\frac{3}{2}})_c.$

Now if $\qquad\qquad \beta = \dfrac{C}{n-2s},$ (13)

equation (12) may be written

$$y^{n-2s} = \frac{\beta}{\beta+\tau}.$$ (14)

But from equation (5) we have $T/T_c = y^{\frac{2}{7}(n+1)}$, so that

$$\frac{T}{T_c} = \left(\frac{\beta}{\beta+\tau}\right)^{\gamma},$$ (15)

where $\qquad\qquad \gamma = \dfrac{2}{7}\dfrac{n+1}{n-2s}.$ (16)

We now have an expression for T in terms of the optical depth and the two exponents n and s.

The thermal emission of radio frequency at the relevant temperatures is simply proportional to the temperature since the Planck function

† D. F. Martyn, *Proc. Roy. Soc.* A, **193**, 44 (1948), equation (16).

assumes this simple form when $RT \gg h\nu$ (Rayleigh–Jeans formula). Then, considering emission in the vertical direction, the *effective temperature of the centre of the disk* T_E is given by

$$T_E = \int_0^\infty T e^{-\tau}\, d\tau. \tag{17}$$

Using equation (15) we get

$$T_E = T_c \int_0^\infty \left(\frac{\beta}{\beta+\tau}\right)^\gamma e^{-\tau}\, d\tau = T_c \beta e^{\beta} E_\gamma(\beta). \tag{18}$$

In the special case $n = 2s$, we have $\tau = -C\lambda^2 \ln y$ and $e^{-\tau} = y^{C\lambda^2}$. We then have

$$T_E = T_c \frac{7C\lambda^2}{7C\lambda^2 + 2 + 4s}. \tag{19}$$

Woolley and Allen† have made a comparison between radio effective temperatures calculated in this way and a number of observations of quiet radio emission at various frequencies, and found that $\gamma = 1$ fitted the observations well. They supposed s to be small, and hence that $n = \frac{2}{5}$. Table LIII shows a model of the quiet chromosphere according

TABLE LIII

Model Chromosphere

Height (cm.) multiply by 10^8	Kinetic Temperature °K.	$\log N$	$\log N_e$	$\log N_p$	$\log N_{\mathrm{H}}$
0	5,040	15·9	12·1	11·2	15·9
1	5,040	13·8	10·6	10·6	13·8
2	5,040	12·7	10·0	10·0	12·7
3	5,040	12·0	9·7	9·7	12·0
4	5,040	11·5	9·4	9·4	11·5
5	5,040	11·0	9·2	9·2	11·0
6	6,300	10·7	10·4	10·4	10·4
6·001	14,500	10·2	10·2	10·2	9·4
6·01	36,000	9·8	9·8	9·8	5·7
6·1	91,000	9·4	9·4	9·4	3·9
7	230,000	9·0	9·0	9·0	2·6
8	300,000	8·9	8·9	8·9	2·3
10	400,000	8·8	8·8	8·8	2·1
14	526,000	8·7	8·7	8·7	1·8
19	645,000	8·6	8·6	8·6	1·6
26	760,000	8·5	8·5	8·5	1·4
33	850,000	8·5	8·5	8·5	1·3
39	930,000	8·4	8·4	8·4	1·2
46	1,000,000	8·4	8·4	8·4	1·1

N = number of atoms and ions per c.c., N_e = electrons per c.c., N_p = protons per c.c., N_{H} = neutral H atoms per c.c.

† R. v. d. R. Woolley and C. W. Allen, *M.N.* **110**, 358 (1950).

to Woolley and Allen. They used Baumbach's electron densities, so that the electron densities which are shown for the upper chromosphere should be reduced, according to van de Hulst. Otherwise the table fits most of the observations mentioned in this chapter, except that it gives no reason for the appearance of He and He⁺ lines in the flash

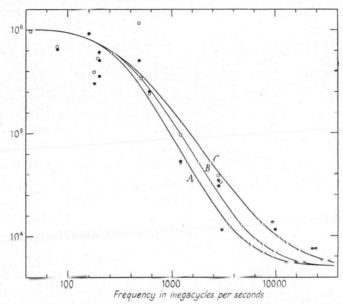

Fig. 44. Relation between radio frequency and the effective temperature at the centre of the solar disk. Plotted points are taken from solar radio-noise observations listed by J. L. Pawsey and D. E. Yabsley (*Aust. J. Sci. Res.* **2,** 198 (1948)) (filled-in circles) and from *Bulletin of Solar Activity* (1949) (circles). The original observations give the apparent temperature of the whole Sun. This has been reduced to the effective temperature at the centre of the disk by applying a correction for limb brightening and the extension of the corona. The curves shown are computed from equation (18) with $\gamma = 1$, $s = 0$, and $C = 3 \cdot 2 \times 10^{-5}$, curves A, B, and C corresponding to $n = 0$, $\frac{1}{6}$, and $\frac{2}{5}$ respectively. The higher frequencies show best agreement with the computed curve for $n = \frac{2}{5}$.

spectrum, and does not explain Redman's line widths. It is, of course, not only possible, but likely, that the chromosphere is so irregular that any particular line of sight in the flash spectrum samples a variety of hot and cold spots; and it may well be that this is the reason why the He lines requiring considerable excitation appear at the same height as neutral metallic ions such as Cr, Mn, Fe, etc.

6. The ultra-violet spectrum of the chromosphere

We have already discussed in Section 7.2 of Chapter XI the radiation from the corona, some of which (for example the Mg X lines) is at a high frequency, and is much more abundant than photospheric radiation at such frequencies. We may expect to find a considerable emission of high-frequency radiation from the chromosphere, if the increase in density compensates for the drop in temperature from coronal values, as turns out to be the case. This radiation has a close connexion with the *Ionosphere*. The ionosphere is the name given to the upper layers of the Earth's atmosphere (at heights above 100 km.) in which there is considerable ionization, the electron population exceeding 10^6 per c.c. Although the origin of these electrons is not yet (1950) established with certainty, it is supposed that they are liberated from terrestrial gases, probably from O_2 and O and perhaps N_2 and N, through photo-ionization by the solar radiation. Now the ionization potentials are as follows: O_2, 12·2 volts; O, 13·61 volts; N, 14·55 volts; and N_2, 15·58 volts: so that rather high-frequency radiation is concerned. There are at least three recognized regions in the ionosphere (called E, F_1, and F_2) and it is supposed that at least two different processes are involved. (For example E may be formed by the process $O_2+h\nu \rightarrow O_2^+ +e$ and F by $O+h\nu \rightarrow O^+ +e$.) Further the number of quanta falling on 1 sq. cm. of the Earth's atmosphere normal to the Sun per second can be established. From the work of Allen[†] we may suppose the following numbers of quanta required (at sunspot minimum):

E region   .   . 5×10^8 quanta

F_1 and F_2 regions   . 2×10^9 quanta each.

The emission averaged over all outward directions per sq. cm. per second from a black body at temperature T in the frequency range ν to $\nu+d\nu$ is $\pi B(\nu, T)\, d\nu$ so that the number of quanta emitted will be

$$\frac{2\pi\nu^2}{c^2}\frac{1}{e^{h\nu/RT}-1}\, d\nu.$$

Integrating from $\nu = \nu_0$ to $\nu = \infty$ with $e^{h\nu_0/RT} \gg 1$ we get for the number of quanta per sq. cm. per second with energy greater than $h\nu_0$

$$\frac{2\pi}{c^2}\frac{RT}{h}\nu_0^2 e^{-h\nu_0/RT}.$$

If these are emitted by a sphere of radius a, the solar radius, and received on 1 sq. cm. normal to the centre at a distance r, the mean radius of the earth's orbit, the number received is

$$\frac{2\pi}{c^2}\left(\frac{a}{r}\right)^2\frac{RT}{h}\nu_0^2 e^{-h\nu_0/RT}.$$

[†] C. W. Allen, *Terr. Mag.* **53**, 433 (1948).

With $a = 6\cdot95 \times 10^{10}$ cm. and $r = 1\cdot496 \times 10^{13}$ cm., we have the numbers of quanta received shown in Table LIV.

TABLE LIV

Logarithm of the Number of Quanta received per sq. cm. by the Earth's Atmosphere

Black-body temperature	Limiting energy in volts 12·2	13·61	14·55
5,000°	7·84	6·51	5·62
6,000°	9·97	8·88	8·15
7,000°	11·50	10·58	9·96

Accordingly, if the Sun radiated like a black body at 6,000° in the far ultra-violet, there would be enough quanta to form the ionosphere, but if at 5,000° there would be far too few.

As far as photospheric radiation is concerned there are far too few quanta. In the Lyman continuum, for example, the absorption coefficient, due to hydrogen atoms in the ground state, is about 6×10^6 times the mean coefficient due mainly to negative ions, and in the sense of Chapter IV we have $k_\lambda = 6 \times 10^6 \bar{k}$. The absorption is therefore so heavy that $\tau_\lambda = 1$ occurs at $\bar\tau = 1\cdot3 \times 10^{-7}$, where we have

$$T = T_0(1 + \tfrac{3}{2} \times 1\cdot3 \times 10^{-7})^{\frac{1}{4}},$$

which is very nearly T_0 itself, that is 4,830°. This is less than 5,000° and, as Table LIV shows, yields far too few quanta, the logarithm of the total number required being 9·65. The ionizing quanta must come from the chromosphere and corona.

While an investigation of the chromosphere itself may decide the precise spectral regions in which the quanta occur, and so assist the solution of the ionospheric problem of identifying the particular photoelectric processes in various regions, the ionospheric observational data is itself a check on chromospheric theory, by setting an upper limit to the number of quanta that the chromosphere (and corona) can emit outwards.

In the case of an ion confined to a relatively thin sheet, such as for example O^{++} or N^{++}, the emission can be estimated without taking self-absorption into account. The continuous emission is (cf. Chapter XI, Section 7.2)

$$\int \alpha N_e^2 p\, dv,$$

the integral extending over the volume of the chromosphere and corona. The fraction p will, of course, only have non-zero values in the sheet where the ions concerned lie. From Chapter XI, equation (24), the line emission is given by the volume integral of

$$pN_e^2\frac{12\pi e^4 f}{(2\pi mRT)^{\frac{1}{2}}}\frac{1}{h\nu}\{e^{-y}-yE_1(y)\},$$

where $y = h\nu/RT$. It is, of course, necessary to use Table LI, or an equivalent table, in order to decide the values of p in any particular case.

Where the atoms are not confined to a thin sheet the emission in a direction inclined at an angle θ to the vertical is

$$\int \alpha N_e^2 p\,.\,e^{-\tau_\lambda \sec\theta}\sec\theta\,dx,$$

in which τ_λ is the optical depth in the particular continuum. The important case is the Lyman continuum in which the optical depth is small so long as the hydrogen atoms are mainly ionized, but becomes appreciable within 100 km. if the atoms are mainly neutral. The number of quanta emitted in all directions from the entire region in which hydrogen is mainly ionized is, as before,

$$Q = \int p\alpha N_e^2\,dh.$$

We may put $\alpha = b/T^{\frac{1}{2}}$ (where $b = 1\cdot8\times10^{-11}$). Introducing the approximations used in Section 5.1 we find

$$Q = pb(h_c-h_i)\frac{N_c^2}{T_c^{\frac{1}{2}}}\int_{y_i}^{1} y^{2s-\frac{5}{7}(n+1)}\,dy,$$

the lower limit of the integral being the value of y appropriate to the division between neutral and ionized hydrogen. Neglecting s we find

$$Q = 7pb\frac{h_c-h_i}{2-5n}\frac{N_c^2}{T_c^{\frac{1}{2}}}\{1-y_i^{(2-5n)/7}\}.$$

When $n = \frac{2}{5}$ this form for Q becomes indeterminate but it readily follows that in this case

$$Q = pb(h_c-h_i)N_c^2\,T_c^{-\frac{1}{2}}\ln\left(\frac{1}{y_i}\right).$$

The value of y_i is found from $(T_i/T_c)^{\frac{5}{2}} = y_i^{n+1}$, or $y_i = (T_i/T_c)^{\frac{7}{2}}$ when $n = \frac{2}{5}$. Woolley and Allen calculate that hydrogen is half ionized when $T = 6,300°$. This gives $y_i = 8\cdot3\times10^{-4}$ and $\ln(1/y_i) = 7\cdot1$. It is clear that Q is not very sensitive to the value of T_i adopted. With $p = \frac{7}{8}$ and $h_c-h_i = 4\times10^9$ cm. we have

$$Q = 2\cdot8\times10^{13}\text{ quanta.}$$

These quanta are emitted in all directions of which one-half are outwards. The number received by 1 sq. cm. of the earth's atmosphere is

$$q = \tfrac{1}{2}(a/r)^2 Q = 3 \cdot 0 \times 10^8 \text{ quanta.}$$

To this must be added the emission from regions in which the atmosphere is opaque to the Lyman continuum. From Table LIV it is seen that the number of quanta is unimportant if the temperature is as low as 5,500° but that it is far greater than the observed number received by the ionosphere ($2 \cdot 5 \times 10^9$) if an effective temperature of the Lyman continuum is even as much as 7,000°. For this reason, it seems clear that ionospheric observation demands a temperature *much lower* than 30,000° in any chromospheric region where hydrogen is mainly neutral.

TABLE LV

The Number of Quanta available to the Ionosphere
(*Multiply by* 10^8)

Spectral range (volts)	12·2 to 13·6	13·6 to 14·6	14·6 to 15·6	15·6 to 50	50 to 100	> 100
Chromospheric line spectrum	0·3 N III 4 II	0·6 N IV	0·6 O III	14 many ions	5 × 10⁻⁵ Fe VII 5 × 10⁻³ Fe VIII 0·04 Fe IX	2·2 × 10⁻⁵ C VI 1·8 × 10⁻⁵ Si V
Chromospheric continuum	..	3 0	2·3	0·1	..	..
Corona	..	..	..	2 Mg X	..	..
Total	4	4	3	16	0·04	4 × 10⁻⁵

Table LV shows the number of quanta arriving per sq. cm. normal to the Sun's rays per second at the top of the Earth's atmosphere. It is taken from the work of Woolley and Allen, but the logarithm of the number of electrons per c.c. at all heights has been reduced by 0·3, to suit van de Hulst's electron densities rather than Baumbach's (as used by Woolley and Allen). A discussion of this point is given in Chapter XI, Section 4.2. The total number of quanta with energy greater than 12·2 volts received per sq. cm. per second by the ionosphere is $2 \cdot 7 \times 10^9$, according to this estimate. This agrees surprisingly well with Allen's estimate of $2 \cdot 5 \times 10^9$ for the number of quanta required.

XIII

STARS OTHER THAN THE SUN

1. Review of earlier chapters

THE theory developed in the earlier chapters of this book has been, for the most part, of a general nature, applicable as much to the atmosphere of a star as to that of the Sun; yet most of the comparisons with observation have been comparisons with the solar atmosphere. This is because the Sun has obvious advantages over the stars as a test object for a great deal of astrophysical theory; in it alone can centre to limb variations be observed easily, and in it alone can the structure of the outermost layers be plainly discerned. On the other hand the stellar atmospheres have certain advantages over the Sun, regarded as testing grounds for physical theory; they present, for example, a wide range of temperatures. It is the purpose of this chapter to give a sketch of the observational material which specially bears on the theoretical topics dealt with earlier in the book, and a very brief indication of special developments in the general theory which are specifically aimed at stars other than the Sun.

It is convenient to review at this point some of the results of Chapters I and IV. The first approximation to the temperature distribution in an atmosphere in radiative equilibrium is

$$T^4 = T_0^4(1+\tfrac{3}{2}\tau),$$

where $d\tau = -\bar{k}\rho\,dx$, and $\bar{k}$ is defined by

$$\bar{k} = \int k_\nu F_\nu\,d\nu \Big/ \int F_\nu\,d\nu.$$

Two approximations to $\bar{k}$ are

(i) Rosseland's mean: $\displaystyle \int \frac{1}{k_\nu}\frac{dB(\nu,T)}{dT}\,d\nu \Big/ \int \frac{dB(\nu,T)}{dT}\,d\nu,$

(ii) Chandrasekhar's mean: $\displaystyle \int k_\nu F_\nu^1\,d\nu \Big/ \int F_\nu^1\,d\nu,$

where F_ν^1 is the flux in a grey atmosphere with the same surface temperature as the star. The mean coefficient $\bar{k}$ can be calculated if the temperature and pressure (especially the electron pressure) are known, and if the sources of opacity are fully understood. It is perhaps unnecessary to add this latter qualification, though there may be some doubt here in the case of the coolest stars. Since $dp = -g\rho\,dx$, the pressure depends only on gravity and temperature. Accordingly, a stellar atmosphere is characterized by two independent variables, and only two, if we suppose that the chemical composition of all stellar atmospheres is the same.

If T_0 and g are given, and also the chemical composition of the atmosphere, T and p may be supposed known at all reasonably small optical depths, and also the associated quantities $\bar{k}$, k_ν, and the ionization of the various elements. The emergent intensity is given by

$$I_\nu(0, \theta) = \int_0^\infty e^{-\tau_\nu \sec\theta} B(\nu, T) \sec\theta \, d\tau_\nu, \tag{1}$$

and the surface flux $F_\nu(0) = \pi \mathfrak{F}_\nu(0)$ is obtained from this by

$$F_\nu(0) = \int_0^{\frac{1}{2}\pi} I_\nu(0, \theta) 2\pi \sin\theta \cos\theta \, d\theta. \tag{2}$$

Inserting the expression for $I_\nu(0, \theta)$ in equation (2) and carrying out the θ integration, we get

$$\mathfrak{F}_\nu(0) = 2 \int_0^\infty B(\nu, T) E_2(\tau_\nu) \, d\tau_\nu, \tag{3}$$

where $E_2(\tau_\nu) = \int_1^\infty e^{-\tau_\nu w} w^{-2} \, dw$. If $\bar{k}/k_\nu$ is independent of depth

$$T^4 = T_0^4[1 + \tfrac{3}{2}(\bar{k}/k_\nu)\tau_\nu].$$

The total flux per sq. cm. per sec. F is equal to $\int F_\nu \, d\nu$, and the total emission from the star L, is given by

$$L = 4\pi R^2 F, \tag{4}$$

where R is the radius of the star. The effective temperature of the star T_e is defined by

$$F = \pi \mathfrak{F} = \sigma T_e^4, \tag{5}$$

where σ is Stefan's constant ($5 \cdot 670 \times 10^{-5}$ ergs cm.$^{-2}$ sec.$^{-1}$ deg.$^{-4}$). Thus T_e is the temperature of a black body which would radiate the same flux as the star itself. We have seen in Chapter I that, in the special case where k_ν is independent of ν, $T_e = 2^{\frac{1}{4}} T_0$. This is, however, not true in general (see Section 3.2 of this chapter).

It is not true in general that the star as a whole radiates like a black body at temperature T_e, that is to say F_ν is not equal to $\pi B(\nu, T_e)$. It would scarcely be necessary to caution the reader who has followed the sequence of equations just given against assuming this simple result, if it were not for the fact that practically all astrophysical literature written before about 1930 admits it, at all events as a working approximation. The error can be considerable.

2. The observed characteristics of stars

2.1. *Spectral types*

An important method of classifying stars depends upon the strength of lines in their spectra. The spectral classes are ordered in the sequence

$$O,\ B,\ A,\ F,\ G,\ K,\ M,$$

being, generally speaking, a sequence of descending T_0. Types R, N, and S, which are later than M, but which do not form a regular sequence, are also recognized. (The departure from alphabetical sequence became necessary when it was understood that the original alphabetical sequence did not follow surface temperatures as it was supposed to do.) The spectral classes have been further subdivided by decimals, that is classes within type A such as $A0$, $A2$, $A3$, $A5$ are recognized (but $A4$, $A6$, $A8$, and $A9$ are omitted), and empirical criteria have been found which permit classification of spectra of stars of the same spectral type according to the star's surface gravity. To see that this is possible, suppose that spectral type was judged by the degree of ionization of *one* element, then all stars are judged to have the same spectral type in which ionization of this element has a certain value. Since

$$\log\{x/(1-x)\} = -5040\chi/T + \tfrac{5}{2}\log T - 0\cdot48 + \log 2\varpi - \log p_e,$$

a certain family of values of T and p_e define the spectral type. The separation of this family into particular pairs of values could clearly be done by considering the ionization of another element with a very different value of χ. In this way we have a means of recognizing a distinction between giants (large radius and small gravity) and dwarfs (small radius and high gravity), written, for example, $gK0$ and $dK0$ But as many as five luminosity (that is gravity) classes are recognized in the classification of Morgan, Keenan, and Kellman. The connexion between surface gravity and luminosity cannot be fully understood without reference either to the theory of the internal constitution of the stars, or to the facts of stellar statistics, into neither of which it is our purpose to enter. To understand spectral classification it is necessary to remark that the theory demands what the observations show, relations between mass, radius, and luminosity. Stars with high luminosity are referred to as giants, and those of low luminosity as dwarfs. It is found that the giants have much smaller surface gravities than the dwarfs.

The main development of the system of spectral classification can be found in the following references:

Harvard System, or Henry Draper System. This system is described in the first volume of the Henry Draper Catalogue, which is volume 91 of the *Annals of Harvard College Observatory* (1918). The classification is one-dimensional, having been devised long before absolute magnitude effects were recognized by Adams and Kohlschütter.† This is by far the most familiar system of classification in astronomical use. Spectral types are designated by a capital letter and a number between 0 to 9 inclusive.

The Mount Wilson System is described in the *Astrophysical Journal*, vol. 87, p. 187 (1935). Spectra are again designated by a capital letter and a number, but some qualifying letters in ordinary type are sometimes added. In the catalogue of results, the absolute visual magnitude is shown separately for each star. The process used is described by Dr. Adams and his collaborators as follows:

> From a group of spectrograms of the same spectral type and differing absolute magnitudes (determined from other sources), spectral lines are chosen which change in intensity with the absolute magnitude: the intensity of each variable line relative to a neighbouring line of nearly fixed intensity is measured in steps; then empirical calibrating curves are drawn connecting the intensity differences with absolute magnitude. The process is repeated in turn for each spectral type.

Although the spectral-type criteria in the Mount Wilson System are the same as the Harvard criteria, the types assigned to particular stars often differ (Mount Wilson classes are mostly based on slit spectra of moderate dispersion, and Harvard classes on slitless spectra—in the case of the HD catalogue, low dispersion slitless spectra).

The Yerkes System is described by Morgan, Keenan, and Kellman in *An Atlas of Stellar Spectra*, University of Chicago Press (1943). These authors adopt essentially the Harvard and Mount Wilson classification, but include other work, especially work on *B* stars. They make, however, an explicit effort to rationalize the steps by making them correspond to equal intervals of gradient (Section 2.3). The luminosity classes are determined in the following manner: (1) an approximate spectral type is determined; (2) the luminosity class is determined; (3) by comparison with stars of similar luminosity, an accurate spectral type is found. The *Atlas* recognizes five luminosity classes, from I, super-giants, to V, 'main sequence' stars. Since the suitability of the various criteria depends on the dispersion used, the actual criteria are not specified in a hard and fast manner. Instead, particular stars are named as examples

† W. S. Adams and A. Kohlschütter, *Ap. J.* **40**, 385 (1914).

of the classes and types. For example, the standard stars of type $B0$ are the following:

γ Cas $B0$ IV	κ Ori $B0$ II
φ^1 Ori $B0$ III	δ Sco $B0$ IV
ϵ Ori $B0$ I	τ Sco $B0$ V

These stars are all $B0$ stars in the HD System, but some differences occur. For example, 139 Tau is $B0{\cdot}5$ II in the Yerkes System and $B2$ in HD.

2.2. *Stellar magnitudes*

The brightness of the stars is expressed in a magnitude scale, which, though very ancient, is very convenient. Hipparchus divided the naked-eye stars into six magnitudes, the first being the brightest and the sixth the faintest visible to the naked eye. It was found by Sir John Herschel that the stars of the first magnitude were about 100 times as bright as those of the sixth, and in about 1850 Pogson proposed that the magnitude scale should be such that a star of magnitude n should emit exactly 100 times as much light as a star of magnitude $n+5$. Accordingly, if two stars have light intensities l_1 and l_2, their magnitudes m_1 and m_2 are related by

$$m_1 - m_2 = -2{\cdot}5\log(l_1/l_2). \tag{6}$$

Magnitudes as observed are called apparent. When corrected for the distance of the star, that is to say referred to the magnitude which the star would show if it were removed to a standard distance, which is chosen as 10 parsecs, they are called *absolute* magnitudes. The absolute magnitude M, the apparent magnitude m, and the parallax p (in seconds of arc) are related by

$$M = m + 5 + 5\log p. \tag{7}$$

Magnitudes were originally judged by the naked eye. *Visual* magnitudes are judged in this way by a hypothetical standard observer. (As a refinement he should judge the magnitude at a standard zenith distance, to take account of differential atmospheric absorption.) *Photographic* magnitudes are magnitudes judged by a photographic plate which has not been sensitized to red light. There is, of course, a considerable difference between photographic and visual magnitude systems; the photographic magnitude of a star minus the visual magnitude is called the *colour index*, which is conventionally taken to be zero for stars of type $A0$, and amounts to about $-0^{\mathrm{m}}{\cdot}3$ for the bluest stars and to $+2^{\mathrm{m}}{\cdot}0$ for the reddest.

Magnitudes observed with panchromatic photographic plates through colour filters which cut out the blue and violet light (and therefore, to some extent, imitate the human eye) are called *photovisual* magnitudes.

If

$i(\lambda)\,d\lambda$ is the light in wave-lengths between λ and $\lambda+d\lambda$ received per second on unit area normal to the direction of the star, just outside the Earth's atmosphere;

$a(\lambda)$ the fraction of the light transmitted by the Earth's atmosphere;

$t(\lambda)$ the fraction of the light transmitted by the telescope (equal to unity in the case of naked-eye observations);

$s(\lambda)$ the response of the observing mechanism, including filters (if any);

then the measured intensity is

$$I = \int i(\lambda)a(\lambda)t(\lambda)s(\lambda)\,d\lambda. \tag{8}$$

All the factors except $i(\lambda)$ are irrelevant, and it is desirable to set up a system of monochromatic magnitudes which eliminates all other factors. This, however, has not yet been done on a large scale (1950). The most important system of magnitudes remains the *International Photovisual Scale*, IPv, which is defined by a table published in the *Transactions of the International Astronomical Union*, vol. 1 (1922). This table shows the photovisual magnitudes of a sequence of stars in the neighbourhood of the North Pole from $+2^{\mathrm{m}}{\cdot}08$ to $+17^{\mathrm{m}}{\cdot}47$, and also photographic magnitudes of the same stars with an additional list which extends the photographic scale to $+20^{\mathrm{m}}{\cdot}10$. The zero points of these scales are conventional.

The *effective wave-length* λ_e of a system of measuring magnitudes is defined as follows. If we write $\sigma(\lambda)$ for the product $a(\lambda)t(\lambda)s(\lambda)$, the effective wave-length λ_e is defined by

$$\lambda_e = \frac{\int \lambda i(\lambda)\sigma(\lambda)\,d\lambda}{\int i(\lambda)\sigma(\lambda)\,d\lambda}. \tag{9}$$

Results of some value can be obtained by assuming that the energy distribution in a stellar spectrum is similar to that of a black body whose temperature is called the colour temperature of the star. This is found empirically to be a good approximation, at all events in early type stars (B to G) and in the range of wave-lengths in the photovisual system.

If T_c is the colour temperature of a star, the *isophotal wave-length* λ_i is defined by

$$B(\lambda_i, T_c) = \text{const.} \times \int B(\lambda, T_c)\sigma(\lambda)\, d\lambda. \tag{10}$$

Defined in this way, there will be a family of values of λ_i for every choice of the constant. The constant was chosen by Seares and Miss Joyner as follows: for a wave-length λ_E there is some temperature T_0 for which $B(\lambda, T_0)$ is a maximum for variations in λ. In symbols $\lambda_{\max} = \lambda_E$ when $T = T_0$. (If λ_E is in microns, $T_0 = 2{,}886/\lambda_E$.) Then the constant is such that

$$B(\lambda_i, T_c) = B(\lambda_E, T_0) \frac{\int B(\lambda, T_c)\sigma(\lambda)\, d\lambda}{\int B(\lambda, T_0)\sigma(\lambda)\, d\lambda}, \tag{11}$$

a definition which, of course, makes λ_i equal to λ_E for $T_c = T_0$. Now if the star radiates like a grey body at T_c, we can establish a relation between the monochromatic magnitude at the effective wave-length λ_E of the system (or indeed at any other wave-length) and the IPv of the star with the help of the isophotal wave-lengths λ_i. In practice λ_E is chosen to make T_0 equal to the colour temperature of the $A0$ stars.

Suppose that over the relevant region of the spectrum the stars radiate like grey bodies, or

$$F_\lambda(0) = g \times \pi B(\lambda, T_c),$$

where g is a factor proper to each star but independent of λ, and T_c is the colour temperature. If d is the apparent diameter of the star in radians, then the radiation received per sq. cm. per sec. at the Earth is

$$i(\lambda) = \tfrac{1}{4}gd^2 \times \pi B(\lambda, T_c). \tag{12}$$

Monochromatic magnitudes are defined by

$$m_\lambda - m_\lambda' = -2 \cdot 5\{\log i(\lambda) - \log i'(\lambda)\}, \tag{13}$$

but the International photovisual magnitudes are defined by

$$m_{\mathrm{pv}} - m_{\mathrm{pv}}' = -2 \cdot 5\left\{\log \int i(\lambda)\sigma(\lambda)\, d\lambda - \log \int i'(\lambda)\sigma(\lambda)\, d\lambda\right\}. \tag{14}$$

If we make use of the isophotal wave-length λ_i, we have from (11)

$$\int B(\lambda, T_c)\sigma(\lambda)\, d\lambda = kB(\lambda_i, T_c),$$

where $k = \int B(\lambda, T_0)\sigma(\lambda)\, d\lambda / B(\lambda_E, T_0)$. Then

$$\int i(\lambda)\sigma(\lambda)\, d\lambda = \tfrac{1}{4}gd^2 \times \pi k B(\lambda_i, T_c). \tag{15}$$

If λ_i is not very different from λ_E,

$$B(\lambda_i, T_c) = B(\lambda_0, T_c) + (\lambda_i - \lambda_E)\left\{\frac{\partial B(\lambda, T_c)}{\partial \lambda}\right\}_{\lambda_E}. \tag{16}$$

From equations (13) and (14) we now obtain

$$m_{\lambda_E}-m'_{\lambda_E} = m_{\text{pv}}-m'_{\text{pv}}+2\cdot5(\lambda_i-\lambda_E)\frac{\partial}{\partial\lambda}\log B(\lambda, T_c)$$

$$-2\cdot5(\lambda'_i-\lambda_E)\frac{\partial}{\partial\lambda}\log B(\lambda, T'_c). \quad (17)$$

Equation (17) enables us to convert magnitude differences from the International system to a monochromatic system if the isophotal wave-lengths λ_i are known.

Effective wave-lengths and isophotal wave-lengths of the International Photovisual System have been determined by Seares and Miss Joyner.[†] Their results are shown in Table LVI.

TABLE LVI

Effective Wave-lengths and Isophotal Wave-lengths of the International Photovisual System

Colour temperature $T_c\,°K.$	Effective wave-length $\lambda_e\,(A)$	Isophotal wave-length $\lambda_i\,(A)$	Colour temperature $T_c\,°K.$	Effective wave-length $\lambda_e\,(A)$	Isophotal wave-length $\lambda_i\,(A)$
30,000	5,415	..	7,000	5,437	5,435
22,000	5,418	5,424	6,000	5,442	5,439
17,000	5,420	5,426	5,000	5,449	5,443
13,700	5,423	5,427	4,000	5,460	5,445
11,000	5,426	5,428	3,500	5,468	5,448
9,000	5,430	5,431	3,000	5,478	5,454

As has already been said, all magnitude systems are difference systems, and a conventional zero has been supplied. To determine the actual flux for a given stellar magnitude, appeal must be made to some comparison between a star of known magnitude and a laboratory source of light, or between a star and the Sun.

According to Minnaert's revision of Abbot's values[‡] the actual solar flux $\pi\mathfrak{F}_\lambda(0)$ at $\lambda5,430$ A is $\pi\times2\cdot77\times10^8$ ergs per sq. cm. per sec. per hundred angstroms. The total output per second is obtained by multiplying this figure by $4\pi R^2$, where $R = 6\cdot960\times10^{10}$ cm. Minnaert's figure should be diminished by $2\cdot4$ per cent. because Abbot's scale of pyrometry was too high (see Chapter I, Section 4.2). Applying this correction we get for the total output between $\lambda5,480$ A and $\lambda5,380$ A

$$5\cdot17\times10^{31} \text{ ergs sec.}^{-1}$$

[†] F. H. Seares and M. C. Joyner, *Ap. J.* **98**, 302 (1943).
[‡] M. Minnaert, *B.A.N.* **2**, 75 (1924).

T

The amount received per sq. cm. at a distance from the Sun equal to the mean radius of the Earth's orbit, or $1 \cdot 496 \times 10^{13}$ cm., is

$$1 \cdot 838 \times 10^4 \text{ ergs cm.}^{-2} \text{ sec.}^{-1}$$

The Sun's International photovisual magnitude is $-26 \cdot 84$, according to Kuiper.[†] It therefore delivers to the Earth $10^{10 \cdot 736}$ times as much light as a star of zero magnitude—in *every* wave-length, if the star has exactly the same spectral type as the Sun. Hence the amount received per sq. cm. per sec. per 100 A at $\lambda 5,430$ A from a star of type $dG0$ and magnitude $0^\text{m} \cdot 00$ IPv is $3 \cdot 37 \times 10^{-7}$ ergs,

and the logarithm of the energy received from any star of this spectral type is $\bar{7} \cdot 53 - 0 \cdot 4 m_\text{pv}.$ (18)

In the case of other spectral types, equation (17) must be used. If λ_i, T_c refer to the star considered and λ_i', T_c' to type dwarf $G0$, the logarithm of the energy received is

$$\bar{7} \cdot 53 - 0 \cdot 4 m_\text{pv} - (\lambda_i - \lambda_E) \frac{\partial}{\partial \lambda} \log B(\lambda, T_c) +$$

$$+ (\lambda_i' - \lambda_E) \frac{\partial}{\partial \lambda} \log B(\lambda, T_c'),$$ (19)

where $\lambda_E = 5,430$ A. The correction term

$$2 \cdot 5 (\lambda_i - \lambda_E) \frac{\partial}{\partial \lambda} \log B(\lambda, T_c)$$

is as follows:

$T_c \,^\circ K.$	*Correction*
22,000	$+0^\text{m} \cdot 0039$
14,300	$+0^\text{m} \cdot 0017$
6,750	$-0^\text{m} \cdot 0012$
3,000	$+0^\text{m} \cdot 0182$

This correction is inappreciable, except possibly in the case of the coolest stars, as the International magnitudes are not known within $0^\text{m} \cdot 01$. Hence for all practical purposes formula (18) is sufficient.

2.3. *Stellar colours*

The difference between the International Visual Magnitude and the International Photographic Magnitude is the International Colour Index. Both scales have arbitrary zeros: these were adjusted to make the average of the colour indices of $A0$ stars in the North Polar Sequence vanish. The colour index of a star is closely related to the spectral type

† G. Kuiper, *Ap. J.* **88**, 429 (1938).

of the star, unless it is seen through absorbing matter in interstellar space, in which case the star appears too red (that is, space reddened). According to Seares and Miss Joyner the stars in the North Polar Sequence are actually reddened, so that the colour indices of stars seen without appreciable reddening are all slightly more negative than the indices of stars of the same spectral type in the North Polar Sequence. Table LVII, which is taken from the work of Seares and Miss Joyner, shows the colour indices of unreddened stars listed according to their HD spectral type.

TABLE LVII

Colour Indices of Unreddened Stars

Spectral type	Colour index	Spectral type	Colour index	
			Giants	Dwarfs
B5	−0·39	G0	+0·60	+0·42
A0	−0·15	G5	+0·78	+0·64
A5	0·00	K0	+1·06	+0·89
F0	+0·12	K2	+1·25	+1·01
F5	+0·26	K5	+1·45	..

A much more accurate measurement of the colour of a star is given by the gradient, ϕ_λ, defined by

$$\phi_\lambda = -\frac{d}{d(1/\lambda)}\ln\{\lambda^5 i(\lambda)\}. \tag{20}$$

In the special case of a grey body, that is if $i(\lambda) = \text{const.} \times B(\lambda, T_c)$, we have

$$\phi_\lambda = \frac{c_2}{T}\Big/(1 - e^{-c_2/\lambda T}), \tag{21}$$

where $c_2 = hc/R$ and has the value 14,387 when λ is in microns and T in degrees K.

Gradients are determined in practice by measuring magnitude differences between stars at two or more wave-lengths. If two stars have monochromatic magnitudes m_r and m_r' at some red wave-length λ_r, and m_b, m_b' at λ_b,

$$m_r - m_r' = -2\cdot5\log\frac{i(\lambda_r)}{i'(\lambda_r)} = -1\cdot086\ln\frac{i(\lambda_r)}{i'(\lambda_r)},$$

with a similar expression for $m_b - m_b'$. The difference between the gradients is therefore given by

$$\phi - \phi' = \frac{m_b - m_b' - (m_r - m_r')}{1\cdot086(\lambda_b^{-1} - \lambda_r^{-1})}, \tag{22}$$

the gradient referring to the mean wave-length chosen. The gradient is usually expressed on such a scale that λ is in microns (1 micron equals 10,000 A).

Gradients in the visible spectrum have been determined at the Royal Observatory, Greenwich,[†] relative to terrestrial sources of known colour temperature. An acetylene lamp was used at first, and replaced in later measurements by a tungsten filament lamp. In the comparison between stars and lamp, wave-lengths between 6,486 A and 4,429 A were used, the mean wave-length being 5,000 A. Over this range of wave-lengths no sensible departures from black-body distributions were observed: that is, it was possible to represent every $i(\lambda)$ for a star by some constant multiplied by $B(\lambda, T_c)$, T_c being the colour temperature of the star.

The Greenwich observers found a considerable dispersion in the gradient of B-type stars: this is no doubt due to space reddening for the most part (it is possible that there is an intrinsic reddening of B-type spectra). The dispersion in A-type stars is much smaller, and for sixteen stars of Harvard type $A0$, the mean gradient is

$$\phi_0 + 0 \cdot 00 \pm 0 \cdot 02,$$

where ϕ_0 is the mean gradient of the Greenwich standard stars, which must be determined by comparison with a laboratory source. Greaves[‡] gives $\phi_0 = 1 \cdot 1 \pm 0 \cdot 1$ (for the mean wave-length 5,000 A) from which the mean colour temperature of the $A0$ stars is $15,600°$ K.

The Greenwich system has been extended to the southern stars by Gascoigne.[§] Table LVIII shows the gradients of unreddened stars listed according to their spectral type (Yerkes), and is taken from Gascoigne's work. Any revision of the Greenwich zero will, of course, affect these results.

An important series of observations has been conducted by Barbier and Chalonge and their collaborators.[‖] The spectra were observed from $\lambda4,500$ A to $\lambda3,150$ A, and the gradients of the stars were compared with that of a hydrogen discharge tube. It was found that the gradient ϕ_1 between $\lambda4,500$ A and $\lambda3,700$ A (mean wave-length 4,250 A) differs from ϕ_2, the gradient between $\lambda3,700$ A and $\lambda3,150$ A (mean wave-length

† Royal Observatory, Greenwich, *Observations of Colour Temperatures of Stars, 1926–1932.*

‡ W. M. H. Greaves, *M.N.* **108**, 240 (1948).

§ S. C. B. Gascoigne, ibid. **110**, 15 (1950).

‖ D. Barbier and D. Chalonge, *Ann. d'Ap.* **4**, 30 (1941).

TABLE LVIII

Gradients and Colour Temperatures of Unreddened Stars

Spectral type	Gradient	Colour temperature
B0	0·73	40,000° K.
B5	0·88	22,600
A0	1·10	15,600
A5	1·40	11,000
F0	1·66	9,000
F5	1·90	7,700
dG0	2·23	6,500

It should be noted that when the temperature is much greater than 50,000° K., the gradient is insensitive to T_c; for when T_c is sufficiently large (21) reduces to

$$\phi_\lambda = \lambda + \tfrac{1}{2}c_2/T + \dots,$$

and when $T = 50,000°$ K., $\tfrac{1}{2}c_2/T = 0\cdot143$. Accordingly, doubling T only changes ϕ by $0\cdot07$.

3,500 A), and there is usually a discontinuity at $\lambda 3,700$ A, which is approximately the wave-length at the head of the Balmer series of hydrogen. The discontinuity is measured by D, which is defined by

$$D = \log(I_1/I_2),$$

where I_1 is the intensity at $\lambda 3,700$ A obtained by producing the curve of intensity from longer wave-lengths, and I_2 by producing the curve from shorter wave-lengths. The quantity D as defined above is *not* a magnitude difference. D is almost always positive (an exception being γ Cas, a star which has a variable value of D and which, at times, shows bright hydrogen emission lines), but $\phi_1 - \phi_2$ may have either sign. When the stars are grouped according to spectral type, both D and $\phi_1 - \phi_2$ have their maximum at type $A0$, where the mean value of D is $0\cdot47$, and happens to be numerically equal to the mean value of $\phi_1 - \phi_2$. Fig. 45 shows the variation with HD spectral type of D and $\phi_1 - \phi_2$ found by Barbier and Chalonge for normal stars.

2.4. *Effective temperatures*

Although the effective temperature T_e is a simple theoretical concept, since it is defined by equations (4) and (5) of this chapter which give

$$L = 4\pi R^2 \sigma T_e^4,$$

it cannot be determined very satisfactorily from observation. This is partly because the radius R of the star cannot be observed except in very special cases, and partly because the radiation from the star in

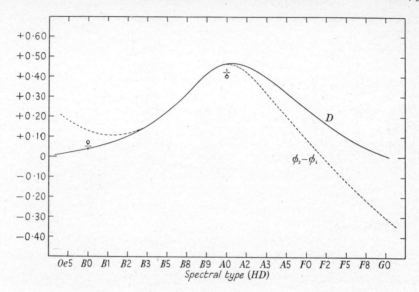

FIG. 45. Variation of D and $\Delta\phi$ with spectral type. The full curve gives the mean magnitude D of the Balmer discontinuity, and the dashed curve the difference $\Delta\phi = \phi_2 - \phi_1$ between the gradient at $\lambda 3,700$ A on either side of the discontinuity for normal stars according to Barbier and Chalonge (*Ann. d'Ap.* **4**, 30 (1941)). The points for individual stars are scattered, but D is hardly ever negative. On the other hand $\phi_2 - \phi_1$ is frequently negative even for spectral types for which the mean difference is positive. The two sets of points plotted in the figure indicate the values of D (circles) and $\phi_{3,500} - \phi_{4,250}$ for Pannekoek's flux model $A0$ star (Section 3.21) and Miss Underhill's model $B0$ star (Section 3.22).

quite extensive spectral regions cannot be observed (on account of absorption in the Earth's atmosphere) so that the total radiation L has to be inferred from radiation in the accessible spectral regions. The magnitude which corresponds to L is called the bolometric magnitude.

Corrections from visual to bolometric magnitude are given by Hertzsprung[†] and by Eddington,[‡] both of whom assumed that the stars radiated like black bodies at a temperature T_e. These have been discussed by Kuiper,[§] who gave, in addition to the theoretical values, empirical bolometric corrections based on a survey of the observational material available.

If satisfactory bolometric corrections exist, we can construct the apparent bolometric magnitude m_{bol} of any star from its observed magnitude and spectral type (the latter being required for the correction)

† E. Hertzsprung, *Zs. f. Wissenschaftliche Photographie*, **4**, 49 (1906); **30**, 173 (1929).
‡ A. S. Eddington, *Internal Constitution of the Stars* (Cambridge), p. 138.
§ G. Kuiper, *Ap. J.* **88**, 429 (1938).

and then, if the parallax p is known, we can compute the absolute bolometric magnitude M_{bol} from

$$M_{bol} = m_{bol} + 5 + 5 \log p.$$

The conversion of M_{bol} to L is best effected through the Sun's absolute bolometric magnitude $M_\odot$, which is $+4^m \cdot 62$ according to a critical discussion by Kuiper. We then have

$$\log(L/L_\odot) = 0 \cdot 4(4 \cdot 62 - M_{bol}). \tag{23}$$

If the stellar radius is expressed in terms of the solar radius as unit, the stellar effective temperature T_e can be found from the effective temperature of the Sun $T_\odot$ by the relation

$$\left(\frac{T_e}{T_\odot}\right)^4 = \frac{1}{R^2}\frac{L}{L_\odot}. \tag{24}$$

We now consider special cases where the radius R can be determined. A few stars are so large and so close that an apparent angular diameter can be detected with an interferometer. If the apparent angular diameter of a star is d and the parallax p (both in seconds of arc), then the radius in astronomical units is $\frac{1}{2}d/p$, and the radius R in units of the Sun's radius is $107 \cdot 7 \times d/p$. Accordingly R^2 is proportional to d^2/p^2. But the absolute luminosity L is related to the apparent luminosity l by $L = l(0'' \cdot 1/p)^2$, so that when the quotient L/R^2 is found from the observed quantities, the parallax drops out. This gives

$$4 \log T_e - 4 \log T_\odot = -4 \cdot 217 - 2 \log d - 0 \cdot 4 m_{bol}. \tag{25}$$

TABLE LIX

Effective Temperatures of Stars from Interferometer Measures

Star	d'' (obs.)	m_{bol}	$\log T_e$	$T_e \,°K.$	Spectrum
α Boo	$0'' \cdot 020$	$-0 \cdot 80$	$3 \cdot 63$	4,280	$K2$ pec.
α Tau	$0 \cdot 020$	$-0 \cdot 44$	$3 \cdot 60$	3,960	$K5$ III
α Ori	$0 \cdot 041$	$-1 \cdot 59$	$3 \cdot 55$	3,590	$M2$ I b
β Peg	$0 \cdot 021$	$+0 \cdot 37$	$3 \cdot 51$	3,200	$M2$ II–III
o Cet	$0 \cdot 047$	$-0 \cdot 14$	$3 \cdot 38$	2,400	$(gM\ 6)$
α Sco	$0 \cdot 040$	$-1 \cdot 24$	$3 \cdot 53$	3,360	$M1$ I b

Table LIX shows effective temperatures of six stars whose diameters have been measured by Pease with the 20-ft. interferometer at Mount Wilson. The bolometric magnitude is taken from Kuiper. In the case of o Ceti, which is a variable (Mira), the result refers to the maximum light, and is therefore only approximate.

The radius can also be measured if the star is an eclipsing binary with a good spectroscopic orbit. The spectroscopic measures give the velocity in kilometres per second and the period, from which can be deduced $a \sin i$, the semi-axis major of the relative orbit multiplied by the sine of the inclination of the orbit. If the stars pass one in front of the other so that an eclipse is seen, the light curve can be used to find this inclination, and also the radii of the two stars in units of the semi-axis of the orbit. The radii may therefore be found in kilometres. If a reliable parallax has been found for the system, the apparent magnitudes can be converted to absolute magnitudes, and the effective temperatures deduced from the equation

$$\log T_e = 3\cdot759 - \tfrac{1}{2}\log(R/R_\odot) + 0\cdot1(4\cdot62 - M_{\mathrm{bol}}).$$

Table LX gives the results of some reductions by means of this formula.

TABLE LX

Effective Temperatures of Eclipsing Binaries

Star	Type	m_{pv}	Parallax	M_{pv}	B.C.	M_{bol}	$R/R_\odot$	$T_e\,°K.$	Ref.
SZ Cas A ⎱	O9 or	..	..	−3·84	−3·12	−6·96	7·5	30,100	1
SZ Cas B ⎰	B0	..	..	−1·84	−2·80	−4·64	3·3	26,700	1
μ_1 Sco A ⎱	B3	3·69	0″·0074	−1·96	−1·66	−3·62	5·26	16,700	2
μ_1 Sco B ⎰		3·98	,,	−1·67	−1·66	−3·33	5·86	14,800	2
β Per	B8 V	2·22	0″·032	−0·26	−1·04	−1·30	2·53	14,000	2
α Cr B A	A0 V	2·29	0″·041	+0·37	−0·72	−0·35	2·28	11,900	3
β Aur A ⎱	A2 IV	2·76	0″·037	+0·60	−0·53	+0·07	2·49	10,400	2
β Aur B ⎰		2·89	,,	+0·73	−0·53	+0·20	2·28	10,500	2
YY Gem A ⎱	K6+	9·57	0″·073	+8·89	−1·32	+7·57	0·66	3,580	2
YY Gem B ⎰		9·81	,,	+9·13	−1·32	+7·81	0·60	3,560	2

Spectral types are Yerkes, where available. Bolometric corrections are from Kuiper. Other data are from (1) Wesselink, *Ann. Leiden*, **17**, iii (1950); (2) N. Milford, *Ann. d'Ap.* **3**, 225 (1950); (3) J. Stebbins, *Washburn Publ.* **15**, 56 (1928). The absolute magnitude of *SZ* Cas is known because it is a member of a cluster (NGC 1502).

There are difficulties in the computation of effective temperatures of eclipsing binaries connected with lack of knowledge of the darkening of the limb of the star, and with tidal distortion, both of which introduce uncertainty into R; furthermore, not many eclipsing systems have good parallaxes. But the results of these reductions give our *only* values of the effective temperatures of early type stars.

3. Theoretical work on stellar spectra

3.1. *Maximum intensities of lines in the spectral sequence*

Consider a series of atmospheres, all of the same composition and all at the same electron pressure, that is both constant from top to bottom of each atmosphere, and also constant from one atmosphere to the next, but at different temperatures. As we go from the coldest atmosphere towards increasingly hotter atmospheres the atoms of a particular element, say iron, will at first be almost entirely in the neutral state; but, as the temperature increases, the proportion of singly ionized to neutral atoms will increase. At still higher temperatures the number of doubly ionized atoms will exceed that of the singly ionized atoms, and so on; so that each stage of ionization, except the neutral and completely stripped stages, must show a maximum concentration somewhere in the temperature series.

We can give mathematical expression to this idea by considering a hypothetical element with only three possible states—neutral, singly ionized, and doubly ionized. Consider thermodynamic equilibrium at temperature T and electron pressure p_e, and let x and x' be the fraction of atoms in the singly and doubly ionized states respectively (so that $1-x-x'$ is the fraction in the neutral state). Then writing C for $2(2\pi m R)^{\frac{3}{2}} R h^{-3}$, we have from Saha's equation

$$\frac{xp_e}{1-x-x'} = \frac{\varpi C}{b(T)} T^{\frac{5}{2}} e^{-I/RT},$$

$$\frac{x'p_e}{x} = \frac{\varpi' C}{b'(T)} T^{\frac{5}{2}} e^{-I'/RT},$$

the dashes referring, in every case, to the second stage of ionization. We can eliminate x' and get

$$\frac{1}{x} = 1 + \frac{b(T)p_e}{\varpi C} T^{-\frac{5}{2}} e^{I/RT} + \frac{\varpi' C}{b'(T)p_e} T^{\frac{5}{2}} e^{-I'/RT}. \qquad (26)$$

Ignoring variations in $b(T)$ and $b'(T)$, the maximum of x occurs where $(\partial x/\partial T)_{p_e} = 0$, that is where

$$p_e = C\left\{\frac{\varpi \varpi'}{b(T)b'(T)}\right\}^{\frac{1}{2}} \left\{\frac{I'+\frac{5}{2}RT}{I+\frac{5}{2}RT}\right\}^{\frac{1}{2}} e^{-\frac{1}{2}(I+I')/RT}. \qquad (27)$$

There is another case in which a maximum occurs and admits of a simple demonstration, namely, lines due to atoms absorbing in an excited state. Consider a neutral atom which has an excited state with an excitation potential χ_r. The fraction f_r of neutral atoms in this state is given (in thermodynamic equilibrium) by

$$f_r = \frac{g_r}{b(T)} e^{-\chi_r/RT},$$

and the fraction n_r of the total number of atoms which are neutral and in this state is

$$n_r = f_r(1-x).$$

But

$$1-x = \frac{b(T)p_e}{b(T)p_e + \varpi C T^{\frac{5}{2}} e^{-I/RT}},$$

so that

$$n_r = \frac{p_e g_r e^{-\chi_r/RT}}{b(T)p_e + \varpi C T^{\frac{5}{2}} e^{-I/RT}}.$$

Ignoring variations in $b(T)$ as before, we find that for constant p_e the fraction n_r has a maximum at a temperature such that

$$p_e = \frac{\varpi C}{b(T)} \frac{I - \chi_r + \frac{5}{2}RT}{\chi_r} T^{\frac{5}{2}} e^{-I/RT}. \qquad (28)$$

Equations (27) and (28) are due to Fowler and Milne.[†] These authors found that a scale of temperature from 3,900° for type $K5$ to 16,000° for type $B2$ was consistent, within reasonable limits, with the assumption that $p_e = 1 \cdot 3 \times 10^2$ dynes per sq. cm. for all stars—so far as the maximum strength of various lines in the spectral sequence was concerned. These results can be refined by recognizing that p_e is not constant with depth, or from star to star, and using values of p_e calculated according to the method of model atmospheres, and by paying attention to the theory of formation of absorption lines to give more precision to the idea of maximum strength of a line. In some cases (notably the strong principal line of Ca^+) the maximum is not sharp, and some criterion other than maximum strength might more usefully be employed.

The method was carried forward by Milne himself, and by Russell, whose work on the subject is the most complete treatment extant. Russell used Pannekoek's values for the stellar absorption coefficient which did not include terms due to negative ions. The reader is referred to his original paper in the *Astrophysical Journal*, **78**, 239 (1933), or to an account of Russell's work in Rosseland's *Theoretical Astrophysics*.

3.2. *Model stellar atmospheres*

The actual structure of a stellar atmosphere depends on the opacity as a function of the depth. Since this is not usually related to the gas pressure in a simple manner, it is not possible to work out general relations, even of an approximate nature, and recourse is had, in modern work, to numerical solutions of the differential equations, using tabular connexions between $p, p_e, \bar{k}$, and $\theta = 5,040/T$. This method of investigating theoretical stellar atmospheres is the more satisfactory since the quantities which one is anxious to compare with observation—equivalent

† R. H. Fowler and E. A. Milne, *M.N.* **83**, 403 (1923); **84**, 499 (1924).

widths, gradients, Balmer discontinuities—are not related to the constants of the atmosphere by neat analytical expressions, so that to secure adequate values of them one is compelled to use numerical methods, whether the atmosphere was built up from physical theory numerically or analytically.

There are, of course, great disadvantages in numerical work. It is often hard to discern the relations between cause and effect, and hard to put right the consequence of a defect in the original physical premises. Where the numerical work is heavy, there is a great risk that the discovery of some modification to the premises will render much labour useless. These disadvantages are at present far outweighed by the difficulty of making an analytical solution.

3.21. *Incomplete stellar models*

Before going on to give an account of model atmospheres constructed by Strömgren,† Rudkjöbing,‡ and Miss Underhill,§ in which the equation of hydrostatic equilibrium is solved numerically and the gas pressure and electron pressure tabulated as a function of optical depth, we remark that the stellar energy curve can be found from a model which does not solve this equation, if some simplifying approximation is introduced, for example supposing that $k_\nu/\bar{k}$ is independent of depth and can be found: for then the formula for the surface flux $F_\nu(0)$ makes no further reference to the electron pressure.

Two examples of approximate formulae may be quoted. The problem is, in every case, to find an approximate expression for $I_\nu(0, \theta)$ and then carry out a θ-integration:

(i) If $B(\nu, T)$ is assumed to be given by the linear form

$$B(\nu, T) = a_\nu + b_\nu \tau_\nu, \tag{29}$$

a θ-integration may be carried out simply. We have

$$I_\nu(0, \theta) = \int\limits_0^\infty e^{-\tau_\nu \sec\theta} B(\nu, T)\sec\theta \, d\tau_\nu \tag{30}$$

and

$$H_\nu(0) = \tfrac{1}{2} \int\limits_0^{\frac{1}{2}\pi} I_\nu(0, \theta)\cos\theta \sin\theta \, d\theta. \tag{31}$$

Using the approximation (29), equation (30) gives $I_\nu(0, \theta) = a_\nu + b_\nu \cos\theta$. Hence from (31) we get

$$H_\nu(0) = \tfrac{1}{4} a_\nu \left(1 + \frac{2}{3}\frac{b_\nu}{a_\nu}\right).$$

† B. Strömgren, *Publ. Copenhagen Obs.*, No. 138 (1944).
‡ M. Rudkjöbing, ibid., No. 145 (1947).
§ A. Underhill, ibid., No. 151 (1950).

Now $a_\nu = B(\nu, T_0)$, and

$$b_\nu = \left(\frac{dB_\nu}{d\tau_\nu}\right)_0 = \frac{\bar{k}}{k_\nu}\left(\frac{dB_\nu}{dT}\frac{dT}{d\tau}\right)_0.$$

This gives

$$\frac{b_\nu}{a_\nu} = \frac{3}{8}\frac{\bar{k}}{k_\nu}\frac{\alpha}{1-e^{-\alpha}},$$

where $\alpha = h\nu/RT_0$. The emergent flux $F_\nu(0) = 4\pi H_\nu(0)$. Hence

$$F_\nu(0) = \pi B(\nu, T_0)\left(1 + \frac{1}{4}\frac{\bar{k}}{k_\nu}\frac{\alpha}{1-e^{-\alpha}}\right). \tag{32}$$

This formula has been used by Unsöld.†

(ii) On the other hand, there exists an expression for $I_\nu(0, \theta)$, namely

$$I_\nu(0, \theta) = (2h\nu^3/c^2)\alpha^{-5}f(\alpha, p), \tag{33}$$

where $p = \frac{3}{2}(\bar{k}/k_\nu)\cos\theta$, and $f(\alpha, p)$ is a tabulated function:

$$f(\alpha, p) = \alpha^5\int\limits_0^\infty \frac{e^{-x}\,dx}{\exp\{\alpha(1+px)^{-\frac{1}{4}}\}-1}.$$

The expression (33) is accurate except in so far as the temperature distribution is not $T^4 = T_0^4(1+\frac{3}{2}\tau)$, and in so far as $k_\nu/\bar{k}$ is not independent of depth. But if $I_\nu(0, \theta)$ is computed from $f(\alpha, p)$ we are still faced with a θ-integration. Chandrasekhar and Breen‡ have calculated a function $\mathscr{F}(\alpha', \beta)$ which avoids this difficulty by evaluating the integral in equation (3). In terms of this function the surface flux is given by

$$F_\nu(0) = \pi B(\nu, T_0)\mathscr{F}\left(\frac{h\nu}{RT_e}, \frac{k_\nu}{\bar{k}}\right), \tag{34}$$

where the temperature T_e may be taken to mean $2^{\frac{1}{4}}T_0$, and is not necessarily the effective temperature of the star, which is determined by $\int F_\nu(0)\,d\nu$. Before this was done Pannekoek§ computed the flux from $f(\alpha, p)$ using a mean value of $\cos\theta$. To show how this can be carried out, we remark that if $B(\nu, T) = a_\nu + b_\nu\tau_\nu$, then

$$H_\nu(0) = \frac{1}{2+\sqrt{3}}I_\nu\left(0, \cos^{-1}\frac{1}{\sqrt{3}}\right). \tag{35}$$

The proof is as follows. Using Eddington's approximation $K_\nu = \frac{1}{3}J_\nu$ we have

$$H_\nu = \frac{dK_\nu}{d\tau_\nu} = \frac{1}{3}\frac{dJ_\nu}{d\tau_\nu},$$

---

† A. Unsöld, *Zs. f. Ap.* **8**, 235 (1934).

‡ S. Chandrasekhar and F. Breen, *Ap. J.* **105**, 461 (1947). Quoted in *Radiative Transfer* (Oxford), chapter xi, section 80.1.

§ A. Pannekoek, *M.N.* **95**, 529 (1935); *Ap. J.* **84**, 481 (1936).

where
$$J_\nu = B_\nu + \frac{2b_\nu - 3a_\nu}{3 + 2\sqrt{3}}\, e^{-\sqrt{3}\,\tau_\nu}.$$

Thus
$$H_\nu(0) = \frac{1}{3}\left(\frac{dJ_\nu}{d\tau_\nu}\right)_0 = \frac{a_\nu}{2 + \sqrt{3}}\left(1 + \frac{1}{\sqrt{3}}\frac{b_\nu}{a_\nu}\right).$$

But
$$I_\nu(0, \theta) = a_\nu\left(1 + \cos\theta\, \frac{b_\nu}{a_\nu}\right).$$

Hence
$$H_\nu(0) = \frac{1}{2 + \sqrt{3}}\, I_\nu\left(0, \cos^{-1}\frac{1}{\sqrt{3}}\right).$$

Pannekoek transfers this mean value of $\cos\theta$ from the case
$$B(\nu, T) = a_\nu + b_\nu\, \tau_\nu$$
to the case $T^4 = T_0^4(1 + \tfrac{3}{2}\tau)$, and writes

$$H_\nu(0) = \frac{1}{2 + \sqrt{3}} \int\limits_0^\infty e^{-\sqrt{3}\,\tau_\nu} B(\nu, T)\sqrt{3}\, d\tau_\nu = \frac{2h/c^2}{2 + \sqrt{3}}\left(\frac{RT_0}{h}\right)^3 \alpha^{-2} f\left(\alpha, \frac{\sqrt{3}}{2}\frac{\bar{k}}{k_\nu}\right). \tag{36}$$

Since this formula assumes $T^4 = T_0^4(1 + \tfrac{3}{2}\tau)$, all that is now required to calculate the surface flux is a value of T_0 and a table of values of $\bar{k}/k_\nu$. Pannekoek constructed such a table of values of the absorption coefficient applicable to $T_0 = 10{,}080 \times 2^{-\frac{1}{4}} = 8{,}428^\circ$ K. The absorption did not include the effect of negative ions, but this is not a serious objection at the temperature concerned. With these values of $\bar{k}/k_\nu$ he calculated the flux from equation (36) with $T_0 = 8{,}428^\circ$ K. The results of the calculations are given in Table LXI. We shall refer to this as Pannekoek's model, although it is not a model in the sense that a table of values of p or p_e as functions of τ is obtained; it only gives the surface flux. The scheme might therefore be called an *incomplete model*.

TABLE LXI

Monochromatic Fluxes on Pannekoek's Model

Flux equals $\mathfrak{F}_\lambda$ multiplied by π

$\lambda(A)$	$\bar{k}/k_\lambda$	$\log \mathfrak{F}_\lambda$	$\lambda(A)$	$\bar{k}/k_\lambda$	$\log \mathfrak{F}_\lambda$
911−	00·00	12·00	3,646+	3·35	15·82
911+	11·08	16·16	4,000	2·53	15·72
1,000	8·43	16·08	5,000	1·35	15·42
1,500	2·51	15·70	6,000	0·84	15·18
2,000	1·05	15·52	7,000	0·57	14·98
2,500	0·54	15·46	8,206−	0·35	14·76
3,000	0·31	15·42	8,206+	1·27	14·88
3,646−	0·17	15·34	9,000	0·80	14·62
3,646+	3·35	15·82	12,000	0·38	14·28

In Fig. 46 the surface flux is plotted in frequency units. By numerical integration we find

$$\mathfrak{F} = \int \mathfrak{F}_\nu \, d\nu = 2 \cdot 24 \times 10^{11} \text{ ergs cm.}^{-2} \text{ sec.}^{-1}$$

Now the effective temperature of the star is given by $\pi \mathfrak{F} = \sigma T_e^4$. Hence $T_e = 10{,}550°$ K., a result which differs from the effective temperature of a grey atmosphere, $2^{\frac{1}{4}}T_0$, namely $10{,}080°$ K.

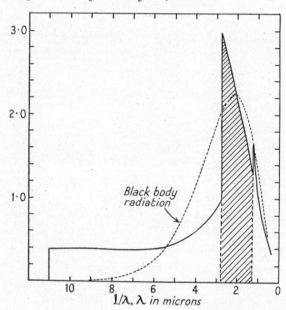

FIG. 46. Monochromatic flux from Pannekoek's model $A0$ star. The ordinate gives $\mathfrak{F}_\nu$ in units of 10^{-4} ergs cm.$^{-2}$ sec.$^{-1}$, the flux being $\pi \mathfrak{F}_\nu$. The hatched area marks the spectral region between the Balmer and Paschen limits, corresponding roughly to the visible part of the spectrum.

The gradients and Balmer discontinuity $D = \log(\mathfrak{F}_{3,646^+}/\mathfrak{F}_{3,646^-})$ for Pannekoek's model are given in Table LXII. The model represents quite well a star of type $A0$ for which $\phi_{5\,000} = 1 \cdot 1 \pm 0 \cdot 1$ (Greaves), and $D = 0 \cdot 47$, $\phi_2 - \phi_1 = 0 \cdot 47$ (Barbier and Chalonge).

3.22. Complete stellar models

Additional information can be obtained from numerical models which actually solve the equation of hydrostatic equilibrium. In these, the electron pressure is found at all optical depths. This has several advantages: the value of $k_\nu/\bar{k}$ is found in a more satisfactory way (it is a function of the optical depth, and if it is tabulated as such, there is no need to choose a mean value of the electron pressure); if the electron pressure is tabulated, it is possible to work out ionization at various depths, and carry out a detailed calculation of equivalent widths ; and finally, if the pressure is found at various depths, it is possible to find the top of the convection zone and introduce a change in the temperature gradient at this point.

TABLE LXII

Gradients and Balmer Discontinuity in Pannekoek's Model

$\lambda(A)$	$\log \mathfrak{F}_\lambda$	$2 \cdot 5 \log \lambda^5 \mathfrak{F}_\lambda$ λ *in microns*	Δm	$1 \cdot 086 \Delta(1/\lambda)$ λ *in microns*	ϕ
3,000	15·42	32·025			
			0·850	0·641	1·32
3,646⁻	15·34	32·875			
			..	..	..
3,646⁺	15·82	34·075			
			0·400	0·445	0·90
4,286	15·63	34·475			
			0·325	0·362	0·90
5,000	15·42	34·800			
			0·375	0·362	1·04
6,000	15·18	35·175			

$$\phi_{5,000} = 0 \cdot 97, \quad \phi_{3,500} - \phi_{4,250} \doteq 0 \cdot 42; \quad D = 0 \cdot 48$$

Strömgren considered stars of types $A5$ to $G0$, in which absorption due to negative hydrogen ions H⁻ is important. He assumed at the outset that the approximate temperature distribution $T^4 = T_0^4(1 + \frac{3}{2}\tau)$ was sufficiently accurate for his purposes, τ being derived from the Rosseland mean opacity $\overline{k}$. Now the equation of hydrostatic equilibrium is

$$\overline{k}\,dp = g\,d\tau, \tag{37}$$

and $\overline{k}$ is, in general, dependent on the electron pressure. Strömgren starts by constructing tables showing $\overline{k}$ and p_e as functions of $\theta = 5{,}040/T$ and p: for if $\overline{k}$ is known as $\overline{k}(\theta, p)$ and $\theta = \theta_0(1 + \frac{3}{2}\tau)^{-\frac{1}{4}}$, equation (37) may be solved by numerical integration to give values of p at each optical depth. From these may be found p_e and $\overline{k}$, with the help of the original tables. This is the object of the work.

The tables are constructed as follows. Given θ and p_e, the degree of ionization of every constituent of the atmosphere is computed by Saha's equation, without correction (Chapter IX, Section 4). If there are N_H hydrogen atoms per c.c. and N_H/A metal atoms of all kinds taken together, and if x_H is the ionization of hydrogen and α_i, x_i the relative abundance ($\sum \alpha_i = 1$) and the degree of ionization of the ith metal in the mixture, the number of electrons per c.c. N_e is given, as in Chapter IX, Section 3.1, by

$$N_e = N_H x_H + (N_H/A) \sum \alpha_i x_i.$$

Writing x_M for $\sum \alpha_i x_i$, we have

$$N_e = N_H(x_H + x_M/A).$$

Now A is of order 10^3, and N, the total number of particles, is practically equal to the number of hydrogen atoms and ions plus the number of electrons liberated from hydrogen, or $N = N_H(1 + x_H)$. But

$$p_e/p = N_e/N;$$

therefore

$$\frac{p_e}{p} = \frac{x_H}{1 + x_H} + \frac{1}{A}\frac{x_M}{1 + x_H}.$$

In this expression the second term is negligible unless x_H is small compared with unity: accordingly, we have with sufficient accuracy

$$\frac{p_e}{p} = \frac{x_H}{1 + x_H} + \frac{x_M}{A}. \tag{38}$$

From (38) p can be calculated for every pair of values of θ and p_e, and if a table of values is made, p_e can be found for every pair of values of p and θ by interpolation.

Likewise, a pair of values of θ and p_e determine the opacity $\bar{k}$. In the stars from type $A5$ to $G0$ the only contributor that need be considered is hydrogen, but a distinction must be made between negative ions, atoms in the ground state, and atoms in the excited states. For neutral hydrogen the absorption coefficient per hydrogen atom in the ground (or excited) state is

$$\kappa_\nu(n) = \frac{64\pi^4}{3\sqrt{3}}\frac{me^{10}}{ch^6}\frac{g_\nu(n)}{n^5}\frac{1}{\nu^3}, \quad \nu > \nu(n).$$

Setting all the Gaunt factors equal to unity and using Boltzmann's equation, the absorption coefficient due to all the excited states which are effective at a particular frequency, per hydrogen atom in the ground state, is

$$a_\nu(H) = \frac{64\pi^4}{3\sqrt{3}}\frac{me^{10}}{ch^6}\frac{1}{\nu^3}\sum_{n=n_0}^{\infty}\frac{1}{n^3}e^{-\chi_n/RT},$$

where $n_0 = 1$ for $h\nu > 13{\cdot}59$ volts, $n_0 = 2$ for $h\nu > 13{\cdot}59/2^2$, etc., and $\chi_n = 13{\cdot}59(1 - 1/n^2)$ volts. The total absorption coefficient per hydrogen atom in the ground state is

$$a_\nu = a_\nu(H) + a_\nu(H^-) \times p_e/\{2(2\pi m)^{\frac{3}{2}}(RT)^{\frac{5}{2}}h^{-3}\varpi(H^-)e^{-I(H^-)/RT}\}. \tag{39}$$

Now the number of hydrogen atoms in the ground state per gramme of the atmosphere is practically $(1 - x_H)/m_H$. Accordingly k_ν, the continuous absorption coefficient per gramme of the atmosphere, is

$$k_\nu = \frac{1}{m_H}(1 - x_H)a_\nu. \tag{40}$$

The Rosseland mean $\bar{k}$ is given by

$$\frac{1}{\bar{k}} = \frac{15}{4\pi^4} \int_0^\infty \frac{1}{k_\nu} \frac{u^4 e^{-u}\, du}{(1-e^{-u})^3}, \qquad (41)$$

where $u = h\nu/RT$. Thus $\bar{k}$ can be found for every pair of values of θ and p_e from equations (39), (40), and (41).

Suppose that tables have been prepared showing p_e and $\bar{k}$ as dependent on θ and p. We have to use equation (37) to build up a table of values of p, p_e, and $\bar{k}$ for ascending values of τ, given θ_0, g, and A. The first step from $\tau = 0$ to small values is made with $\theta = \theta_0$, constant. Since p_e starts from zero $a_\nu = a_\nu(\mathrm{H})$, from (39), and x_H is nearly equal to unity, so that

$$p_e/(1-x_\mathrm{H}) = 2(2\pi m)^{\frac{3}{2}}(RT)^{\frac{5}{2}} h^{-3} \varpi e^{-I/RT} = \kappa(\theta_0),$$

$$k_\nu = \frac{1}{m_\mathrm{H}} a_\nu p_e/\kappa(\theta_0), \qquad \bar{k} = \mathrm{const.} \times p_e = k_0 p_e.$$

Then, from equation (37), we have

$$k_0 p_e\, dp = g\, d\tau,$$

and, from (38) with $x_\mathrm{H} \sim 1$, we find $p_e \sim p$. Hence $p\, dp = (g/k_0)\, d\tau$, which gives

$$p^2 = (2g/k_0)\tau, \qquad (42)$$

an equation which can only be used for values of τ so small that $\theta \doteq \theta_0$, and further, with p so small that $x_\mathrm{H} \sim 1$. Equation (42) does, however, enable us to get away from p_e zero. When this start has been made, p can be built up from $dp = (g/\bar{k})\, d\tau$, $\bar{k}$ being a tabulated function of p and θ $[= \theta_0(1+\frac{3}{2}\tau)^{-\frac{1}{4}}]$. Equation (42) may be compared with equation (24) of Chapter IX.

In the actual construction of Strömgren's tables, $a_\nu(\mathrm{H}^-)$ was replaced by a constant ($2\cdot6 \times 10^{-17}$ cm.^{2} per negative hydrogen ion), since well established values were not available at the time. [Strömgren gives alternative tables constructed by Rudkjöbing using a slightly different hypothesis about $a_\nu(\mathrm{H}^-)$.] The tables of ionization, of opacity, and of the relations between p, p_e, $\bar{k}$, and θ are followed by *Model Stellar Atmospheres*, that is, tabulated solutions of equation (37) which show θ, $\log p$, $\log p_e$, and $\log \bar{k}$ for ascending values of τ. These are worked out for various values of $\log A$ and $\log g$, and for $\theta_0 = 1\cdot0$, $0\cdot9$, $0\cdot8$, and $0\cdot7$. Special tables for $\theta_0 = 1\cdot041$ and $\log g = 4\cdot44$, representing the Sun, are also given. The model solar atmosphere calculations have been repeated by Münch (Chapter IX, Section 3.2), using Chandrasekhar and Breen's values of the absorption coefficient of H^-, the temperature distribution from Chandrasekhar's fourth approximation, and the Chandrasekhar mean instead of the Rosseland mean opacity.

As was shown in Chapter X, convection occurs when

$$\left(\frac{d\log T}{d\log p}\right)_{\text{radiative}} \geqslant \left(\frac{d\log T}{d\log p}\right)_{\text{adiabatic}}.$$

In Strömgren's work the radiative solution is carried out with $\theta = \theta_0(1+\frac{3}{2}\tau)^{-\frac{1}{4}}$ beyond the convection zone. A small table shows pressure and temperature (but not optical depth) with the adiabatic gradient.

When the boundary temperature T_0 ($= 5,040/\theta_0$) is much greater than the values considered by Strömgren, say $\theta_0 = 0\cdot2$, negative hydrogen ions no longer make an appreciable contribution to the continuous absorption, and the opacity is due to atomic hydrogen and helium. There is, in addition, scattering due to free electrons, of amount $\sigma_e = 8\pi e^4/3m^2c^4$ per electron. The equation of transfer is

$$\cos\theta\,\frac{dI_\nu(\theta)}{\rho\,dx} = -\left(k_\nu + \frac{n_e\,\sigma_e}{\rho}\right)I_\nu(\theta) + k_\nu\,B(\nu, T) + \frac{n_e\,\sigma_e}{\rho}\,J_\nu,$$

which leads in the usual way to

$$J = H(2+3\tau),$$

with
$$\bar{k} = \int\left(k_\nu + \frac{n_e\,\sigma_e}{\rho}\right)F_\nu\,d\nu \Big/ \int F_\nu\,d\nu.$$

In other words, the electron scattering can be treated exactly as if it were true absorption.

In the early type stars, hydrogen is almost completely ionized, and helium is nearly all once ionized: nearly all the particles are H$^+$ and He$^+$ and an equal number of free electrons, so that the electrons are almost exactly half the total population, and we have

$$p_e = \tfrac{1}{2}p,$$

a convenient fact which removes the necessity for constructing ionization tables. On the other hand radiation pressure cannot be neglected, and equation (37) must be replaced by

$$\bar{k}\,(dp_g + dp_r) = g\,d\tau.$$

Since $dp_r/d\tau = (\sigma/c)T_e^4$, where σ is Stefan's constant, we have

$$\frac{dp_g}{d\tau} = \frac{g}{\bar{k}} - \frac{\sigma}{c}\,T_e^4. \tag{43}$$

Model B star atmospheres have been computed by Rudkjöbing and by Miss Underhill. Rudkjöbing uses the Rosseland mean $\bar{k}$ and avoids the use of equation (43) by taking an effective value of g, constant with depth. Miss Underhill uses (43), and adopts the Chandrasekhar mean $\bar{k} = \int k_\nu F_\nu^1 \, d\nu \big/ \int F_\nu^1 \, d\nu$. Both of these means are approximations to the correct mean $\bar{k} = \int k_\nu F_\nu \, d\nu \big/ \int F_\nu \, d\nu$, which suffers, of course, from the disadvantage that it cannot be calculated until F_ν is known: it can therefore only be found by successive approximation.

TABLE LXIII

Monochromatic Surface Flux for Miss Underhill's Model Atmosphere

($\theta = 0 \cdot 2$; $\log g = 4 \cdot 20$)

λ (A)	$\log \mathfrak{F}_\lambda$	λ (A)	$\log \mathfrak{F}_\lambda$
504·3$^+$	17·977	1,458	18·207
567·8	17·894	1,716	17·988
694·4	17·738	2,083	17·733
758·7	17·757	2,652	17·368
911·6$^-$	17·745	3,646$^-$	16·886
911·6$^+$	18·833	3,646$^+$	16·958
1,006	18·733	4,234	16·702
1,122	18·582	5,048	16·413
1,268	18·418	6,251	16·055
1,458	18·207	8,204$^-$	15·595

Miss Underhill's model atmosphere was computed with $\theta_0 = 0 \cdot 2$, and $\log g = 4 \cdot 20$. Table LXIII gives the surface value of $\mathfrak{F}_\lambda$ for the model; the actual flux is $\pi \mathfrak{F}_\lambda$. The effective temperature of the model is given by $T_e^4 = (\pi/\sigma)\mathfrak{F}$, where

$$\mathfrak{F} = \int \mathfrak{F}_\lambda \, d\lambda = 32 \cdot 72 \times 10^{12} \text{ ergs cm.}^{-2} \text{ sec.}^{-1}$$

Hence $\qquad\qquad\qquad T_e = 36{,}800^\circ \text{ K}.$

This effective temperature is considerably in excess of $2^{\frac{1}{4}}T_0$, or $30{,}000^\circ$ K., and the calculation shows that $T_e = 2^{\frac{1}{4}}T_0$ may be considerably wrong when k_ν is not independent of ν.

The calculation of gradients and the Balmer discontinuity shown by Miss Underhill's model is given in Table LXIV. The gradient for $\lambda 5{,}000$ A is $0 \cdot 60$, which is somewhat less than Gascoigne's value for unreddened $B0$ stars, and the Balmer discontinuity D is near to the value given by Barbier and Chalonge for the same spectral type. However, these quantities do not fix the spectral type very closely. For example, $\phi = 0 \cdot 60$ corresponds to $T_c = 76{,}000^\circ$ K. (notice how different it is from T_0 and T_e), but $T_c = 70{,}000^\circ$ K. gives $\phi = 0 \cdot 629$ and $90{,}000^\circ$ K. gives $\phi = 0 \cdot 584$, so that ϕ is very insensitive to temperature.

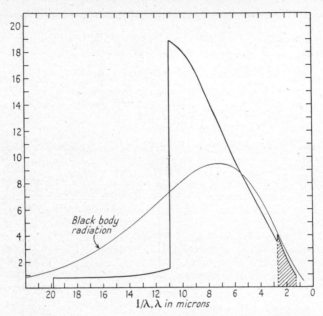

FIG. 47. The monochromatic surface flux of Miss Underhill's model
$B0$ star. The ordinate gives $\mathfrak{F}_\nu$ in units of 10^{-3} ergs cm.$^{-2}$ sec.$^{-1}$,
the flux being $\pi\mathfrak{F}_\nu$. The spectral region between the Balmer and
Paschen limits is indicated by the hatched area. The function $B(\nu, T_e)$
for a black body radiating at the effective temperature of the star
$(T_e = 36,800°$ K.$)$ is also given.

TABLE LXIV

Gradients and Balmer Discontinuity in Miss Underhill's Model

λ (A)	$\log \mathfrak{F}_\lambda$	$2 \cdot 5 \log \lambda^5 \mathfrak{F}_\lambda$ λ *in microns*	Δm	$1 \cdot 086 \Delta(1/\lambda)$ λ *in microns*	ϕ
2,652	17·368	36·215 ⎱			
			0·523	1·107	0·47
3,646⁻	16·886	36·738 ⎰			
			..	..	..
3,646⁺	16·958	36·917 ⎱			
			0·173	0·414	0·42
4,234	16·702	37·090 ⎰			
			0·232	0·414	0·56
5,048	16·413	37·322 ⎰			
			0·266	0·414	0·64
6,251	16·055	37·588 ⎰			

$$\phi_{5,000} = 0 \cdot 60, \quad \phi_{3,500} - \phi_{4,250} \doteq 0 \cdot 05; \quad D = 0 \cdot 07$$

The identity of the model with type $B0$ is better established by Miss
Underhill's calculations of the equivalent widths of lines in the spectrum
of the model atmosphere.

TABLE LXV

Calculated Equivalent Widths compared with Observed Values for Early Type Stars

Element	λ (A)	Computed	τ Sco B0 V (Unsöld)	10 Lac O9 V (Aller)
C II	4,267	0·099	0·115	0·081
C III	4,187	0·085	0·065	0·089
Si III	4,820	0·050	0·071	< 0·050
Si IV	4,089	0·209	0·174	0·270

The equivalent widths, whose ratios are sensitive to the temperature, show that the spectral type of Miss Underhill's model must be close to B0.

3.23. *Determination of stellar diameters from observations of brightness*

Two methods of determining stellar radii theoretically have been used. One method which employs bolometric corrections to find the total luminosity of a star, and uses the relation $L = 4\pi R^2 \sigma T_e^4$, has already been mentioned in Section 2.4 of this chapter. There is in addition a method given by Russell, which uses the monochromatic flux. These two methods are illustrated in this section by data from the Sun, and from Pannekoek's and Miss Underhill's models. These data are given in Table LXVI; they are, unfortunately, very inhomogeneous, but they suffice to illustrate the principles involved.

TABLE LXVI

Flux of Energy from the Sun and from Stellar Models, with Temperatures

Object	$\pi \mathfrak{F}_\lambda \, \Delta\lambda$ Flux at λ5,430 A for $\Delta\lambda = 100$ A	$\pi \mathfrak{F}$ Total flux	$2^{\frac{1}{4}}T_0$	T_e	T_c
	Multiply by 10^8	Multiply by 10^{11}			
Sun . . .	8·70	0·616	..	5,740	7,200
Pannekoek's model	63·4	7·03	10,080	10,550	18,500
Underhill's model .	626·0	1,046	30,000	36,800	75,000

Fluxes are in ergs cm.$^{-2}$ sec.$^{-1}$ The data for the Sun are experimental. The gradient of the Sun is taken to be $\phi = 2\cdot00$. The values of T_c are in each case computed from ϕ for λ5,000 A.

Now the bolometric corrections are devices for converting the measured magnitudes into bolometric magnitudes, which give the total flux. If we follow the simple assumption made by Hertzsprung and Eddington that the stars radiate like black bodies at a temperature T_e, or, in symbols,

$$\mathfrak{F}_\lambda = B(\lambda, T_e),$$

then the magnitude difference of the two stars, defined in the notation of Section 2.2 by equation (14), is given by

$$m-m' = 2 \cdot 5 \Big\{ \log \int d'^2 B(\lambda, T'_e)\sigma(\lambda) \, d\lambda - \log \int d^2 B(\lambda, T_e)\sigma(\lambda) \, d\lambda \Big\},$$

d being the apparent diameter, and $\sigma(\lambda)$ the selection function of the measuring system. But the difference between the bolometric magnitudes of the same stars is

$$m_{\text{bol}} - m'_{\text{bol}} = 2 \cdot 5 \{ \log(d'^2 T'^4_e) - \log(d^2 T^4_e) \},$$

so that

$$(m_{\text{bol}} - m) - (m'_{\text{bol}} - m') = 2 \cdot 5 \Big\{ \log \int T_e^{-4} B(\lambda, T_e)\sigma(\lambda) \, d\lambda -$$
$$- \log \int T'^{-4}_e B(\lambda, T'_e)\sigma(\lambda) \, d\lambda \Big\}, \quad (44)$$

and the bolometric correction $\Delta m = m_{\text{bol}} - m$ can be computed as a function of T_e from Planck's function and a table of values of $\sigma(\lambda)$. There is an arbitrary constant to be assigned: the correction is conventionally taken to be zero when $T_e = 6{,}500°$ K. Values of Δm for the international photovisual system, after Hertzsprung, are shown in Table LXVII.

TABLE LXVII

Theoretical Bolometric Corrections to Photovisual Magnitudes

$T_e °K.$	Δm	$T_e °K.$	Δm	$B.C.$
2,000	−4·69	10,000	−0·28	−0·57
3,000	−1·74	12,000	−0·55	−0·98
4,000	−0·64	15,000	−0·97	−1·51
5,000	−0·18	20,000	−1·61	−2·18
6,000	−0·02	25,000	..	−2·69
8,000	−0·06	30,000	..	−3·12

Since the stars do not radiate like black bodies, an amendment to Δm is necessary. Thus Kuiper writes B.C. $= \Delta m + \delta m$, where δm is smaller than Δm, and finds δm from various models calculated by Pannekoek. Since negative ions were not taken into account, the models of solar and later types are not trustworthy. Kuiper also gives empirical bolometric corrections which are obtained from radiometric measurements. Now the radiometer responds to all the radiation which penetrates the Earth's atmosphere, and therefore fails to indicate the bolometric magnitude only in so far as the Earth's atmosphere cuts off the ultra-violet and bands in the infra-red. Radiometric measurements would therefore give a very poor indication of the total light from a B star, or even an A star, but for stars of solar type a considerable fraction of the light reaches the Earth's surface, and the radiometer may be supposed to give a reasonable indication of the total light. Table LXVII gives theoretical bolometric corrections B.C. $= \Delta m + \delta m$ to photovisual magnitudes for temperatures above 10,000° K. after Kuiper. Table LXVIII shows Kuiper's empirical corrections for later type stars with the spectral type as argument.

TABLE LXVIII

Empirical Bolometric Corrections to Photovisual Magnitudes of Late Type Stars after Kuiper

Spectral type	Dwarfs	Giants	Super-giants	Spectral type	Dwarfs	Giants	Super-giants
F2	−0·04	−0·04	−0·04	K0	−0·11	−0·54	−0·93
F5	0·04	0·08	0·12	K2	0·15	0·72	1·20
F8	0·05	0·17	0·28	K3	0·31	0·89	1·35
G0	0·06	0·25	0·42	K4	0·55	1·11	1·56
G2	0·07	0·31	0·52	K5	0·85	1·35	1·86
G5	0·10	0·39	0·65	M0	1·43	1·55	2·2
G8	−0·10	−0·47	−0·80	M1	−1·70	−1·72	−2·6

Taking the international photovisual system to be simply a monochromatic system at $\lambda 5,430$ A, relative bolometric corrections can be readily formed from Table LXVI, for then

$$m_{\mathrm{pv}} - m'_{\mathrm{pv}} = 2 \cdot 5 \{ \log \mathfrak{F}'_{5,430} - \log \mathfrak{F}_{5,430} \},$$

and then

$$m_{\mathrm{bol}} - m'_{\mathrm{bol}} = 2 \cdot 5 \{ \log T'^4_e - \log T^4_e \},$$

so that

$$\mathrm{B.C.} - (\mathrm{B.C.})' = -2 \cdot 5 \left\{ \log \left(\frac{\mathfrak{F}'_{5,430}}{T'^4_e} \right) - \log \left(\frac{\mathfrak{F}_{5,430}}{T^4_e} \right) \right\}.$$

Taking the bolometric correction to the Sun to be $-0 \cdot 10$, we find for Pannekoek's model B.C. $= -0 \cdot 59$, and for Miss Underhill's model B.C. $= -3 \cdot 53$; Kuiper gives B.C. $= -0 \cdot 68$ for $T_e = 10,500°$ K., and B.C. $= -3 \cdot 6$ for $T_e = 36,800°$ K. The basis is not quite the same as we have used but the difference is inconsiderable.

Radii are actually determined, in this method, from absolute photovisual magnitudes, by

$$M_{\mathrm{bol}} = M_{\mathrm{pv}} + \mathrm{B.C.},$$

and

$$\log(R/R_\odot) = 7 \cdot 518 - 2 \log T_e - 0 \cdot 2(4 \cdot 62 - M_{\mathrm{bol}}).$$

To use the method, it is necessary to know the effective temperature of the star from its spectrum, and as the diameter in kilometres (as distinct from an apparent diameter in seconds of arc) is wanted it is also necessary to known the parallax of the star accurately.

An alternative method of determining stellar radii is due to Russell, Dugan, and Stewart.[†] Suppose that we have some means of ascertaining (perhaps from the spectral type) the monochromatic surface flux of a star, $\pi \mathfrak{F}_\lambda$. The total radiation emitted in wave-lengths from λ to $\lambda+d\lambda$ is $4\pi^2 R^2 \mathfrak{F}_\lambda \, d\lambda$, and the absolute monochromatic magnitude M_λ is given by

$$M_\lambda = \text{const.} - 5\log R - \tfrac{5}{2}\log \mathfrak{F}_\lambda.$$

Hence radii can be determined from

$$\log(R/R_\odot) = -\tfrac{1}{2}\log(\mathfrak{F}_\lambda/\mathfrak{F}_{\lambda,\odot}) - \tfrac{1}{5}(M_\lambda - M_{\lambda,\odot}). \tag{45}$$

Russell, Dugan, and Stewart give a numerical formula for visual magnitudes, which they take to be practically equal to monochromatic magnitudes at $\lambda 5,290$ A, assuming that $\mathfrak{F}_\lambda = B(\lambda, T_e)$.

Table LXVI gives values of $\mathfrak{F}_\lambda$ from which monochromatic temperatures T_λ defined by $\mathfrak{F}_\lambda = B(\lambda, T_\lambda)$ can be found. Values of T_λ are given in Table LXIX, which also shows values of R from (45) in units of the correct radius $\{B(\lambda, T_e)/\mathfrak{F}_\lambda\}^{\frac{1}{2}}$. The radii found from T_e are not greatly in error: but if the radius is wanted more accurately, it is just as easy to construct $\mathfrak{F}_\lambda$ for a model as it is to construct a bolometric correction. The effective temperature T_e should not really be used in Russell's method.

TABLE LXIX

Monochromatic Temperatures

Object	Monochromatic temperature for $\lambda 5,430$ A	Radius deduced from equation (45) using T_e
Sun . . .	5,860° K.	0·955
Pannekoek's model	10,180	1·052
Underhill's model .	32,400	1·095

Beals[‡] has calculated the radii of very early type stars using Russell's method. For these stars no well-established relation between temperature and spectral type exists, but one may eventually be found from the level of excitation in the spectra (He II, C IV, N V, O V, etc.). In determining the radii of these stars, Russell's method has the advantage that there is no need to find a bolometric correction and an unwanted effective temperature—all that is needed is a relation between the ionization and $\mathfrak{F}_\lambda$.

But the effective temperature remains an important concept, since it gives a direct calculation of the luminosity, through $L = 4\pi R^2 \sigma T_e^4$,

† H. N. Russell, R. S. Dugan, and J. Q. Stewart, *Astronomy*, vol. 2, 1st ed., p. 732.
‡ C S. Beals, *J.R.A.S. Canada*, **34**, 169 (1940).

which is of prime interest in the theory of the Internal Constitution of the Stars. Bolometric corrections will always be needed on this account. Otherwise one might describe stellar atmospheres better by avoiding the use of bolometric corrections and effective temperatures; one should then seek relations between monochromatic absolute magnitudes, ionization, and gradient, using if necessary some temperature such as $2^{\frac{1}{4}}T_0$, which is easily related to the ionization of the outer layers of a star.

APPENDIX

USEFUL CONSTANTS AND FORMULAE

1. *Physical Constants*

Quantity	Symbol	Unit	Number	Logarithm
Mass of the hydrogen atom .	m_{H}	gm.	$1 \cdot 674 \times 10^{-24}$	$\overline{24} \cdot 2237$
Mass of the electron . .	m	gm.	$9 \cdot 107 \times 10^{-28}$	$\overline{28} \cdot 9593$
Charge of the electron . .	e	e.s.u.	$4 \cdot 802 \times 10^{-10}$	$\overline{10} \cdot 6814$
Velocity of light . . .	c	cm. sec.$^{-1}$	$2 \cdot 998 \times 10^{10}$	$10 \cdot 4769$
Planck's constant . .	h	erg sec.$^{-1}$	$6 \cdot 624 \times 10^{-27}$	$\overline{27} \cdot 8212$
Stefan's constant . .	σ	erg cm.$^{-1}$ sec.$^{-1}$deg.$^{-4}$	$5 \cdot 670 \times 10^{-5}$	$\overline{5} \cdot 7536$
Boltzmann's constant . .	R	erg deg.$^{-1}$	$1 \cdot 380 \times 10^{-16}$	$\overline{16} \cdot 1399$
Physical gas constant $= R/m_{\mathrm{H}}$	$\mathbf{R}$	erg deg.$^{-1}$ mol.$^{-1}$	$8 \cdot 245 \times 10^{7}$	$7 \cdot 9162$
Radius of the first Bohr orbit for hydrogen . . .	a_0	cm.	$0 \cdot 5292 \times 10^{-8}$	$\overline{9} \cdot 7237$
$\pi e^2/mc$	. .	. .	$0 \cdot 02654$	$\overline{2} \cdot 4239$
$2(2\pi m R)^{\frac{3}{2}}h^{-3}$ . . .	. .	. .	$4 \cdot 830 \times 10^{15}$	$15 \cdot 6839$

2. *Astronomical Constants*

Quantity	Symbol	Unit	Number	Logarithm
Mass of the Sun . . .	$M_{\odot}$	gm.	$1 \cdot 991 \times 10^{33}$	$33 \cdot 2991$
Radius of the Sun . .	$R_{\odot}$	cm.	$6 \cdot 960 \times 10^{10}$	$10 \cdot 8426$
Surface gravity of the Sun .	$g_{\odot}$	cm. sec.$^{-2}$	$2 \cdot 740 \times 10^{4}$	$4 \cdot 4378$
Luminosity of the Sun. .	$L_{\odot}$	erg sec.$^{-1}$	$3 \cdot 87 \times 10^{33}$	$33 \cdot 5877$
Luminosity of the Sun within 100 Angstroms at λ 5,430 A	$L_{\odot,5430}$	erg sec.$^{-1}$	$5 \cdot 16 \times 10^{31}$	$31 \cdot 7126$
Angular diameter of the Sun at the Earth's mean distance .	. .	. .	$959'' \cdot 6$	. .
Astronomical unit in cm. .	. .	cm.	$1 \cdot 496 \times 10^{13}$	$13 \cdot 1750$
Parsec in cm. . . .	. .	cm.	$3 \cdot 086 \times 10^{18}$	$18 \cdot 4894$

Numerical values of the constants given in this Appendix are based on *Astrophysical Quantities* by C. W. Allen (in preparation).

3. *Useful Relations*

$$1 \text{ electron volt} = 1 \cdot 602 \times 10^{-12} \text{ ergs}$$

$$\lambda_{\text{angstroms}} \times \chi_{\text{volts}} = 1 \cdot 2395 \times 10^4$$

RT in volts for $T = 10,000°$ K. is $0 \cdot 8616$ volts.

Temperature associated with 1 volt when working in common logarithms is $5,040 \cdot 4°$ K. Thus we write $e^{h\nu/RT} = 10^{\chi\theta}$, where χ is in volts, and $\theta = 5,040/T$, that is

$$h\nu/RT = 2 \cdot 3026\chi\theta.$$

4. *Physical Formulae*

4.1. *Maxwellian distribution of velocities*

4.11. The number of particles with *velocity components* in a given direction within the range u to $u+du$:

$$f(u)\,du = \left(\frac{M}{2\pi RT}\right)^{\frac{1}{2}} e^{-\frac{1}{2}Mu^2/RT}\,du.$$

The average positive velocity in the given direction is

$$\bar{u} = 2\int_0^\infty uf(u)\,du = \left(\frac{2RT}{\pi m}\right)^{\frac{1}{2}}.$$

4.12. The number of particles with *space velocities* within V to $V+dV$ ($V^2 = u^2 + v^2 + w^2$):

$$f(V)\,dV = 4\pi\left(\frac{M}{2\pi RT}\right)^{\frac{3}{2}} e^{-\frac{1}{2}MV^2/RT}V^2\,dV.$$

The most probable space velocity V_0 is the value of V for which the function $f(V)$ has its maximum (or the modal value of the space velocity), and is given by

$$V_0 = \left(\frac{2RT}{M}\right)^{\frac{1}{2}}.$$

The average space velocity is

$$\overline{V} = \int_0^\infty Vf(V)\,dV = \frac{2}{\sqrt{\pi}}V_0.$$

4.13. The number of particles with energies within ϵ to $\epsilon+d\epsilon$:

$$\mu(\epsilon)\,d\epsilon = \frac{4\pi}{(2\pi RT)^{\frac{3}{2}}}(2\epsilon)^{\frac{1}{2}}e^{-\epsilon/RT}\,d\epsilon.$$

The average energy is $\qquad \bar{\epsilon} = \int_0^\infty \epsilon\mu(\epsilon)\,d\epsilon = \frac{3}{2}RT.$

4.2. Saha's formula

The degree of ionization in thermodynamic equilibrium at temperature T for an atom (or ion) with ionization potential I ergs is given by

$$\frac{xN_e}{1-x} = 2(2\pi mRT)^{\frac{3}{2}}h^{-3}e^{-I/RT}B_{p+1}(T)/B_p(T),$$

where $x/(1-x)$ is the ratio of the number of atoms in the $(p+1)$th and pth stages of ionization, I is the pth ionization potential, and $B_p(T)$ is the partition function of the pth stage of ionization. If most of the atoms in this stage are in the ground state, $B_p(T)$ is nearly equal to the statistical weight of this ground state, and $B_{p+1}(T)/B_p(T)$ is approximately the ratio of the statistical weights of the two ground states. Introducing the electron pressure p_e by the relation $p_e = N_e RT$, and writing χ for the ionization potential in volts, Saha's formula may be written

$$\log\frac{x}{1-x} = -5040\chi/T + \tfrac{5}{2}\log T - 0\!\cdot\!48 + \log 2\varpi - \log p_e,$$

where ϖ is the ratio of the statistical weights of the ground states of the ion and the atom in the adjacent lower stage of ionization, and p_e is in *dyne cm.*$^{-2}$

4.3. Planck's function†

The intensity (not energy density) of black-body radiation at temperature T is as follows:

4.31. *Formula in frequency units*

$$B(\nu, T)\,d\nu = \frac{2h\nu^3/c^2}{e^{h\nu/RT}-1}\,d\nu.$$

4.32. *Formula in wave-length units*

$$B(\lambda, T)\,d\lambda = \frac{2hc^2/\lambda^5}{e^{hc/\lambda RT}-1}\,d\lambda = \frac{c_1/\lambda^5}{e^{c_2/\lambda T}-1}\,d\lambda.$$

When the wave-length is in centimetres

$$c_1 = 2hc^2 = 1\!\cdot\!1905 \times 10^{-5} \text{ erg cm.}^{-2} \text{ sec.}^{-1} \text{ sterad.}^{-1},$$

$$c_2 = hc/R = 1\!\cdot\!4387 \text{ cm. deg.}$$

4.33. *The integrated Planck function*

$$B(T) = \int_0^\infty B(\nu, T)\,d\nu = \frac{2R^4T^4}{c^2h^3}\int_0^\infty \frac{x^3\,dx}{e^x-1}.$$

Since

$$\int_0^\infty \frac{x^3\,dx}{e^x-1} = \frac{\pi^4}{15},$$

we have $B(T) = \dfrac{\sigma}{\pi}\,T^4$, where σ is Stefan's constant $\dfrac{2\pi^5}{15}\dfrac{R^4}{e^2h^3}$.

† The function is tabulated by A. N. Lowan and G. Blanch, *J.O.S.A.* **20**, 70 (1940).

INDEX OF AUTHORS

INDEX OF SUBJECTS

PRINTED IN
GREAT BRITAIN
AT THE
UNIVERSITY PRESS
OXFORD
BY
CHARLES BATEY
PRINTER
TO THE
UNIVERSITY